HANDBOOK OF
Stress and Strength

HANDBOOK OF
Stress and Strength
DESIGN AND MATERIAL APPLICATIONS

Charles Lipson
Professor, Mechanical Engineering
University of Michigan

Robert C. Juvinall
Professor, Mechanical Engineering
University of Michigan

The Macmillan Company, New York
Collier-Macmillan Ltd., London

First Printing

Library of Congress catalog card number: 63—10398

The Macmillan Company, New York
Collier-Macmillan Canada, Ltd., Galt, Ontario
DIVISIONS OF THE CROWELL-COLLIER PUBLISHING COMPANY

Printed in the United States of America

Symbols

a   =   Major radius of contact area

b   =   Minor radius of contact area

BHN =   Brinell Hardness Number

c   =   Distance from neutral axis to the extreme fibre in bending, in.

E   =   Linear modulus of elasticity, psi

f   =   Coefficient of friction

G   =   Torsional modulus of elasticity, psi

I   =   Rectangular moment of inertia, in.^{4}

J   =   Polar moment of inertia, in.^{4}

ksi =   Thousands of pounds per square inch (kilo-pounds per square inch)

K_t =   Theoretical, or geometric stress concentration factor

K_f =   Fatigue stress concentration factor

M   =   Moment, in. lb.

P   =   Force, lb.

p   =   Contact pressure, psi

p_o =   Maximum value of contact pressure, psi

psi =   Pounds per square inch

q   =   Notch sensitivity

R_c =   Rockwell C hardness number

S   =   Strength, psi or ksi

$\quad S_u$ = ultimate strength

$\qquad S_{ut}$ = ultimate strength in tension

$\qquad S_{uc}$ = ultimate strength in compression

$\qquad S_{us}$ = ultimate strength in shear

$\quad S_y$ = yield strength

$\qquad S_{yt}$ = yield strength in tension

$\qquad S_{yc}$ = yield strength in compression

$\qquad S_{ys}$ yield strength in shear

$\quad S_n$ = endurance strength of a part

$\quad S_n'$ = endurance limit of a material

T   =   Torque, in. lb.

V   =   Transverse shear force, lb.

y   =   Perpendicular distance from neutral bending plane to point considered, in.

Z   =   Rectangular section modulus $(\frac{I}{C})$, in.^{3}

Z'   =   Polar section modulus $(\frac{J}{R})$, in.^{3}

σ =   Normal stress, psi or ksi

     σ_a = normal stress due to axial load

     σ_b = normal stress due to bending load

     σ_1, σ_2, σ_3 = principal stress

δ =   Linear deflection, in.

ϵ =   Strain, in/in.

θ =   Angular deflections, radians (one radian = $\dfrac{180}{\pi}$ = 57.7°)

τ =   Shear stress, psi or ksi

μ =   Poisson's ratio

Contents

PART II: CONSIDERATION OF STRENGTH

PART III: BALANCING STRENGTH AND STRESS

PART IV: ELASTIC DEFLECTION AND ELASTIC STABILITY

PART V: CHARTS

* Also see Figure 21-20a through 21-24b for properties of aluminum.

Introduction

Chapter 1

INTRODUCTION

A rational approach to a structural problem involves a recognition that the solution calls for the determination of two factors: one of stress, the other of strength. By stress is meant the significant stress, that is, the stress imposed on a member by service loads, assembly conditions, and fabrication. This stress can be static, dynamic, or a combination of the two. If static, it can result from conditions such as the driving torque of an engine, a preload of a suspension spring, or cold straightening of a shaft in production. If dynamic, it can be produced by the torsional fluctuations of a drive shaft, gust loads on an airplane structure, or the reaction of automobile suspension parts to road irregularities.

By strength is meant the significant strength (the allowable stress), or the maximum stress which the material in its fabricated form can sustain when subjected to significant stress, that is, to service loads, assembly conditions, and fabrication. Strength, as defined here, takes into account hardness of the material, size of the member, surface conditions, type of service loading, life expectancy, etc.

Stress and strength, thus defined, are concepts strictly interwoven according to some as-yet-to-be-defined relation.

A review of structural problems reveals that generally they can be grouped into three broad classifications:

1. Problems involving evolution of a new part or structure.
2. Problems involving a modification of an existing part or structure.
3. Problems involving a determination of the cause of failure.

1. **Evolution of New Parts or Structures.** In designing new parts or structures, the principal consideration from the structural viewpoint is that the part carry service loads without failure. Problems of this type are conventionally approached from one of two viewpoints, depending on the conditions prevailing at the time the problem is postulated:

(a) estimate the strength of the material which will be used in fabricating the member, and on this basis calculate the required size and shape;

(b) estimate the approximate size of the part on the basis of past experience, space limitation, existing design codes, etc., and from this determine whether the part thus designed will have sufficient strength to withstand service loads. It is apparent that both methods of approach involve balance between stress and strength.

2. **Modification of an Existing Part or Structure.** Generally, the need for modifying an existing member arises from the fact that the function of the part has

3

been changed or the method of fabrication is to be modified. The former would occur in case of a demand for an increased performance, such as greater output from an output from an engine or an increased capacity of a machine tool. The latter would arise in cases where a stamping is to be used in place of a forging or a casting for economy or ease of manufacture. The saving could result from numerous considerations, such as less expensive materials, increased rate of production, or a need for less material.

To evaluate the effect of these changes, it is necessary to compare the new member with some standard, such as the existing member. As a rule, therefore, all these problems can be postulated as follows: How does design A compare with design B, or material A with material B, or process A with process B, or any combination of the above with any other combination? For example, suppose a part that is known to be satisfactory in service has a 20 per cent greater stress because of some design modification. To determine whether the redesigned part will be satisfactory, it is necessary to determine whether the margin of safety is adequate. This can be done by calculating the margin of safety of the old design with the 20 per cent added stress, or by determining the margin of safety of the redesigned part. In either case it is still a problem of balance between stress and strength.

3. **Determination of the Cause of Failure.** The only failures of concern to the designer are those in which the design can be assumed to be faulty. Failures that are caused by the material being subpar or by the fabrication not meeting specifications are problems of production and not of design.

The obvious cause of a structural failure is the fact that the stresses imposed on the member by service loads are greater than its strength, and the immediate concern is to find feasible means of eliminating and forestalling such failures.

The general procedure in this case is to check the balance between the stress and the strength, that is, to re-evaluate the loads, the stresses, and the strength in the failed part. In most cases it will be found that the actual loads are different from the assumed loads, the material is below specification, or the actual method of processing has been changed without being brought to the attention of the designer. Usually a remedy can be found that requires only a slight modification in the shape of the member or in its processing. Often it is found that a small change in the shape discontinuity will lower the stresses sufficiently so that a satisfactory balance between stress and strength is achieved.

A second method of overcoming failures involves increasing the hardness of the member. This can be accomplished by changing the heat treatment or by changing the material to obtain higher hardenability with the same process.

If neither of the above methods applies in the specific case, the last resort is to increase the size of the member. This is often undesirable from the viewpoint of both economy and performance. Usually, the cost penalty for a slight increase in size is not only the expense of the added material but also the cost involved in modifying other members of the assembly mating with the redesigned member, so that the final cost may be appreciably higher.

From the preceding discussion it can be concluded that all structural problems involve a balance between stress and strength. The subsequent chapters of this book give a more detailed description of the various factors affecting the stress, the strength, and the means of achieving the balance between the two by the use of a factor of safety.

PART I

Consideration of Stress

Chapter 2

GENERAL CONSIDERATIONS OF STRESS

An adequate analysis of the stresses acting in a machine or structural part often involves consideration of many factors. The total stress may include internal residual stresses resulting from manufacturing processes as well as stresses due to external loads. Also, the external loading may cause stresses which are static, dynamic, or a combination of the two. Furthermore, the stresses causing failure commonly occur at local "stress raisers," or at points of localized load application.

All stresses are commonly resolved into normal stresses (perpendicular to the plane of the cross-section) and shear stresses (in the plane of the cross-section). The relative importance of the two depends upon the material used, and involves generally the application of a "failure theory."

In considering the stresses in a part, one must always have in mind one or more possible modes of failure, such as static yielding, fatigue fracture, surface spalling or pitting, impact fracture, etc. The stresses associated with each of the possible modes of failure are, of course, the stresses of interest. Hence, these are called the *significant stresses*. For example, the significant stress associated with a failure due to general yielding would be the maximum shear stress (or maximum distortion energy, depending on the failure theory assumed applicable) at the point of initial yielding, even though this maximum stress might be applied to the part only once. Repeated application of lower stresses at the same point would not be significant in this instance.

As another example, the significant stress associated with fatigue fracture at the root of a gear tooth would be the repeated bending stress at the origin of fracture. For this example, contact stresses acting on the face of the gear would not be significant. For a pitting or wear type failure of the gear tooth, the reverse would, of course, be true. In the initial design of the gear where neither type of failure has occurred but where both types are possibilities to be considered, both the bending and the surface contact stresses would be regarded as significant stresses.

The calculation of stresses due to external loads presupposes prior knowledge of the nature and magnitude of the loads — or at least reasonable estimates. Frequently, this information is difficult to obtain. In many such cases, stress calculations are limited to relative values, giving a comparison between alternate designs. For example, suppose that we know only that the stress level in "this year's model" of a part is satisfactory, and that the loads involved in "next year's model" will be 50 per cent higher. Without knowing absolute values, a design for "next year's model" can be proposed which will have the required 50 per cent increase in strength.

2.1 Impact Stresses

When a machine or structure is intended to operate under conditions which apply impulsive loading, the design problem is complicated by several additional factors. Even in the most clearly defined cases, the problem of computing loads and stresses under impact considerations is sufficiently involved that theoretical considerations can usually serve only in a qualitative manner to guide the design.

Impact loading does not necessarily involve an impact or a collision of bodies, but simply sudden application of forces or motions to the structure. "Sudden application" is regarded as extending over a time interval which is of the order of, or less than, the lowest natural period of vibration of the structure.

Under impact loading, the machine part or structure is required to absorb a certain amount of kinetic energy, which is temporarily stored in the structure in the form of elastic energy of deformation. In contrast to this, statically loaded parts must withstand only the maximum applied forces.

Impact loading often occurs unexpectedly in service due to the gradually increasing clearances which develop between two mating parts as wear takes place. In this process, a simple dynamic stress changes into an impact stress as wear takes place, often leading to fracture of such parts as the structural members of steering gears and axle journals of vehicles.

In practice, it is common to design parts subjected to impact loading on the basis of multiplying the static stresses by an impact loading factor which is empirically determined. Tests conducted with automotive suspension components, for example, indicate that an impact loading factor of 4 is appropriate for these parts.

Factors associated with designing a part so as to be strong in impact are discussed in article 10.1.

References

Lipson, Noll, and Clock, *Stress and Strength of Manufactured Parts*, McGraw-Hill, 1950.

NOMINAL STRESSES—NORMAL

3.1 Axial Loading, σ_a = P/A (3.1)

In this book, the letter σ is used to designate normal stresses. The subscript "a" is used to indicate axial loading. The units usually used for P, A, and σ, are, respectively, pounds, square inches, and pounds per square inch. The latter is commonly abbreviated as "psi." In order to save writing three zeros, "ksi," designating kilo-pounds (thousands of pounds) per square inch, is often used.

An axially loaded straight round rod having two common types of end connections is shown in Figure 3-1a. "Lines of force flow" have been drawn to illustrate the general nature of the stress distribution in cross sections at various distances from the ends. A substantially uniform distribution is reached at points about three diameters from the end fittings, in most cases.

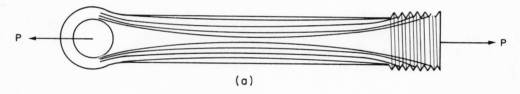

(a)

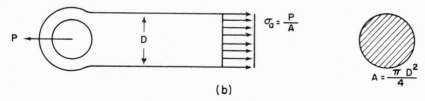

(b)

Figure 3—1. Axial loading.

Figure 3-1b illustrates equilibrium of the left portion of the link under the action of the external force at the left, and the tensile stresses acting on the cutting plane. The uniform stress distribution implied by Equation (3.1) requires fulfillment of the following conditions:

1. The link must be straight, and the load must be axial. Note that if the

9

load is eccentric by amount "e," a bending moment of magnitude Pe will
be applied to the link in addition to axial load P.

2. There must be no stress raisers near the cross section. Stress raisers
   can be grooves, holes, shoulders, etc. incorporated in the geometry of
   the part; or they can be flaws in the material, such as inclusions or
   blowholes.

3. If the load is compressive, the geometry of the part must be such that
   there is no tendency for buckling to occur. This subject is treated in
   Chapter 18.

4. The cross-section considered must be sufficiently remote from the points
   of loading.

3.2 Bending Loading, $\sigma_b = My/I$ (3.2)

In the above equation:

σ_b = normal stress due to bending (psi).

M = bending moment (in. lb.). (Moments associated with various
beam loadings are given in Table 17-2.)

y = perpendicular distance from the neutral bending plane to the
point under consideration (in.).

I = rectangular moment of inertia of the cross-section about the
neutral bending axis (in^4). (Properties of various sections
are listed in Table 18-1.)

Figure 3-2a shows a bending load applied to a straight beam of cross-section
having two axes of symmetry. Equilibrium of the left portion under the action of the
external moment on the left, and stresses acting on the cutting plane are shown in
Figure 3-2b. Common examples of cross-sections having two axes of symmetry are

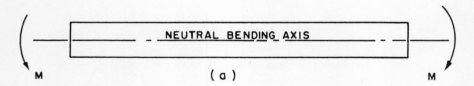

(a)

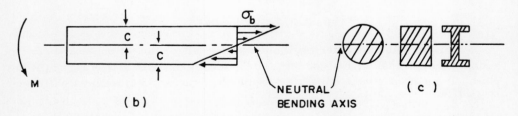

(b)

(c)

Figure 3–2. Pure bending of sections with two axis of symmetry.

shown in Figure 3-2c. Note that the bending stresses marked σ_b in Figure 3-2b are the maximum values of the bending stress, where "y" in Equation (3.2) has been replaced by "c," the distance from the neutral plane to the extreme fibre. By defining the section modulus, Z, as the ratio I/c, we have:

$$\sigma_b \text{ (maximum)} = M/Z \tag{3.3}$$

Note that for sections having two axes of symmetry, the tensile stress σ_b shown at the top of the beam is equal to the compressive stress σ_b at the bottom.

If the beam cross section is not symmetrical about the neutral bending plane, tensile and compressive values of σ_b will in general not be equal. This is shown in Figure 3-3.

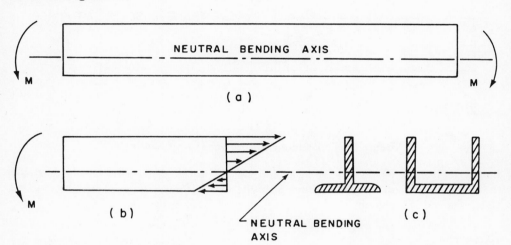

Figure 3–3. Pure bending of sections with one axis of symmetry.

Bending loads are most frequently caused by transverse forces, as shown in Figure 3-4a. Figure 3-4b shows that equilibrium considerations require that the cutting plane experience a transverse shear force as well as bending stresses. The distribution of the transverse shear stresses caused by this shear force is discussed in the next chapter. Note that the magnitude of the bending moment in this case is R_1a, and that the magnitude of the transverse shear force is R_1.

The important assumptions implicit in the bending stress formula are:

1. The beam is initially straight, and the bending loads are in a plane of symmetry.
2. The material obeys Hooke's law (i.e., the material is perfectly elastic, with modulii of elasticity in tension and compression being equal, and with no stresses exceeding the elastic limit).
3. The cross-section considered is sufficiently remote from points of loading and remote from any stress raisers.

An important distinction between normal stresses produced by axial loading and by bending is the difference in stress gradient. Whereas axial loading gives zero gradient for all sizes of samples, bending loading causes gradients which are

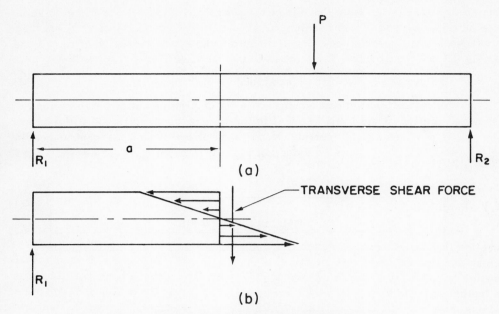

Figure 3—4. Bending due to transverse loading.

increasingly high as the thickness of the sample is reduced. This means that very thin samples loaded in bending have only the thin surface layers stressed to essentially the full M/Z value.

References

1. Lipson, Noll, and Clock, *Stress and Strength of Manufactured Parts*, McGraw-Hill, 1950.
2. Shanley, F. R., *Strength of Materials*, McGraw-Hill, 1957.

Chapter 4

NOMINAL STRESSES—SHEAR

4.1 Direct Loading, $\tau = P/A$ (4.1)

In this book, the letter τ is used to designate shear stresses. Equation (4.1) implies that direct shear stresses are assumed to be distributed uniformly over the cross-section. Although this condition is probably never fully realized, it is approximated in cases involving bolts, rivets, pins, snap-rings, etc. Figure 4-1 illustrates a typical example. The pin is shown yielded in shear in order to illustrate the shear stress more clearly. In this example, the load P is carried in shear through two areas in parallel; hence the area A used in Equation 4.1 is twice the cross-section area of the pin.

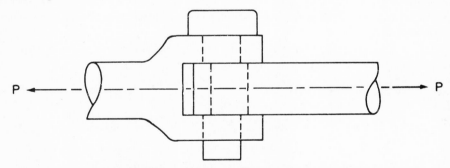

Figure 4—1. Direct shear loading (showing failure in double shear).

In order for Equation (4.1) to provide a reasonable approximation of the maximum direct shear stress in Figure 4-1, there should be a minimum of clearance at all points, and all deflections except the primary shear deflection should be negligible. Under these ideal conditions, the direct shear deflection will also be negligible, unless shear yielding occurs.

4.2 Torsional Loading of Round Bars, $\tau = Tr/J$ (4.2)

In the above equation:

τ = shear stress (psi).

T = torque (in. lb.).

13

r = radial distance from the axis of the bar to the point under consideration (in.).

J = polar moment of inertia of the cross section (in.^{4}). (Properties of various sections are listed in Table 18-1.)

Figure 4-2 shows the distribution of shear stresses resulting from a torsional load. This distribution is similar to that for bending, shown in Figure 3-2, except for one important difference. Whereas the maximum bending stresses exist only at the top and bottom of the beam, the maximum torsional stresses exist in the entire outer surface.

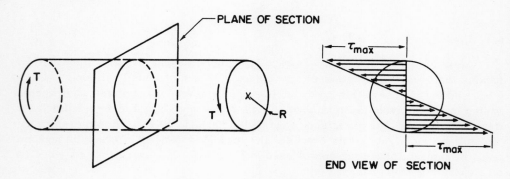

Figure 4—2. Shear due to torsion.

The maximum shear stress due to torsion is obtained from Equation (4.2) by using the maximum value of r; namely, the radius of the outer surface, R. By defining the polar section modulus, Z', as J/R, we have:

$$\tau \text{ (maximum)} = T/Z' \tag{4.3}$$

The important assumptions involved in the torsional stress formula are:

1. The bar must be straight and round (it may be solid or hollow), and the torque must be applied about the longitudinal axis.
2. The material must be perfectly elastic within the stress range involved.
3. The cross section considered must be sufficiently remote from points of load application and from any stress raisers.

The standard formulas for nominal stress are often used to obtain rough approximations in cases where the assumptions are not completely satisfied. Application of Equation (4.2) to a rectangular cross-section bar affords a striking example where this can *not* be done. To illustrate this point, take a common rubber eraser and mark on it the three elements shown as 1, 2, and 3, in Figure 4-3a. Now twist the eraser about the longitudinal axis and observe the shear distortion of the three elements, numbered 1, 2, and 3. Equation (4.2) implies that element 2 should distort the most, as it is farthest from the neutral axis, whereas element 1 should distort the least. These results could not be farther from the truth. Element 2 (if it could be drawn small enough) does not distort at all, while element 1 experiences the maximum distortion of any element on the entire surface.

4.3 Torsional Loading of Rectangular Bars, $\tau_{max} = T\alpha ba^2$ (4.4)

In the above equation:

τ_{max} = maximum shear stress in the middle of the wide sides (psi).

T = torque (in. lb.).

a,b - as defined in Figure 4-3b (in.).

α - a numerical factor having values given in Table 4-1.

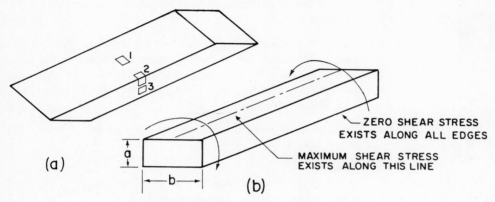

Figure 4—3. Torsion in rectangular bar.

TABLE 4-1

Factors for Torsion of Rectangular Shafts

b/a	α
1.00	.208
2.50	.231
1.75	.239
2.00	.246
2.50	.258
3.00	.267
4.00	.282
6.00	.299
8.00	.307
10.00	.333
∞	.333

4.4 Transverse Beam Loading, $\tau = \dfrac{V}{Ib} \Sigma \bar{y} A'$ (4.5)

Figure 3-4 illustrates the presence of a transverse shear force in beams subjected to transverse loading. Although the average stress produced by this force is the ratio force/area, the distribution of the stress is not uniform. Fortunately, the maximum shear stress exists at the neutral bending axis (where the normal bending stress is zero), and the shear stress is zero at the extreme fibres (where the normal bending stress is a maximum). The shear stress at any distance from the neutral axis can be computed from Equation (4.5). The symbols in this equation are defined as follows:

τ = transverse shear stress (psi).

V = total shear force in the cross-section (1b.). For example, in Figure 3-4, V = R_1.

I = rectangular moment of inertia of the cross-section about the neutral bending axis (in.[4]).

b = width of cross-section *at the point where the stress is to be determined* (in.).

A' = area of a portion of the cross-section between the level at which the stress is to be determined and the outer fibre (in.[2]). In many cases, the geometry will be such that only one area A' need be considered. In the example below, two such areas are involved.

$\bar{y}$ = distance from neutral bending axis to center of gravity of area A' (in.).

Sample Problem

Determine the distribution of shear stresses in the cross section of the I section shown in Figure 4-4. This section approximates that of a standard 10" I beam.

The average shear stress = τ_{avg} = V/A = V/9.5 in[2] = $\underline{.105V}$

I (from equation in Table 18-1) = $\underline{143 \text{ in.}[4]}$

(1) Determine first the shear stress at neutral axis, n. It is convenient to divide the total cross-hatched area between this location and the extreme fibre into areas A'_1 and A'_2. Applying Equation (4.5):

$$\tau_n = \frac{V}{143(.5)} \left[(2.25)(2.25) + (4.75)(2.5) \right] =$$

.014V $[5.07 + 11.9] = .237V$

$\underline{\tau_n = .237V = 2.26\,\tau_{avg}}$

(2) Consider next the shear stress at q, which is 4½ inches above the neutral axis but still in the web, so that b remains .5". Now, only area A'_2 is between the level being considered and the outer fibre. Thus, dropping the A'_1 term and leaving everything else the same:

$$\tau_q = 0.14V(11.9) = .167V$$

$$\tau_q = .167V = 1.59\,\tau_{avg}$$

(3) Consider now the shear stress at p, which is also essentially 4½ inches above the neutral axis, but at the extreme bottom of the flange. The only difference between the calculation here and the calculation for q

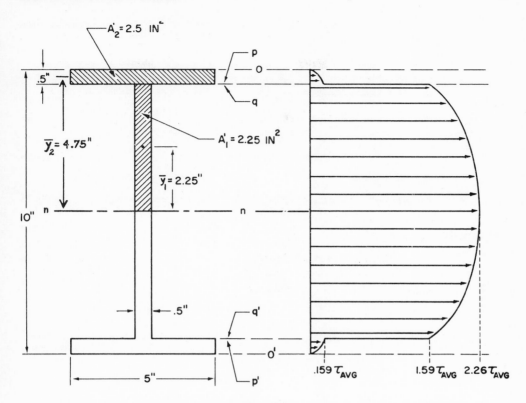

Figure 4–4. Distribution of transverse shear stress in an I section.

is that at q, the width of section (b) is 5″ rather than .5″. Thus, the stresses are reduced by a factor of 10.

$$\tau_p = .0167V = .159 \tau_{avg}$$

(4) Finally, consider the stresses at the extreme top, o. Since there is no area between this point of consideration and the outer fibre, Equation (4.5) indicates that the shear stress at o is zero.

The values calculated above are plotted on the shear distribution curve at the right of Figure 4-4. Due to symmetry, values at q′, p′, and o′, are the same as at q, p, and o, respectively. (Note that for the bottom half of the section the areas considered would conveniently be taken as those areas between the level being considered and the *bottom* extreme fibre.)

The shear stresses plotted in Figure 4-4 are shear stresses tending to produce distortion in a vertical plane containing the longitudinal axis. In addition to these, the flanges experience shear stresses in a horizontal plane. Since these are always lower than the vertical shear stresses at the neutral axis, they are seldom of practical interest, and hence will not be considered here.

Figure 4-5 illustrates the shear stress distribution in round and rectangular sections. Note that the maximum shear stresses in these sections are $1\frac{1}{3} \tau_{avg}$ and $1\frac{1}{2} \tau_{avg}$ respectively.

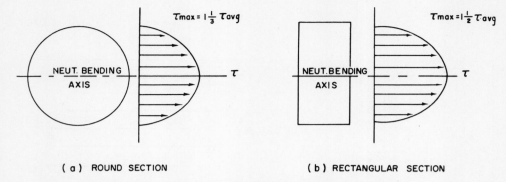

(a) ROUND SECTION   (b) RECTANGULAR SECTION

Figure 4–5. Shear stress distribution in common shapes.

References

1. Timoshenko, S. and MacCullough, G. H., *Elements of Strength of Materials*, Van Nostrand, 1935.
2. Shanley, F. R., *Strength of Materials*, McGraw-Hill, 1957.

Chapter 5

COMBINED STRESSES—MOHR'S CIRCLE REPRESENTATION

Mohr's circle provides a convenient means for representing the normal and shear stresses acting on planes in all directions. Mohr's circles can be quickly constructed for any combination of axial, torsional, bending, and direct shear stresses acting at a point of interest. Values of maximum shear stress and maximum normal stress can then be read directly from the circles. Furthermore, the angular orientation of planes subjected to these maximum stresses is directly indicated.

Whereas the same information can be obtained analytically from the standard combined stress equations (5.1), (5.2), and (5.3), the graphical Mohr method often gives a quicker solution and also a pictorial aid to visualizing the total stress situation at the point under study.

The Mohr circle method will now be used to represent stresses resulting from axial and bending loads, from torsional loads, and finally from combinations of loading.

5.1 Mohr's Circle for Axial and Bending Loads

Figure 5-1 shows a bar loaded in tension. A typical stress element is shown with all of the stresses which act on it.

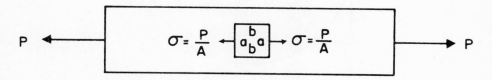

Figure 5–1. Bar loaded in tension.

Figure 5-2 illustrates a Mohr circle representation of the stresses at the point on the bar where the element is drawn. The coordinates of the Mohr plot are σ and τ. Angles measured on the Mohr circle are *twice* the actual angles at the element. This is illustrated in Figure 5-2 as follows:

1. Planes a of the element are subjected to a normal stress of P/A and a shear stress of zero. These values are used as coordinates of point a of the Mohr plot. (Note that in the case of a bending load producing

19

tension in the element shown in Figure 5-1, planes a of the element would be subjected to a normal stress of Mc/I and a shear stress of zero.)

2. Planes b of the element are subjected to no stress. Hence, point b on the Mohr plot is at the origin.

3. Planes a and b are 90° apart on the element of Figure 5-1. Due to the 2:1 angular relationship, points a and b are 180° apart on a Mohr's circle. Thus, points a and b are at opposite ends of a diameter, and the complete circle can be drawn as shown.

4. Suppose we wish to investigate shear stresses which are present in the tensile bar. Points c and d on the circle represent points of maximum (and minimum) shear stress. On the circle, point c is 90° counterclockwise from a; hence, at the actual element, plane c will be 45° (half of 90°) counterclockwise from plane a. Similarly, plane d at the element will be 45° clockwise from a.

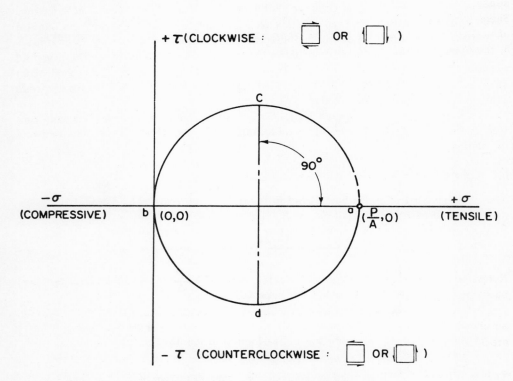

Figure 5-2. Mohr circle for tensile loading.

5. Using the above information, an element oriented so as to experience maximum shear stress is shown in Figure 5-3. The values of normal and shear stress acting on this element are taken directly from the circle. Note carefully the sign convention: positive values of σ are tensile; positive values of τ tend to produce clockwise rotation of the element.

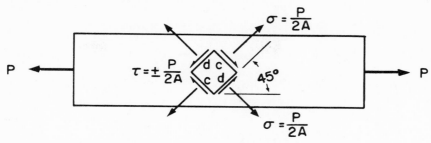

Figure 5–3. Planes of maximum shear stress in a tensile bar.

5.2 Mohr's Circle for Torsional Loads

Figure 5-4 shows a bar loaded in torsion. The shear stresses shown on faces a of the element are equal to T/Z' (or, TR/J), and their clockwise (positive) sense follows directly from an observation of the direction of the torque arrows. Shear stresses on planes $90°$ apart are always equal but opposite; thus, stresses of $-T/Z'$ act on faces b. Note that if it were not for the shear stresses on faces b, the element would not be in equilibrium.

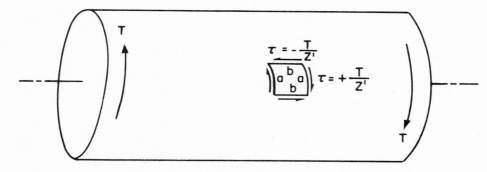

Figure 5–4. Bar loaded in torsion.

Note also that Figure 5-2 affords graphical illustration of the fact that shear stresses on perpendicular planes are equal but opposite.

From the above information, points a and b can be plotted on a Mohr diagram, as shown in Figure 5-5. Since a and b are $90°$ apart on the element, points a and b are $180°$ apart on Mohr's circle and therefore define the circle.

The maximum and minimum normal stresses are represented on the circle as σ_1 and σ_2. These stresses are called *principal stresses*, and for this reason numbers rather than letters are used to designate these points. With this concept in mind, points a and b in Figure 5-2 could also be called points 1 and 2 respectively. Note that planes subjected to principal stresses are never subjected to shear.

Figure 5-6 is like Figure 5-4 except that the element is drawn to contain planes subjected to the maximum and minimum normal stresses, or principal stresses. Note carefully the application of the sign conventions in determining which $45°$ diagonal corresponds to the tensile principal stress and which corresponds to the compressive principal stress.

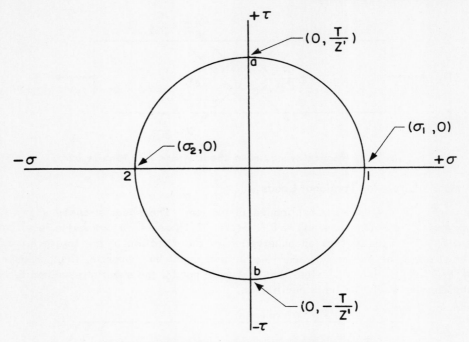

Figure 5—5. Mohr circle for torsional loading.

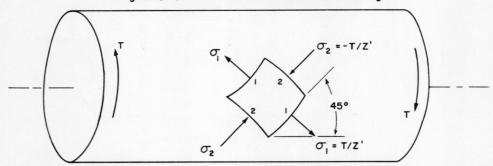

Figure 5—6. Principal stresses for bar loaded in torsion.

5.3 Mohr's Circle for Combined Loading — Sample Problem

Figure 5-7 shows an example of a one-inch diameter solid round bar subjected to both transverse loads and torsion. Two locations of interest are indicated by elements A and B, which are immediately adjacent to the plane of the center load. Both elements are subjected to the maximum torsional stress. In addition, element A is subjected to the maximum bending stress (but zero transverse shear), whereas element B is subjected to the maximum transverse shear stress (but zero bending stress).

(1) The nominal stresses are first calculated:

$$\sigma_b = \frac{M}{Z} = \frac{300(6)}{.098} = 18,300 \text{ psi}$$

$$\tau \text{(due to torque)} \quad = \frac{T}{Z'} = \frac{2000}{.196} = 10,200 \text{ psi}$$

$$\tau_{max} \text{ (transverse)} \quad = (1\tfrac{1}{3}) (300) / .785 = 500 \text{ psi}$$

(2) Figure 5-8 shows elements A and B with the proper stresses applied.

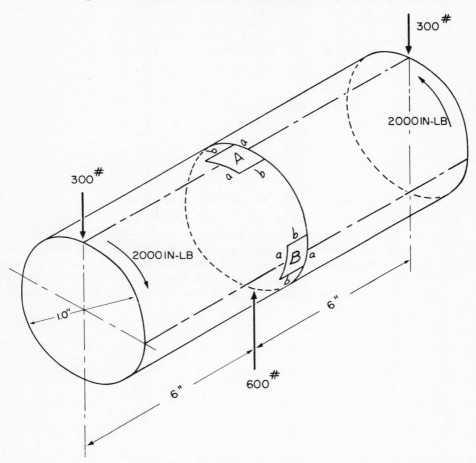

Figure 5–7. Bar subjected to transverse loads and to torsion.

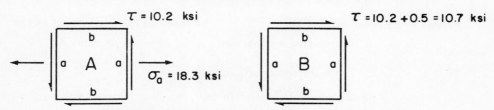

Figure 5–8. Stresses acting on elements A and B.

(3) Figure 5-9 shows Mohr's circle for each location, drawn to the same scale.

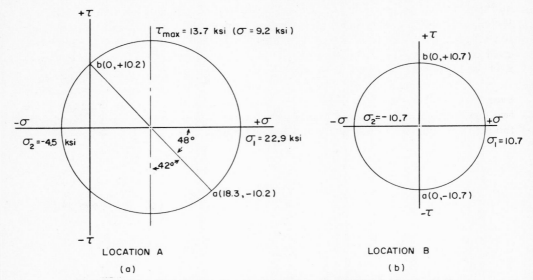

Figure 5–9. Mohr's circles for locations A and B of Figure 5–7.

(4) Obviously, location A is more critical than location B. In practice, this
    is nearly always the case; hence, the transverse shear stresses can
    often be ignored. The only exceptions encountered involve beams which
    are extremely short in comparison with their cross-section.

(5) Figure 5-10 shows directions of maximum normal stress and of maximum
    shear stress for location A. Note that Figure 5-10 is readily derived
    from Figure 5-9.

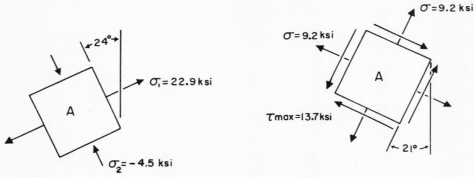

Planes of maximum normal stress   *Planes of maximum shear stress*

Figure 5–10. Maximum shear and normal stresses at point A.

5.4 Mohr's Circle for Three-Dimensional Loading

The plane square elements shown in the preceding articles can be thought
of as cubes by merely extending the elements (which are infinitesimally small) an
incremental distance under the surface. For principal elements, the stresses on the
three pairs of mutually perpendicular faces are σ_1, σ_2, and σ_3, where σ_3 is zero.
The third principal stress is zero because the element face which is part of the

surface is unloaded (except, of course, for atmospheric pressure which may be neglected). We could at this point go back over each of the previous examples and add to the Mohr plot a "point 3" which would be at the origin. We could then draw three circles connecting the three pairs of principal stress points. This is done in Figure 5-11 for the case illustrated in Figure 5-9a.

For this example, the added two circles are of no practical importance. However, if σ_1 and σ_2 are both of the same sign, the addition of $\sigma_3 = 0$ gives rise to two new circles, one of which indicates the true maximum shear stress existing at the point in question. This is illustrated in Figure 5-12.

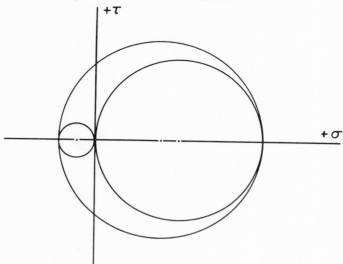

Figure 5–11. Three-dimensional version of Figure 5–9 (a).

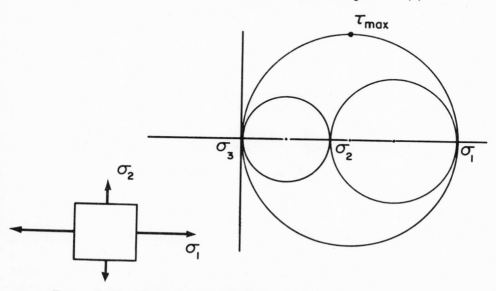

Figure 5–12. Three-dimensional Mohr circle required to show τ_{max}.

A practical example illustrating the necessity of considering the third dimension is afforded by the walls of pressure vessels. At the outer surface of a pressurized cylinder, for example, σ_1 and σ_2 are both tensile, while $\sigma_3 = 0$. At the inner surface, σ_1 and σ_2 are tensile, and σ_3 is compressive (the magnitude being equal to the pressure in the vessel). In either case, principal stress σ_3 participates in determining the maximum shear stress.

5.5 Mohr's Circle Representation of Combined Stress Equations

Figure 5-13 shows the general case of two dimensional stress. Equations (5.1), (5.2), and (5.3) are the conventional "combined stress equations." Figure 5-13b shows how these equations can be developed readily by means of Mohr's circle.

$$\sigma_1, \sigma_2 = \frac{\sigma_x + \sigma_y}{2} \begin{array}{c} + \\ - \end{array} \sqrt{\tau_{xy}^2 + \left(\frac{\sigma_x - \sigma_y}{2}\right)^2} \qquad (5.1)$$

$$\tau_{max} = \begin{array}{c} + \\ - \end{array} \sqrt{\tau_{xy}^2 + \left(\frac{\sigma_x - \sigma_y}{2}\right)^2} \qquad (5.2)$$

$$\phi = \frac{1}{2} \operatorname{Tan}^{-1} \frac{2\tau_{xy}}{\sigma_x - \sigma_y} \qquad (5.3)$$

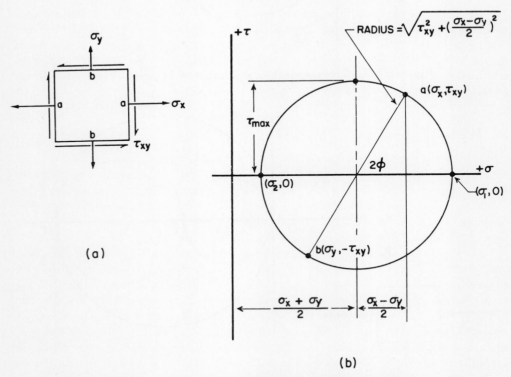

(a)

(b)

Figure 5-13. Combined stress equations illustrated by Mohr's circle.

Chapter 6

STRESS CONCENTRATION (GEOMETRIC OR THEORETICAL)

Up to this point no methods have been discussed for calculating stresses in regions involving fillets, holes, notches, and other section discontinuities commonly classified as stress raisers. In actual machine and structural members, the highest stresses almost invariably exist at such points. As a practical matter, these stresses are normally determined by multiplying the nominal stresses (computed from P/A, Mc/I, etc.) by correction factors known as *stress concentration factors*. The present chapter is concerned exclusively with so-called *geometric* or *theoretical* stress concentration factors which reflect theoretical stress increases caused by the geometry of the stress raiser. These factors are designated by the symbol K_t, and they are based on the assumption that the material involved is perfectly homogenous, isotropic, and elastic.

Theoretical stress concentration factors are seldom applied directly, because (a) for static loading, local yielding generally nullifies the effect of stress concentration provided the material has at least the ductility of hardened steel, and (b) for fatigue loading, the "notch sensitivity" properties of the material modify the effective magnitude of stress concentration. The present study of theoretical stress concentration factors is of importance, however, as it establishes the basis for handling stress concentration associated with fatigue loading (Chapter 11).

6.1 Intuitive Estimate of K_t

An intuitive feeling for stress concentration factors is often helpful in such situations as interpolating or extrapolating from available information to estimate K_t for unlisted cases, making preliminary comparisons of design alternatives, and visualizing possible design changes which would reduce stress concentration. The development of this intuitive judgment is facilitated by visualizing lines of force flow in the region of a stress raiser.

Figure 6-1 illustrates force paths in a tensile member by means of the "flow analogy." The lines of force flow are uniformly distributed in sections sufficiently remote from the notch, but become somewhat concentrated near the surface as they pass through the section containing the notch. The force flow lines are analogous to the streamlines which exist in fluid flowing through a channel having the same shape as the notched bar. Unless obstructed, all flow lines tend to remain straight. In Figure 6-1, flow lines 1, 2, 3, 4, 8, 9, 10, and 11, are forced to bend in order to remain inside the part; but since they tend to deflect as little as possible, the flow lines

27

are crowded together just inside the notch. If flow lines 1, 2, 3 and 4, all tried to pass through the fibre *immediately* adjacent to the surface at the base of the notch, that fibre would elongate excessively. This would cause the neighboring fibres to elongate also, resulting in their sharing a portion of the increased load. Thus, the stress concentration effect extends inward from the surface for a finite distance.

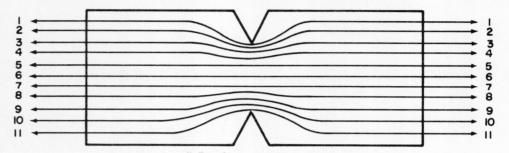

Figure 6–1. Flow lines in notched tensile bar.

Figure 6-2 illustrates force flow lines in a shaft with keyway subjected to torsion. Here, the shear force flow lines lie *in* the cross-section (whereas the tensile flow lines were perpendicular to the cross-section). Note that the corner element, shown enlarged, must be subjected to *zero* shear because it has two exposed sides which cannot be loaded in shear. A more rigorous mathematical analogy relating to Figure 6-2 is the "membrane analogy," treated in standard references in strength of materials.

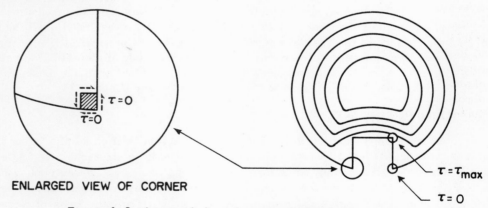

ENLARGED VIEW OF CORNER

Figure 6–2. Lines of shear force in shaft carrying torque.

6.2 Quantitative Determination of K_t

Most of the methods used for determining theoretical or geometric stress concentration factors may be classified in one of three groups: mathematical calculations, measurements on models, and measurements on actual parts.

Mathematical calculations are generally limited to relatively simple two-dimensional forms, or to forms of axial symmetry. Figure 6-3 illustrates a case of interest; namely, that of an elliptical hole in a large plate subjected to tensile loading. If the plate is sufficiently large in comparison with the hole so that the reduction of cross section due to the hole can be neglected (i.e., the plate may be considered "semi-infinite"), the stress concentration factor pertaining to stresses at points 1 of Figure 6-3 is:

$$K_t = 1 + 2\ a/b \qquad\qquad (6.1)$$

The derivation of this equation is based on the theory of elasticity, and is contained in standard texts on this subject. Note the value of K_t obtained from Equation (6.1) for three special cases:

1. For a round hole, $a/b = 1$, and $K_t = 3$.
2. For a crack parallel to the load, a/b approaches zero, and the stress concentration factor approaches unity, thus confirming the obvious fact that there is virtually no stress concentration in this case.
3. For a crack perpendicular to the load, a/b approaches infinity, and K_t also approaches infinity.

Case 3 serves to explain the frequently observed phenomenon of small cracks in machine or structural parts propagating rapidly to cause complete fracture. A comparison of cases 1 and 3 offers an explanation for the common practice of drilling holes at the ends of small cracks in the hope of at least temporarily arresting crack propagation. It should be noted that although drilling the hole greatly reduces K_t, the stress concentration factor of the *crack-hole combination* is greater than 3.

For stress raisers not amenable to mathematical analysis, stress distribution patterns may be evaluated from experimental measurements on models. The most frequently used model study techniques employ the principles of photoelasticity. In these cases, suitably scaled models are made of a transparent material (usually a plastic) which becomes birefringent under stress. The models are loaded in loading fixtures, and the fringe pattern is examined under polarized light. By measuring the relative spacing between the fringe lines, quantitative measurements of stress gradient are obtained. Most photoelastic studies have been limited to two-dimensional cases. Recently, methods have been developed which permit three-dimensional cases to be investigated. (Reference 3)

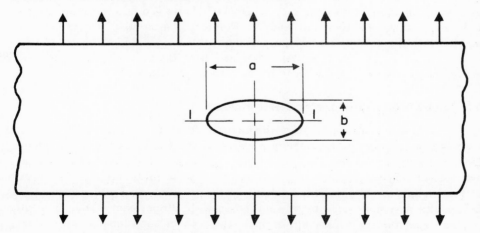

Figure 6-3. Elliptical hole in semi-infinite tensile plate.

Other model methods are sometimes used. For example, rubber models have been used as a means for obtaining large, easily measureable strains. Brittle plaster models have been tried under the theory that fracture of a loaded model occurs when the local stress at the discontinuity reaches the strength of the plaster. In general, however, only the photoelastic method of model study has proven useful.

Measurements of local stresses on actual parts may be made using strain gages or extensometers of short gage length. Locations of points of peak stress, and an estimate of the values of these stresses are often obtained by testing actual parts which have been coated with a calibrated brittle lacquer, such as "Stresscoat," or with "Photostress."

6.3 Charts for Determining K_t

In engineering practice, values of K_t corresponding to various geometric stress raisers are usually obtained from charts which have been prepared on the basis of the mathematical and experimental methods discussed above. A series of such charts is contained in Chapter 20. In using these charts, two points should be carefully noted:

1. Stress concentration factors are different for different types of loading; hence, care must be taken to use stress concentration data corresponding to the type of loading involved.
2. Stress concentration factors are applied to the nominal stress computed for the net section which remains after any notch, groove, hole, etc. has been cut, except in a few specific cases noted in Chapter 20.

6.4 Stress Gradients

In dealing with surface treated parts incorporating stress raisers, it is important to know the stress magnitudes at various levels below the surface as well as the maximum stress which normally exists at the surface. For example, if when going below the surface the strength falls off more rapidly than the stress, the most critical point will be below the surface. The curves in Figures 6-4, 6-5, and 6-6 give stress gradient data pertaining in grooved shafts and notched plates subjected to bending, axial, and torsional loading. References 4 through 10 were used in connection with the development of these curves.

Analysis of fringe patterns obtained from the photoelastic model studies also provides a method for determining the stress gradients.

6.5 Biaxial Effect of Geometric Stress Raisers

Figure 6-1 illustrates how the lines of force flow in a tensile bar become concentrated adjacent to the base of a notch. Since these lines are in tension, they tend to straighten. This, in turn, tends to increase the distance between the two notches, thereby producing transverse tension. As an illustration of the magnitude of this transverse stress, axial loading of the grooved round rod shown in Figure 6-7 results in a transverse tensile stress equal to 20 per cent of the axial stress. In this case, the transverse stress is in the form of hoop tension which tends to expand the diameter at the root of the groove.

Figure 6-8 illustrates the case of a round hole in a semi-infinite plate. This is the usually encountered special case of the elliptical hole illustrated in Figure 6-3. Equation (6.1) indicates that for this case $K_t = 3$, which means that the stresses at points 1 are $3P/A$. The theoretical analysis of this case indicates that at points 2 there exist compressive stresses of magnitude P/A. The reasonableness of this is apparent when one considers that the force flow lines passing immediately adjacent to the hole tend to straighten.

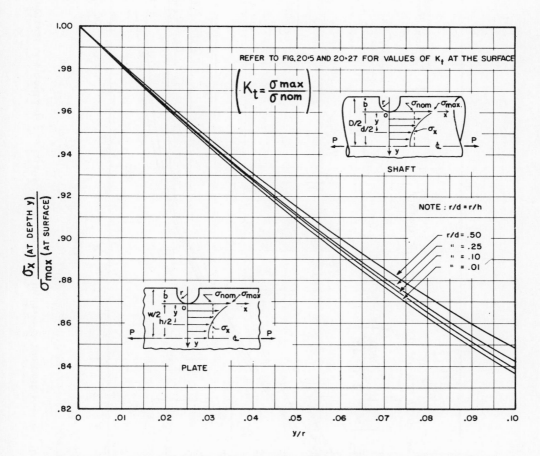

Figure 6—4a. [7] **Stress gradient at circular notch or groove, shafts and flat plates in tension.**

By applying the principle of superposition, the reader will be able to verify the following:

1. When subjected to biaxial tensile stresses of equal magnitude, tensile stresses at points 1 and 2 are of magnitude $2P/A$.
2. When subjected to biaxial normal stresses of equal magnitude but opposite in sign (i.e., tension and compression, or pure shear), the stress magnitudes at points 1 and 2 have absolute values of $4P/A$.

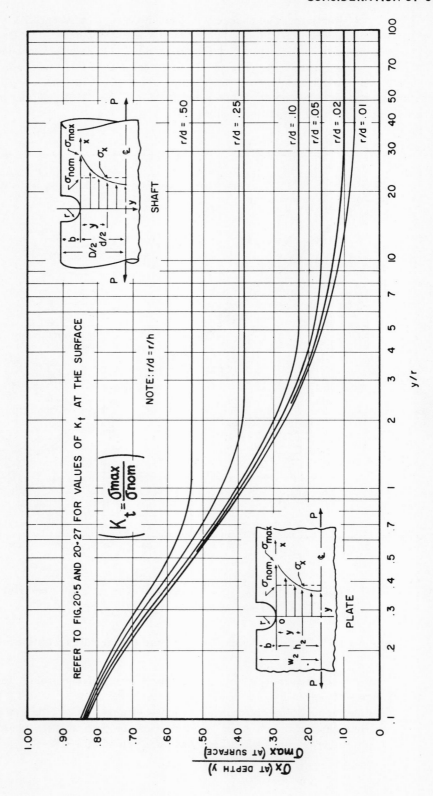

Figure 6–4b.[7] Stress gradient at circular notch or groove, shafts and flat plates in tension.

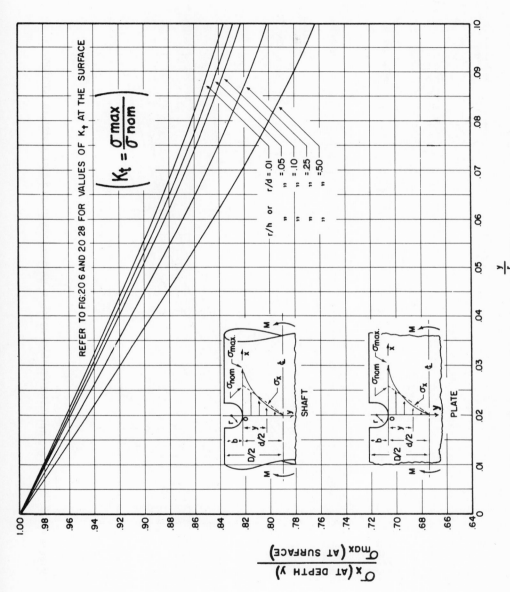

Figure 6–5a.[7] Stress gradient at circular notch or groove, shafts and flat plates in bending.

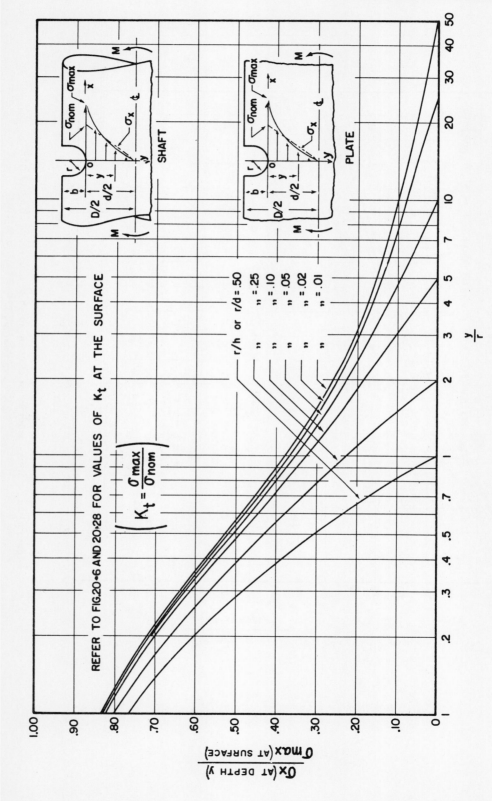

Figure 6–5b. [7] Stress gradient at circular notch or groove, shafts and flat plates in bending.

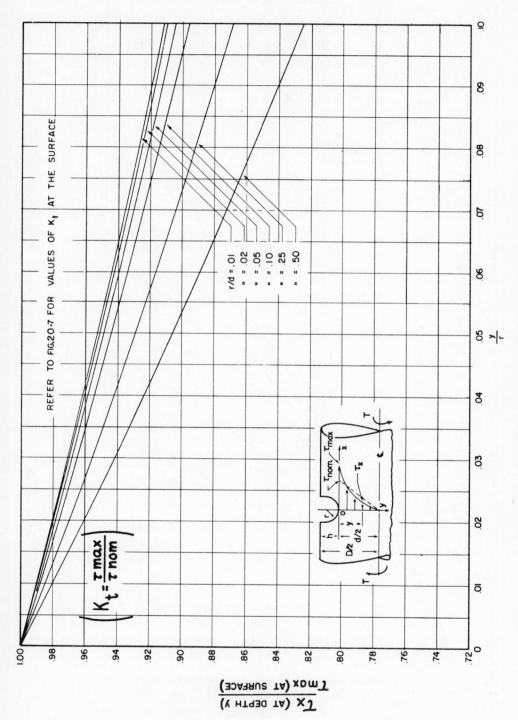

Figure 6–6a. Stress gradient at circular groove, shaft in torsion.

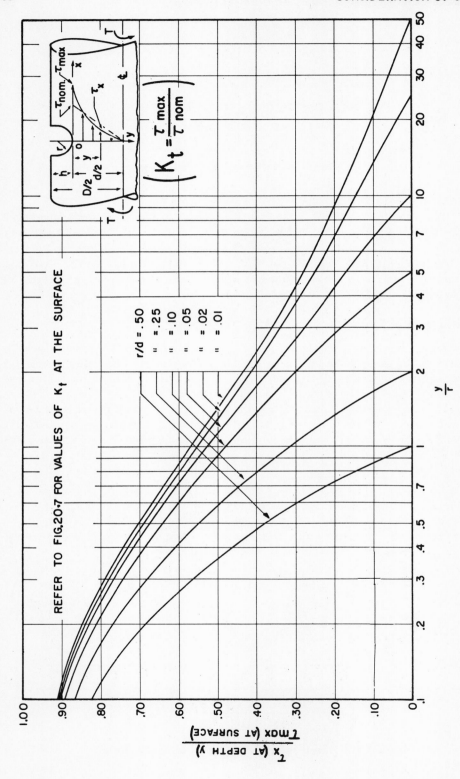

Figure 6–6b.[7] Stress gradient at circular groove, shaft in torsion.

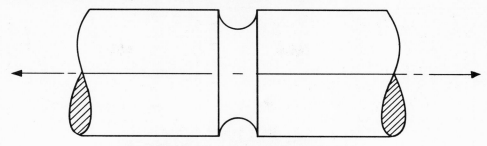

Figure 6—7. Grooved round tensile bar.

The importance of the transverse component of stress depends somewhat upon the manner in which the part tends to fail; i.e., the failure theory which is applicable.   In most cases the influence of the transverse stress on the load required for failure is less than 10 per cent and is commonly neglected.   Also, in some cases the presence of the transverse stress tends to make the part behave in a manner slightly more brittle and less ductile.

6.6 Mitigation of Stress Concentration

Figure 6-9 illustrates three possible modifications of the notched tensile bar shown in Figure 6-1.   In each case the force flow concept indicates (correctly) that the severity of stress concentration has been reduced.   These constitute examples of making a part stronger by *removing* material.

Figure 6-9 also illustrates that often the cumulative effect of a series of stress raisers can be less than the effect of one of the stress raisers individually.   The quantitative effect of multiple notches on K_t is illustrated in Figures 20-39 through 20-42.

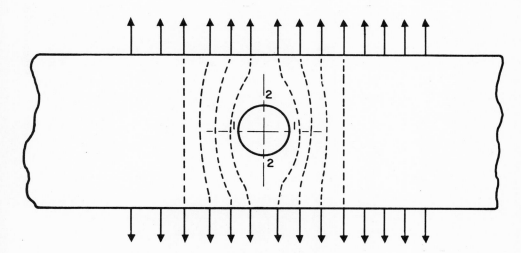

Figure 6—8. Round hole in semi-infinite tensile plate.

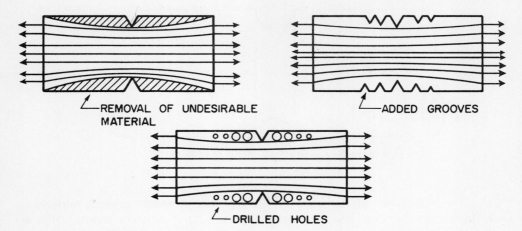

REMOVAL OF UNDESIRABLE MATERIAL

ADDED GROOVES

DRILLED HOLES

Figure 6–9. Means of reducing stress concentration.

Figures 6-10 through 6-16 illustrate practical examples of reducing stress concentration through improved design. In each case the improvement is associated with reducing sharp transitions in the lines of force flow. In many cases, additional stress concentrations are employed as stress relieving notches.

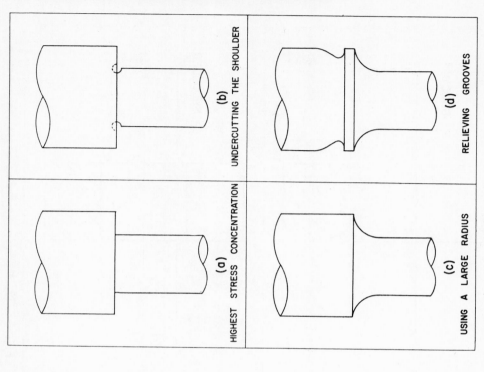

(b) UNDERCUTTING THE SHOULDER

(d) RELIEVING GROOVES

(a) HIGHEST STRESS CONCENTRATION

(c) USING A LARGE RADIUS

Figure 6–11. Methods of reducing stress concentration.

HIGH STRESS CONCENTRATION

ROUGH SURFACE

NO FILLET

SMALL DIA. FOR THREADS

NO SHOULDER OR STRESS RELIEF

REDUCED STRESS CONCENTRATION

SMOOTH SURFACE

GENEROUS FILLET

LARGE DIA. FOR THREADS

SHOULDER AND STRESS RELIEF

Figure 6–10. Methods of reducing stress concentration.

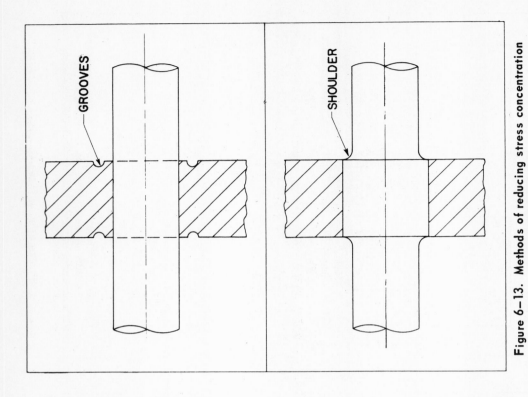

Figure 6–13. Methods of reducing stress concentration in interference fits.

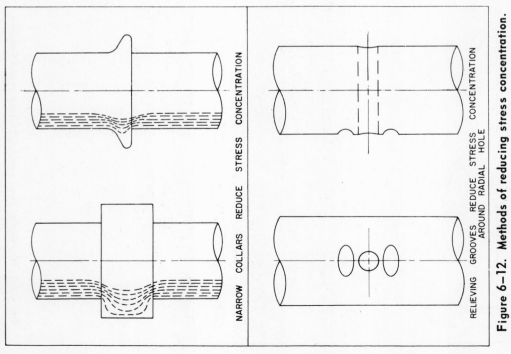

Figure 6–12. Methods of reducing stress concentration.

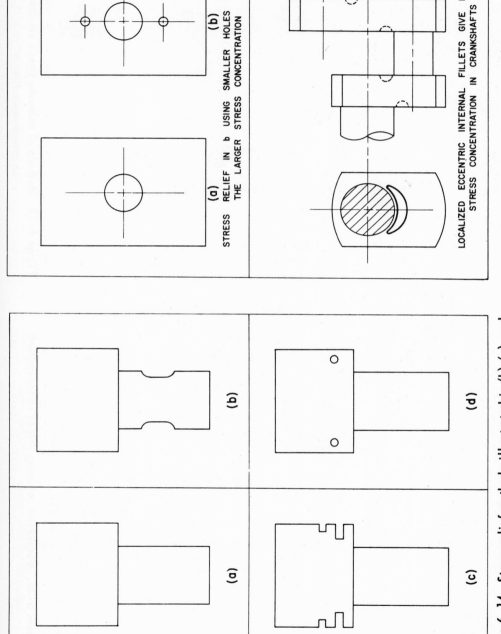

(a)

(b)

STRESS RELIEF IN b USING SMALLER HOLES FLANKING THE LARGER STRESS CONCENTRATION

LOCALIZED ECCENTRIC INTERNAL FILLETS GIVE REDUCED STRESS CONCENTRATION IN CRANKSHAFTS

Figure 6–15. Stress relief.

(a)

(b)

(c)

(d)

Figure 6–14. Stress relief methods illustrated in (b), (c), and (d) reduce the large stress concentrated caused by the sudden change in section.

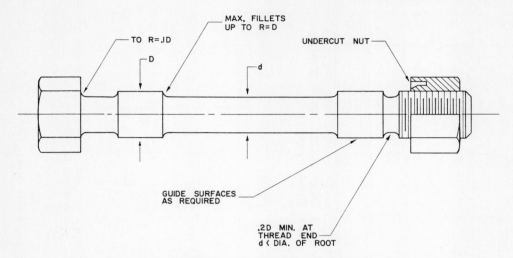

Figure 6–16. Stress relief applied to a large bolt.

References

1. Frocht, M. M., *Photoelasticity*, Wiley, Vol. I, 1941, Vol. II, 1948.
2. Gibson, W. H., "Photoelasticity and Stress Concentration," *Symposium on the Failure of Metals by Fatigue*, Melbourne University Press, Melbourne, Australia, 1947.
3. Hetenyi, M., *Handbook of Experimental Stress Analysis*, Wiley, 1950.
4. Neuber, H., "Theory of Notch Stresses," English Translation, Edwards Bros., Inc., Ann Arbor, Michigan, 1948.
5. Kirsch, G., "Solution for a Thin Plate of Infinite Width with a Hole Under Tension," *Ver. deut. ing.*, Vol. 42, 1959.
6. Tuzi, Z., "Effect of Circular Hole on the Stress Distribution in a Beam Under Uniform Bending Moment," *Phi. Mag.*, p. 210 (February, 1930); also Sci. Papers Inst. Phys. Chem. Research (Tokyo), Vol. 9, p. 65, 1928.
7. Leven, M. M., "Stress Gradients in Grooved Bars and Shafts," *S.E.S.A. Proceedings*, Vol. XIII, No. 1, p. 207, 1955.
8. Howland, C. J. "On the Stresses in the Neighborhood of A Circular Hole in a Strip Under Tension," *Trans. Roy. Soc.*, London, Vol. A229, p. 49, 1929–1930.
9. Timoshenko, S. and Goodier, J. N., *Theory of Elasticity*, McGraw-Hill, 1951, p. 81.
10. Sternberg, E. and Sadowsky, M., "Three Dimensional Solution for the Stress Concentration Around a Circular Hole in a Plate of Arbitrary Thickness," *J. Appl. Mechanics*, Vol. *16*, p. 27 (March 1949).

CONTACT STRESSES

In analyzing contact stresses, the pressure distribution between contacting bodies is first determined. It is then possible to evaluate the stresses at any point of the contact zone.

7.1 Contact Pressure Distribution – Two General Bodies, General Case

According to Hertz, the intensity of pressure, p, over the surface of contact is represented by the ordinates of a semi-ellipsoid constructed on the surface of contact, thus:

$$p = p_o \sqrt{1 - \frac{x^2}{a^2} - \frac{y^2}{b^2}} \qquad (7.1)$$

The maximum pressure exists at the center of the surface of contact and is designated as p_o. Letters a and b denote the semi-axes of the boundary, as shown in Figure 7-1.

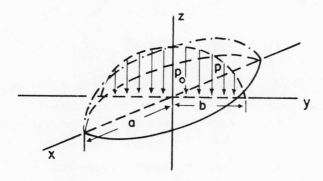

Figure 7–1. Contact pressure distribution – two general bodies.

Since total load, P, is equal to the volume of the semi-ellipsoid, we can write

$$P = \frac{2}{3} \pi \, abp_o \qquad (7.2)$$

43

From this expression the maximum pressure, p_o, is found to be

$$p_o = \frac{3}{2} \frac{P}{\pi \, ab} \qquad (7.3)$$

To calculate p_o we must know a and b, both of which depend on the shape, applied force, and the material properties of the two bodies. Dimensions a and b are given by Timoshenko as

$$a = m \sqrt[3]{\frac{3}{4} \frac{P\Delta}{A + B}}$$

$$\qquad (7.4)$$

$$b = n \sqrt[3]{\frac{3}{4} \frac{P\Delta}{A + B}}$$

where

$$\Delta = \frac{1 - \mu_1^{\,2}}{E_1} + \frac{1 - \mu_2^{\,2}}{E_2}$$

μ_1, μ_2 = Poisson's ratio (of contacting bodies 1 and 2)

E_1, E_2 = Modulii of elasticity (of contacting bodies 1 and 2)

$$A + B = \frac{1}{2} \left(\frac{1}{R_1} + \frac{1}{R_1'} + \frac{1}{R_2} + \frac{1}{R_2'} \right)$$

$$B - A = \frac{1}{2} \left[\left(\frac{1}{R_1} - \frac{1}{R_1'} \right)^2 + \left(\frac{1}{R_2} - \frac{1}{R_2'} \right)^2 \right.$$

$$\left. + 2 \left(\frac{1}{R_1} - \frac{1}{R_1'} \right) \left(\frac{1}{R_2} - \frac{1}{R_2'} \right) \cos 2\psi \right]^{1/2}$$

R_1, R_1', R_2, R_2' = Minimum and maximum radii of curvatures at the point of contact

ψ = Angle between the planes containing the curvatures $(1/R_1)$ and $(1/R_2)$

m, n = Constants depending on the ratio $\dfrac{B - A}{B + A}$

Using the notation, $\cos \theta = \dfrac{B - A}{B + A}$, the values of m and n are given in the following table:

θ	30°	35°	40°	45°	50°	55°	60°	65°	70°	75°	80°	85°	90°
m	2.731	2.397	2.136	1.926	1.754	1.611	1.486	1.378	1.284	1.202	1.128	1.061	1.0
n	0.493	0.530	0.567	0.604	0.641	0.678	0.717	0.759	0.802	0.846	0.893	0.944	1.0

Six important special cases are considered in the succeeding articles.

7.2 Contact Pressure Distribution – Two Spheres

For this case,

$$A + B = \frac{1}{R_1} + \frac{1}{R_2}$$

$$B - A = 0$$

Thus,

$$\frac{B - A}{B + A} = \cos \theta = 0, \text{ and } \theta = 90°.$$

From the preceding table, $m = n = 1.000$. Substituting these results into Equations (7.3) and (7.4):

$$a = b = \sqrt[3]{\frac{3}{4} \frac{P \Delta}{(1/R_1 + 1/R_2)}} \tag{7.5}$$

$$p_o = 0.578 \sqrt[3]{\frac{P(1/R_1 + 1/R_2)^2}{\Delta^2}} \tag{7.6}$$

7.3 Contact Pressure Distribution – Sphere and Flat Plate

If R_2 is infinite, Equations (7.5) and (7.6) apply to the case of a sphere and flate plate, thus:

$$a = b = \sqrt[3]{\frac{3}{4} PR_1 \Delta} \tag{7.7}$$

$$p_o = 0.578 \sqrt[3]{\frac{P}{R_1^2 \Delta^2}} \tag{7.8}$$

7.4 Contact Pressure Distribution – Sphere and Spherical Socket

By giving R_2 a negative sign, Equations (7.5) and (7.6) apply to a sphere in a spherical socket, thus:

$$a = b = \sqrt[3]{\frac{3}{4} \frac{P \Delta}{(1/R_1 - 1/R_2)}} \tag{7.9}$$

$$p_o = 0.578 \sqrt[3]{\frac{P(1/R_1 - 1/R_2)^2}{\Delta^2}} \tag{7.10}$$

7.5 Contact Pressure Distribution — Two Parallel Cylinders

In this case, the area of contact approaches a rectangle, and the distribution of pressure is represented by a semi-elliptical prism. Pressure values are given by Equation (7.11) and the pressure distribution is illustrated by Figure 7-2.

$$p = p_o \sqrt{1 - \frac{y^2}{b^2}} \tag{7.11}$$

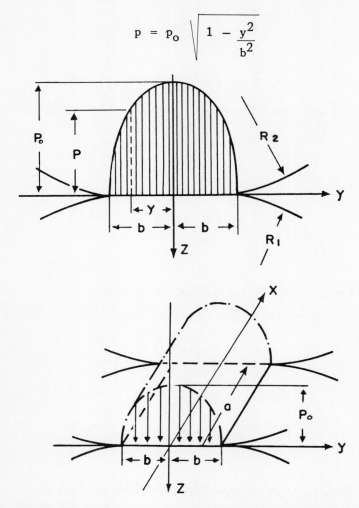

Figure 7-2. Contact pressure distribution — two parallel cylinders.

The volume of the semi-elliptical prism is equal to the total load, P, hence:

$$p = \frac{1}{2} \pi \, bap_o, \tag{7.12}$$

and

$$p_o = 2 \frac{P}{\pi \, ab} \tag{7.13}$$

In this case a is the length of the cylinders.

The equation for b is given by Timoshenko as:

$$b = 1.13 \sqrt{\frac{P}{a} \frac{\Delta}{(1/R_1 + 1/R_2)}} \qquad (7.14)$$

Substituting this expression into Equation (7.13) gives an equation for the maximum pressure, p_0:

$$p_0 = 0.564 \sqrt{\frac{P}{a} \frac{(1/R_1 + 1/R_2)}{\Delta}} \qquad (7.15)$$

7.6 Contact Pressure Distribution — Cylinder and Flat Plate

By letting R_2 = infinity, Equations (7.14) and (7.15) apply to the case of a cylinder and a flat plate, thus:

$$b = 1.13 \sqrt{\frac{PR \Delta}{a}} \qquad (7.16)$$

$$p_0 = 0.564 \sqrt{\frac{P}{aR \Delta}} \qquad (7.17)$$

7.7 Contact Pressure Distribution — Cylinder and Cylindrical Groove

By giving R_2 a negative sign, Equations (7.14) and (7.15) apply to a cylinder in a circular groove thus:

$$b = 1.13 \sqrt{\frac{P}{a} \frac{\Delta}{(1/R_1 - 1/R_2)}} \qquad (7.18)$$

$$p_0 = 0.564 \sqrt{\frac{P}{a} \frac{(1/R_1 - 1/R_2)}{\Delta}} \qquad (7.19)$$

7.8 Stresses in Contact Zone — Concentrated Normal Load

Stresses due to a concentrated normal load (illustrated in Figure 7-3), are given by E. I. Radimovsky as:

$$\sigma_y = \frac{-2P}{\pi z} \sin^2 \theta \cos^2 \theta$$

$$\sigma_z = \frac{-2P}{\pi z} \cos^4 \theta \qquad (7.20)$$

$$\tau_{yz} = \frac{-2P}{\pi z} \sin \theta \cos^3 \theta$$

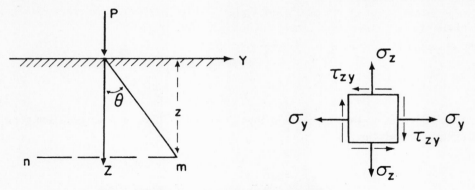

Figure 7–3. Single concentrated normal force.

In Figure 7-4 the values of σ_z and τ_{yz} are plotted for points in the yz-plane located at a depth z below the surface. These values show how the stresses vary along the line m-n due to the concentrated load, P. It can be seen that the shear stress, τ_{yz}, has a different sign on each side of the z axis. Thus, if the load moves along the surface, the shear stress at a fixed point in the yz-plane first increases, then decreases to zero as the load passes over the point, then increases in the opposite direction, and finally decreases to zero.

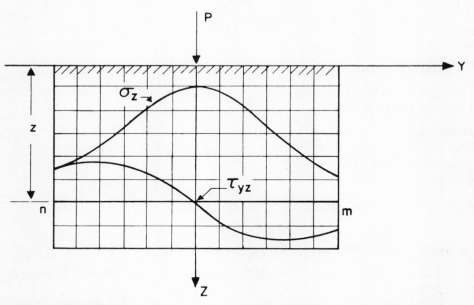

Figure 7–4. Variation of stresses σ_z and τ_{yz} due to concentrated load P.

7.9 Stresses in Contact Zone — Concentrated Tangential Load

Stresses due to tangential loads are of interest because tangential surface loading (due to friction) is often an important factor when considering such members as gears and cams.

According to J. O. Smith and C. K. Liu the equations for the stresses in yz-plane due to concentrated tangential load, Q, are:

$$\sigma'_y = \frac{-2Q}{\pi z} \cos^3 \psi \sin \psi$$

$$\sigma'_z = \frac{-2Q}{\pi z} \cos \psi \sin^3 \psi \qquad (7.21)$$

$$\tau'_{yz} = \frac{-2Q}{\pi z} \cos^2 \psi \sin^2 \psi$$

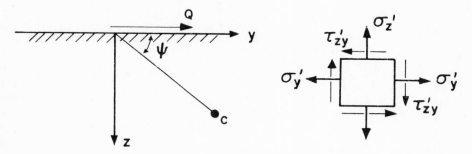

Figure 7–5. Single concentrated tangential force.

It can be seen from the above equations that τ_{yz} and σ'_y have identical forms, so do τ_{yz} and σ_y. Thus, Figure 7-4 can be used for σ'_y which shows that in the case of concentrated tangential loading σ'_y changes sign. Equations (7.21) also show that as ψ varies from $0°$ to $180°$ σ'_y changes sign, but that τ'_{yz} does not.

7.10 Stresses in Contact Zone – Two General Bodies, Normally Loaded

Stresses at points along the z-axis due to the contact of two bodies of general shape have been computed by H. R. Thomas and V. A. Hoersch. The magnitudes of these stresses are plotted in Figure 7-6 for a ratio of contact area semi-axes, b/a, of 0.866. Because of symmetry, stresses σ_x, σ_y, and σ_z are principal stresses. On the $45°$ maximum shear planes, the shear stresses are as follows:

$$\tau_{xz} (45°) = \frac{1}{2} (\sigma_x - \sigma_z)$$

$$\tau_{xy} (45°) = \frac{1}{2} (\sigma_x - \sigma_y) \qquad (7.22)$$

$$\tau_{yz} (45°) = \frac{1}{2} (\sigma_y - \sigma_z)$$

For the case shown in Figure 7-6, $\tau_{xy} (45°) \approx \tau_{xz} (45°)$, and $\tau_{xy} \approx 0$. Hence, only $\tau_{yz} (45°)$ is plotted. This shear stress reaches a maximum value at a depth of about 0.44a.

7.11 Stresses in Contact Zone – Two Spheres Normally Loaded

The equations for stresses at points along the z-axis due to contact of two

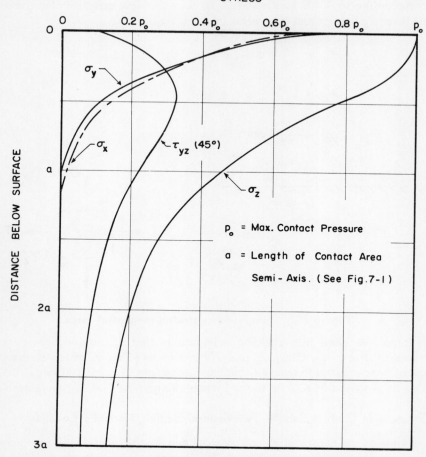

Figure 7–6. Stress gradients due to contact of two bodies of general shape (b/a = 0.866).

spheres have been computed by H. R. Thomas and V. A. Hoersch. These are as follows:

$$\sigma_x = \sigma_y = \frac{2a \left(\frac{1}{R_1} + \frac{1}{R_2} \right)}{\pi \Delta} \left[(1 + \mu) \left(\frac{z}{a} \cot^{-1} \frac{z}{a} - 1 \right) + \frac{1}{2} \frac{a^2}{a^2 + z^2} \right]$$

$$\sigma_z = - \frac{2a \left(\frac{1}{R_1} + \frac{1}{R_2} \right)}{\pi \Delta} \frac{a^2}{a^2 + z^2} \tag{7.23}$$

Since σ_x and σ_y are equal, Equations (7.22) become

$$\tau_{xz} (45^\circ) = \tau_{yz} (45^\circ) = \frac{1}{2} (\sigma_x - \sigma_z)$$

$$\tau_{xy} (45^\circ) = 0 \tag{7.24}$$

STRESS

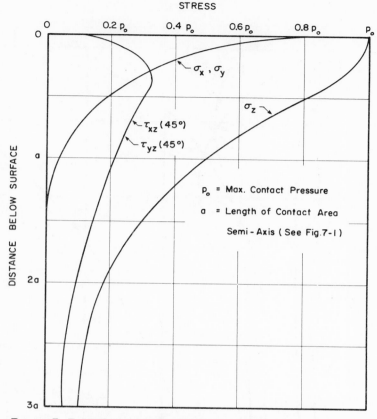

Figure 7–7. Stress gradients due to contact of two spheres.

Variations of these stresses with depth are plotted in Figure 7-7. The magnitudes of the shear stresses τ_{xz} (45°) and τ_{yz} (45°) are greatest at a depth of about half the radius of the contact surface. For $\mu = 0.3$, the magnitude of this stress is approximately 0.33 p_0.

7.12 Stresses in Contact Zone — Two Parallel Cylinders, Normally Loaded

It was shown in article 7.5 that the contact pressure distribution between two cylinders is represented by a semi-elliptical prism (Figure 7-2), and given by Equation (7.11). The stresses associated with a normal load are plotted in Figures 7-8, 7-9, 7-10, 7-11, and 7-12. Figure 7-8 shows the stresses for points on the z-axis (directly under the load). Of the three shear stresses, τ_{xy} (45°), τ_{xz} (45°), τ_{yz} (45°), the highest is τ_{yz} (45°). This stress has a maximum value of approximately 0.3p_0 at a depth of 0.786b.

Figures 7-9, 7-10, 7-11, and 7-12 show the variation of stresses at all points in the contact zone. The magnitudes of normal stresses σ_x, σ_y, and σ_z are highest for the points under the load (stresses at points directly under the load are plotted in Figure 7-8 and are shown again at the zero abscissa points of Figures 7-9 through 7-12). As in the case of the concentrated normal load, the shear stress τ_{yz} changes

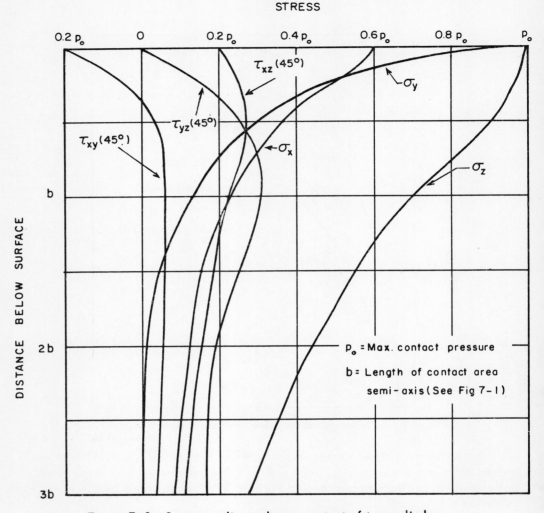

Figure 7–8. Stress gradients due to contact of two cylinders.

sign and is zero directly under the load. The coordinates of points where τ_{yz} is a maximum are, $z = 0.5b$, $y = 0.85b$, and the magnitude is $0.256p_o$. For a moving load, the most critical shear stress is τ_{yz}, as it undergoes a complete stress reversal and has a larger range than any of the 45° shear stresses τ_{yz} (45°), τ_{xz} (45°), and τ_{xy} (45°) plotted in Figure 7-8.

7.13 Summary of Contact Stress Formulas, Normal Loading

Table 7-1 contains a summary of general formulas pertaining to the maximum compressive and maximum shear stresses associated with the six special cases discussed in the previous articles.

TABLE 7-1
Summary of Contact Stress Formulas

No.	GEOMETRY	DISSIMILAR METALS $p_o = \sigma_2 = \sigma_{max}$	SIMILAR METALS: $E_1=E_2=E,\ \mu_1=\mu_2=0.3$			$a=b^*$ (No.1,2,3) b (No.4,5,6)
			$p_o = \sigma_2 = \sigma_{max}$	τ max	Depth at τ max	
1.	Sphere and Flat Plate P = Total load	$.578\left[\dfrac{P}{R^2\left(\dfrac{1-\mu_1^2}{E_1}+\dfrac{1-\mu_2^2}{E_2}\right)}\right]^{1/3}$	$0.388\left[\dfrac{PE^2}{R^2}\right]^{1/3}$	$.33\,p_o$	$.25a$	$1.11\left[\dfrac{PR}{E}\right]^{1/3}$
2.	Two Spheres P = Total Load	$.578\left[\dfrac{P\dfrac{R_1+R_2}{R_1R_2}}{\left(\dfrac{1-\mu_1^2}{E_1}+\dfrac{1-\mu_2^2}{E_2}\right)}\right]^{1/3}$	$0.388\left[PE^2\left(\dfrac{R_1+R_2}{R_2}\right)^2\right]^{1/3}$	$.33\,p_o$	$.25a$	$1.11\left[\dfrac{P}{E}\left(\dfrac{R_1R_2}{R_1+R_2}\right)\right]^{1/3}$
3.	Sphere and Spherical Socket P = Total load	$0.578\left[\dfrac{P\left(\dfrac{R_1-R_2}{R_1R_2}\right)}{\left(\dfrac{1-\mu_1^2}{E_1}+\dfrac{1-\mu_2^2}{E_2}\right)}\right]^{1/3}$	$0.388\left[PE^2\left(\dfrac{R_1-R_2}{R_2}\right)^2\right]^{1/3}$	$.33\,p_o$	$.25a$	$1.11\left[\dfrac{P}{E}\left(\dfrac{R_1R_2}{R_1-R_2}\right)\right]^{1/3}$
4.	Cylinder and Flat Plate $P' = \dfrac{Load}{inch} = \dfrac{P}{a}$	$0.564\left[\dfrac{P'}{R\left(\dfrac{1-\mu_1^2}{E_1}+\dfrac{1-\mu_2^2}{E_2}\right)}\right]^{1/2}$	$0.418\left[\dfrac{P'E}{R}\right]^{1/2}$	$.30\,p_o$	$.79b$	$3.04\left[\dfrac{P'R}{E}\right]^{1/2}$
5.	Two Cylinders $P' = \dfrac{Load}{inch} = \dfrac{P}{a}$	$0.564\left[\dfrac{P'\dfrac{R_1+R_2}{R_1R_2}}{\dfrac{1-\mu_1^2}{E_1}+\dfrac{1-\mu_2^2}{E_2}}\right]^{1/2}$	$0.418\left[P'E\left(\dfrac{R_1+R_2}{R_1R_2}\right)\right]^{1/2}$	$.30\,p_o$	$.79b$	$3.04\left[\dfrac{P'}{E}\left(\dfrac{R_1R_2}{R_1+R_2}\right)\right]^{1/2}$
6.	Cylinder and Cylindrical Groove $P' = \dfrac{Load}{inch} = \dfrac{P}{a}$	$0.564\left[\dfrac{P'\left(\dfrac{R_1-R_2}{R_1R_2}\right)}{\dfrac{1-\mu_1^2}{E_1}+\dfrac{1-\mu_2^2}{E_2}}\right]^{1/2}$	$0.418\left[P'E\left(\dfrac{R_1-R_2}{R_1R_2}\right)\right]^{1/2}$	$.30\,p_o$	$.79b$	$3.04\left[\dfrac{P'}{E}\left(\dfrac{R_1R_2}{R_1-R_2}\right)\right]^{1/2}$

* See Figures 7-1 and 7-2

For the portion of Table 7-1 pertaining to cases involving the two contacting members made of similar metals, it is assumed that $\mu = .3$. For values of μ between 0.25 and 0.35 the tabulated results will be in error by less than 1½ per cent. Table 7-2 contains average values of E and μ for several metals.

TABLE 7-2

E and μ for Various Metals

Metal	E, psi	μ
Aluminum	10.3×10^6	.33
Beryllium copper	18×10^6	.29
Brass	15×10^6	.35
Bronze	15.5×10^6	.35
Cast iron	15×10^6	.26
Copper	15×10^6	.34
Magnesium	6.5×10^6	.35
Steel	29×16^6	.29
Titanium	17×10^6	

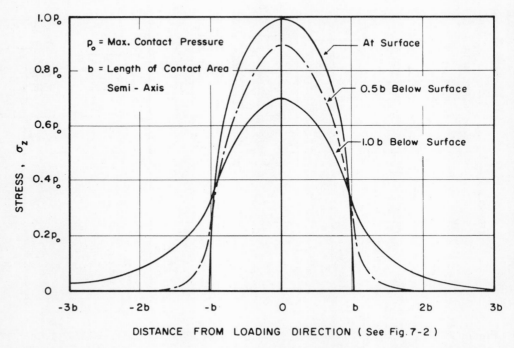

Figure 7–9. σ_z at various points within contact zone – normally loaded cylinders.

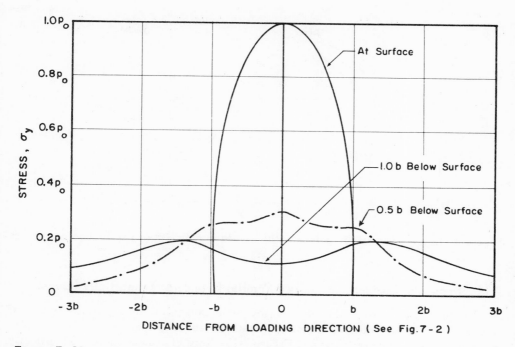

Figure 7–10. σ_y at various points within contact zone – normally loaded cylinders.

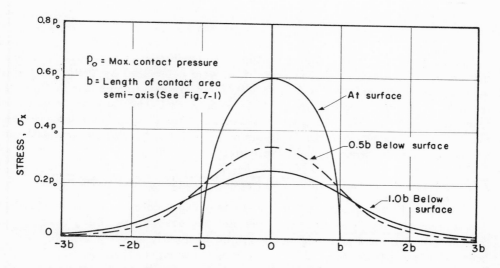

Figure 7–11. σ_x at various points within contact zone – normally loaded cylinders.

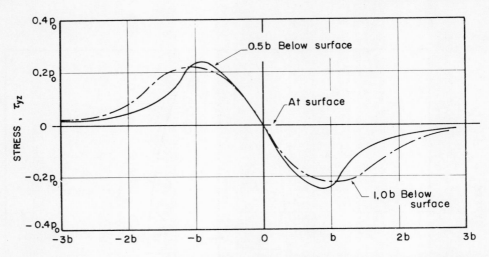

Figure 7–12. τ_{yz} at various points within contact zone – normally loaded cylinders.

7.14 Stresses in Contact Zone – Two Parallel Cylinders, Tangentially Loaded

In analyzing the stresses caused by a tangential load (due to frictional forces), Smith and Liu (Reference 6) assumed an elliptical stress distribution, represented by Equation (7.25) and Figure 7-13. Note that these correspond directly to Equation (7.11) and Figure 7-2 which pertain to the elliptical distribution of normal pressure.

$$q = q_o \sqrt{1 - \frac{y^2}{b^2}} \qquad (7.25)$$

On the basis of the assumed elliptical distribution of tangential pressure, the stress gradients due to a tangential load were determined by Smith and Liu to be as shown in Figures 7-14, 7-15, and 7-16. Note in these figures that the symbols for stress contain the added subscript, t, denoting that these stresses result from tangential loading. Because of the similarity in stress equations it can be seen that τ_{yz} and σ_{zt} have identical forms, as do σ_y and τ_{yzt}. Note also that with tangential loading, the stresses that change sign are σ_{yt} and σ_{zt}.

7.15 Stresses in Contact Zone – Two Parallel Cylinders, Sliding and Rolling

It has been established that the stresses due to combined rolling and sliding can be evaluated by superposition of the stresses due to pure rolling (normal load only, article 7.12) and pure sliding (tangential load only, article 7.14). It has also been established that when rolling and sliding occur together, $q_o = fp_o$ where f is the coefficient of friction of the surfaces of contact. Hence, the stresses due to combined rolling and sliding are obtained by multiplying the stresses in Figures 7-14, 7-15, and 7-16 by the coefficient of friction (thereby expressing them in terms of p_o) and adding them to the stresses given in Figures 7-9, 7-10, and 7-12. This is

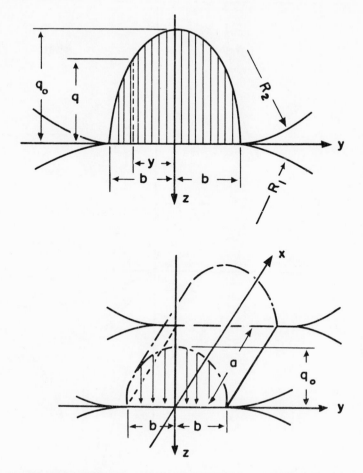

Figure 7-13. Tangential pressure distribution — two parallel cylinders.

done for a coefficient of friction, f, of 1/3, and the resulting stresses are plotted in Figures 7-17, 7-18, and 7-19. In these figures, all stresses are designated with a prime (′) to indicate that they reflect a combination of normal and tangential loading.

Figure 7-17 shows that normal stress σ_y' ranges from $0.67p_0$ (tension) to $-1.20p_0$ (compression). Figure 7-10 shows that when only the normal load is present, stress σ_y varies from zero to $-1.0p_0$. Thus, the addition of sliding with f = 1/3 increased the stress range in the y direction by 87 per cent, and also brought about a reversal in stress direction. This is believed highly significant in explaining fatigue crack initiation and propagation in parts subjected to combined rolling and sliding section.

Figure 7-20 shows values of σ_y' at the surface for three coefficients of friction.

From the theory of elasticity, stress σ_x' is given by

$$\sigma_x' = \mu \ (\sigma_z' + \sigma_y') \tag{7.26}$$

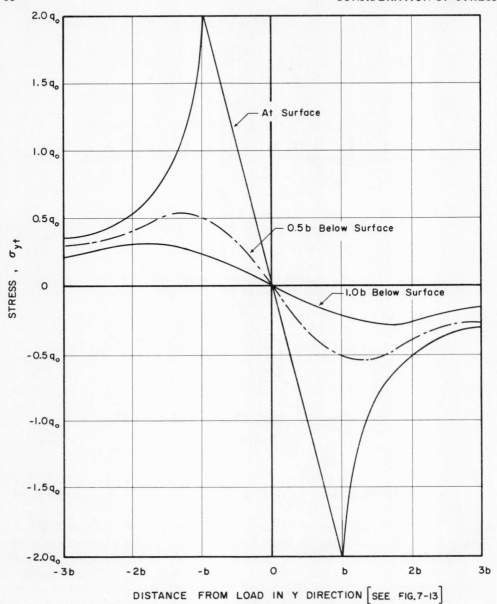

Figure 7–14. σ_{yt} at various points within contact zone —
tangentially loaded cylinders.

By using the methods of Chapter 5 the three principal stresses can be determined. If these principal stresses are σ_1', σ_2', and σ_3' in decreasing order in magnitude,

$$\tau_{max}' = \frac{1}{2}(\sigma_1' - \sigma_3')$$

(7.27)

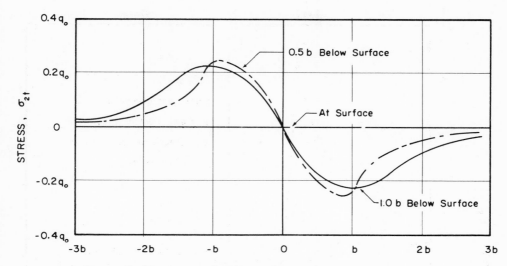

Figure 7–15. σ_{zt} at various points within contact zone —
tangentially loaded cylinders.

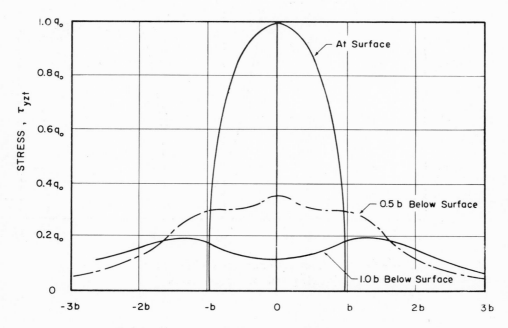

Figure 7–16. τ_{zyt} at various points within contact zone —
tangentially loaded cylinders.

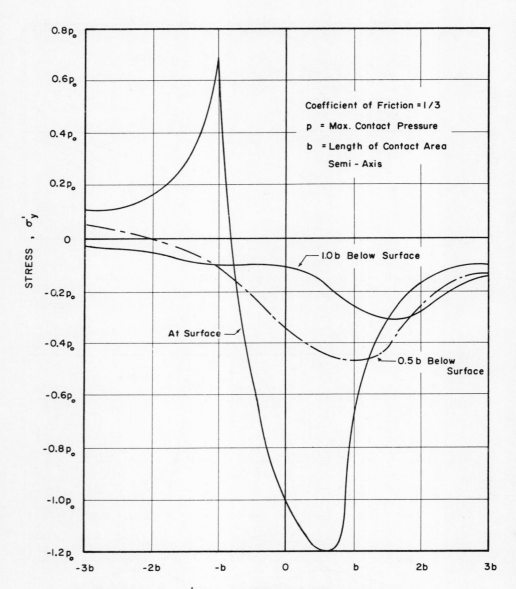

Figure 7–17. σ_y' at various points within contact zone —
sliding and rolling cylinders.

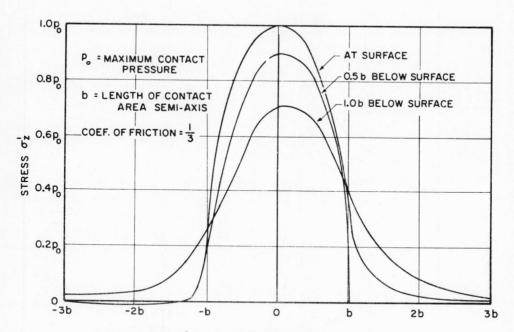

Figure 7–18. σ_z' **at various points within contact zone — sliding and rolling cylinders.**

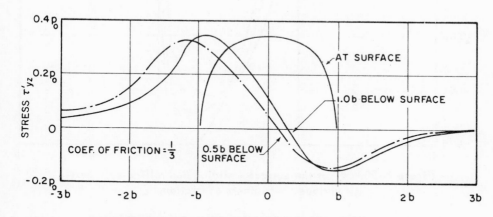

Figure 7–19. τ_{yz}' **at various points within contact zone — sliding and rolling cylinders.**

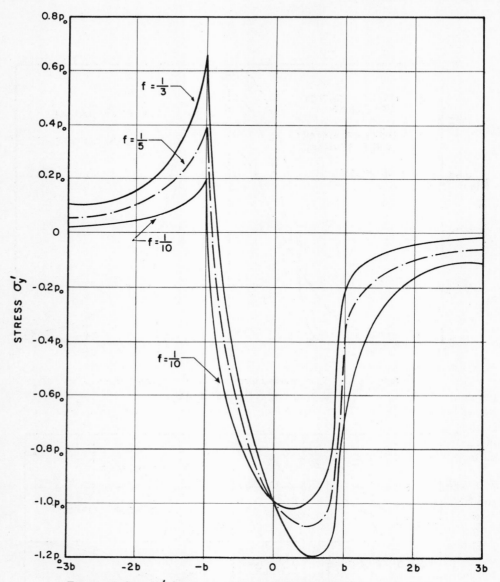

Figure 7–20. σ_y' at the surface – sliding and rolling cylinders, various coefficients of friction.

This maximum shearing stress at the point in question is in a plane bisecting the direction of σ_1' and σ_3'. By using this method it is found that the highest principal stresses are at point A ($z = 0$, $y = 0.3b$) in Figure 7-21, for the case $f = 1/3$, $\mu = 0.25$.

Numerical values of the principal stresses for this case are:

$$\sigma_{1\,max}' = -1.39p_o$$

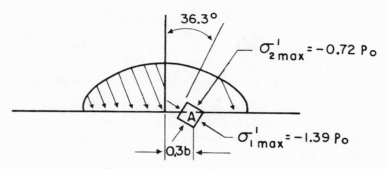

Figure 7–21. Location of maximum principal stresses due to rolling plus sliding.

$$\sigma_{2_{max}}' = -0.72p_0$$

$$\sigma_{3_{max}}' = -0.53p_0$$

From Equation (7.27) the maximum shear stress at the point A is determined as:

$$\tau_{max}' = 0.43p_0$$

Without friction, the highest shear stress was found to be $\tau_{yz}(45°) = 0.3p_0$ at a depth 0.786b below the surface (Figure 7-8). Thus, the friction effect (for $f = 1/3$) results in an increase of maximum shear stress of $(.43 - .30)/.30$, or 43 per cent. Furthermore, the location of the maximum shearing stress is changed by the addition of tangential force from beneath the surface to point A on the surface (Figure 7-21). It was found by J. O. Smith and C. K. Liu that when the coefficient of friction is greater than 1/9 the maximum shear stress occurs at a point on the surface, but when f is less than 1/9, the highest shear stress is below the surface.

7.16 Flash Temperatures and Thermal Stresses — Two Parallel Cylinders, Sliding and Rolling

Combined sliding and rolling of two parallel cylinders results in the production of high flash temperatures which are highly localized in the immediate area of contact. This localized heating is highly important to a consideration of surface failure phenomena. Furthermore, because of differential thermal expansion, it has an important bearing upon the contact zone stresses.

A specific example, illustrating the distribution and order of magnitude of flash temperatures, is shown in Figure 7-22.

Blok derived the following equation for flash temperature.

$$T_f = K \frac{\mu P (V_1 - V_2)}{(C_1 V_1 + C_2 V_2) \sqrt{b}} \tag{7.28}$$

K = Constant.
μ = Coefficient of friction.

P = Normal load per unit and length.

V_1 and V_2 = Surface velocities of cylinders in contact.

C_1 and C_2 = Constants of material which include thermal conductivities, specific heats and densities.

b = Width of band of contact.

T_f = Flash temperature rise (maximum mean surface temperature).

Note that if V_1 and V_2 are increased with the difference $(V_1 - V_2)$ held constant, the resulting flash temperature is reduced. This fact has been often overlooked in connection with proposed scoring criteria, such as PV and PVT, which are proportional to the heat intensity but not the surface temperature.

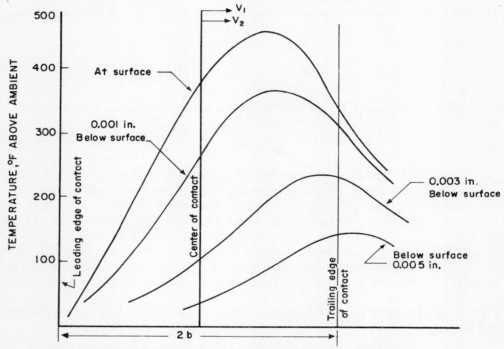

Figure 7–22. Example of flash temperature on and below surface.

It can be shown that the maximum surface temperature varies as $p_o^{3/2}$ with other factors (V_1, V_2, radii, etc.) held constant.

Further investigations into the coefficient of friction as influenced by velocity have resulted in the following formula (Reference 13).

$$T_T = T_B + K \frac{\mu P \left(\sqrt{V_1} - \sqrt{V_2} \right)}{(1 - \frac{S}{50}) \sqrt{b}} \qquad (7.29)$$

T_T = Total surface temperature (flash temperature rise plus ambient).

T_B = Bulk stable temperature of the part.

S = Surface finish r.m.s. micro inches.

Thermal stresses across the contact zone are proportional to temperature. The stresses at the surface represented in Figure 7-22 have been computed. The results are illustrated in Figure 7-23. When this stress pattern is superimposed on the stresses shown in Figure 7-20 ($f = .1$), the complete stress picture results. This is done in Figures 7-24 and 7-25. Data pertaining to these figures is given below:

Radii of Rollers	2.00 and 4.00 inches
V_1	100 in./sec.
V_2	150 in./sec.
Load, P	23,000 lb./in.
Coefficient of Friction, μ	0.1
Materials	Steel on steel

Positive sliding is defined as occurring on the faster of two sliding parts. Note that thermal stresses act to increase the maximum compressive stress for a member in negative sliding more than for a member in positive sliding. It can also be seen that the normal tensile stress is eliminated by the thermal stress indicating that fatigue failure is not likely to occur with positive sliding members since they are stressed only in varying degrees of compression. On the other hand, members in negative sliding are subjected to both tensile and compressive stresses introducing fatigue characteristics and subsequently pitting.

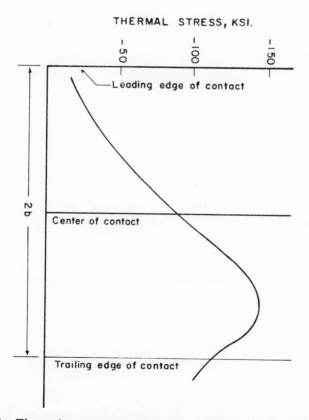

Figure 7-23. Thermal stress at surface of contact (Fig. 7-22 temperatures).

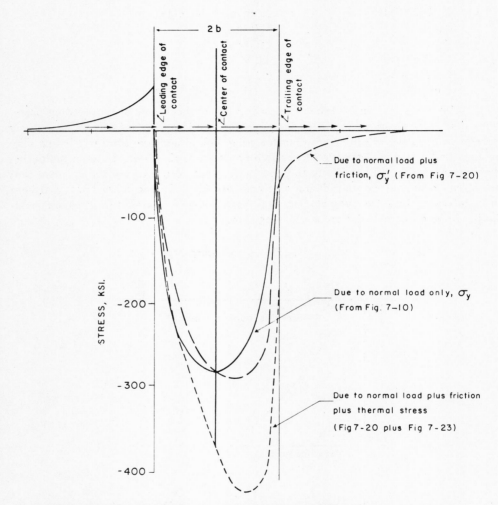

Figure 7-24. Surface stresses, negative sliding (see text for data).

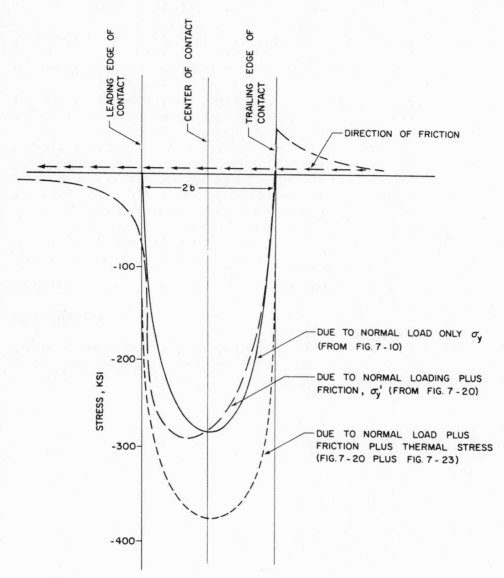

Figure 7–25. Surface stresses, positive sliding (see text for data).

References

1. Roark, R. J., *Formulas for Stress and Strain*, McGraw-Hill, 1954.
2. Buckingham, E., *Analytical Mechanics of Gears*, McGraw-Hill, 1949.
3. Timoshenko, S., *Strength of Materials*, Van Nostrand, 1955.
4. Timoshenko, S. and Goodier, J. N., *Theory of Elasticity*, McGraw-Hill, 1951.
5. Way, Steward, "Pitting Due to Rolling Contact," *Trans. ASME*, Vol. *57*, 1935.
6. Smith, J. O. and Liu, C. K., "Stresses Due to Tangential and Normal Loads on an Elastic Solid with Application to Some Contact Stress Problems," *Jour. of Applied Mechanics*, Vol. *20* (June 1953).
7. Radimovsky, E. I., "Stress Distribution and Strength Condition of Two Rolling Cylinders Pressed Together," University of Illinois Engineering Experiment Station *Bulletin*, Series No. 408, Vol. 50, No. 44, 1953.
8. Buckingham, E. and Talbourdet, G. J., "Recent Roll Test on Endurance Limits of Materials," Mechanical Wear (Symposium), *ASM*, 1950.
9. Faires, V. M., *Design of Machine Elements*, Macmillan, 1941.
10. Thomas, H. R., and Hoersch, V. A., "Stresses Due to the Pressure of One Elastic Solid Upon Another," University of Illinois Engineering Experiment Station *Bulletin* No. 212, 1930.
11. Blok, H., "The Dissipation of Frictional Heat," *Applied Scientific Research*, Section A., Vol. 5, 1955.
12. Kelley, B. W., "A New Look at the Scoring Phenomena of Gears," *SAE Transactions*, Vol. 61, 1953.
13. Kelley, B. W., "The Importance of Surface Temperature to Surface Damage," *Engineering Approach to Surface Damage*, University of Michigan Press, 1958.

Chapter 8

RESIDUAL STRESSES

8.1 Causes of Residual Stresses

The causes of residual stresses include the following:

1. *Mechanical* — loading is of sufficient magnitude to cause plastic deformation. Removal of load allows some elastic relaxation to take place, but due to incomplete relaxation, stresses remain.

2. *Thermal* — non-uniform temperature gradients cause differing degrees of expansion and contraction, accompanied by some degree of plastic deformation. Although mechanical constraint is always involved with plastic deformation, the primary cause of the final stress condition is thermal in nature.

3. *Bulk Phase Transformation* — particular phase transformations require a physical change in volume as one phase decomposes into its transformation products. Perhaps the most common example is the transformation of austenite in steels. Whether martensite or other decomposition products result, a volume increase occurs and residual stresses are created.

4. *Phase Precipitation* — the properties of certain metallic alloys are sometimes controlled by the process known as precipitation or age hardening. Due to a condition of supersaturation, one phase is precipitated and disperses itself through the grains of the matrix. Density differences between matrix and precipitate are considered to be the basic source of stress creation.

5. *Combinations of the Above* — in most cases, the mechanism that causes residual stresses is not singular in nature. Quenching operations may induce thermal, phase transformation, and mechanical mechanisms to contribute to stress creation. Welding operations often introduce phase transformations as well as thermal gradients and plastic flow of the hotter metal.

8.2 Manufacturing Operations Producing Residual Stresses

Typical examples are tabulated below and present the general tendencies to be expected in regard to surface residual stresses only.

The charts, graphs, and other data which follow pertain to the specific examples presented and should not be otherwise interpreted.

Tensile	*Compressive*	*Either*
Welding	Nitriding	Carburizing
	Shot Peening	Rolling
	Flame and Induction	Casting
	Hardening	*Abrasive Metal Cutting
	Heating and Quenching	Non-abrasive Metal Cutting
	Single Phase Materials	*Heat and Quenching Materials that undergo phase transformation

*Majority of commercial situations would probably produce tensile stresses

a. *WELDING*

One important characteristic of spot welding is the presence of a heat source for extremely short periods of time. This creates a large temperature gradient which in turn leads to fast cooling rates as the heat source is removed. Any tendency of the hotter metal to expand is met by restraint from the colder surrounding metal. In addition, phase transformations occur where such a possibility exists. The predominating stresses are usually tensile and a typical biaxial stress distribution is shown in Figure 8-1 (Reference 2). This particular distribution involves a material that had not undergone phase transformation. If this mechanism were also included, the peak tensile stresses would probably be increased.

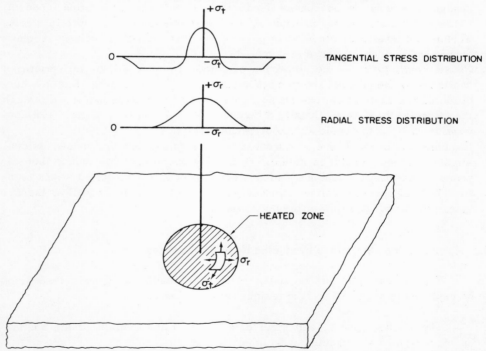

Figure 8–1. Residual stress distribution in a spot welded thin strip (no phase transformation, Reference 2).

Most other welding operations tend to create tensile residual stresses at the surface.

b. CASE HARDENING

Induction hardening consists of heating a relatively shallow layer of a piece of steel to the austenite region and then quenching to produce martensite. Phase transformation, thermal effects, and mechanical restraint all influence the final state of stress which is compressive at the surface. Figure 8-2 (Reference 2) shows a typical distribution that results from this operation. Nitriding, shot peening, and flame hardening are other processes in this category which tend to create surface compressive stresses. Carburizing, however, may lead to either type of stress at the surface. The major difference, from a stress viewpoint, is due to the process itself. Since the entire piece, rather than the surface alone, is heated to high temperatures, the transformation characteristics and cooling rates in the core section can markedly alter the overall stress pattern.

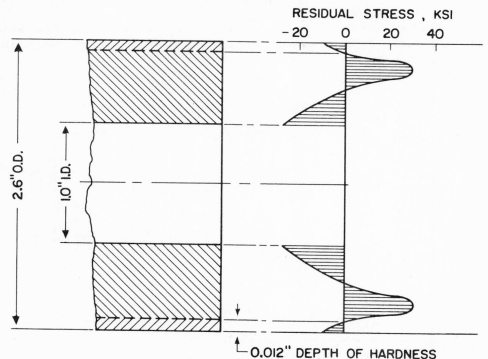

Figure 8-2. Residual stress distribution in an induction hardened crankpin (Reference 2).

c. HEAT TREATING IN GENERAL

The ability of many metals to be hardened by various heat treating operations is one of their most desirable properties. Since heating, then quenching in a cold medium are inherent in this process, it is not surprising to find a stressed end product. In many situations, excessive stresses occur and cause the phenomenon commonly called "quench cracking." Factors such as material composition, size and shape of part, and quenching media introduce so many possible complexities that wide variations in final stress patterns can result. Figures 8-3 (Reference 2) and 8-4 (Reference 3) indicate different patterns that have been found.

d. CASTING

Fundamentally, the cooling of a casting as it solidifies is similar to quenching a piece of metal, but particular characteristics of the casting process cause added complexities. Mold restraint can have a decided influence upon stress patterns and may cause serious consequences, such as hot tears. Figure 8-5 illustrates how such results can occur. The thin rib becomes fully solid before the ends do and as the rib cools and contracts, restraint is afforded by the mold. If the induced stresses exceed the strength of the hotter ends, tears will result as shown. In addition, nonhomogeneity of the structure and uneven cooling rates may lead to center-line shrinkage, interdendritic shrinkage, and blowholes. The resultant stress distribution is thus influenced by many variables.

e. ROLLING

The mechanical working processes are characterized by plastic deformation of the workpiece and, for the purposes of this chapter, this single mechanism will be considered as the sole source of stress creation.

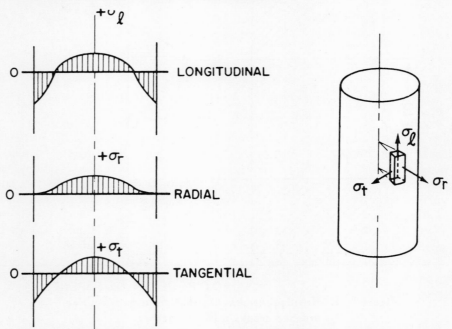

Figure 8–3. Residual stress patterns in a quenched cylindrical bar
(no phase transformation, Reference 2).

Apparently, the resultant stress distribution caused by rolling operations is influenced greatly by the depth of penetration or plastic deformation that is produced. Slight reductions in bar thickness are considered as "surface" or "non-penetrating" rolling while large reductions are classed as "heavy" or "penetrating" rolling. Figure 8-6a (Reference 1) presents a schematic version of these differences

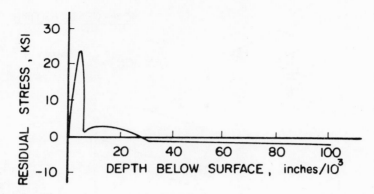

Figure 8–4. Residual stress distribution in a flat bar of AISI 52100 steel after heat treating to obtain a hardness of R_c59 (Reference 3).

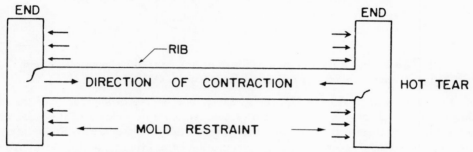

Figure 8–5. Development of hot tears in a casting as it solidifies from a molten state.

as they affect stress patterns in the finished workpiece. A possible explanation of these differences is that surface rolling is similar to shot peening in that the tendency of surface expansion is held back by the interior thereby causing surface compressive stresses. During heavy rolling, plastic deformation results throughout the section and, under load, the full workpiece is subjected to longitudinal tensile stress which is maximum at the surface. This condition prevails because the outer regions of the section thickness experience a greater degree of plastic flow than do the interior regions. Upon passage through the rolls, the external load is released and elastic relaxation follows until an equilibrium of residual stresses is reached. Figure 8-6b is a schematic presentation of a simplified version showing the shift in stress pattern from a loaded to an unloaded condition.

f. NON-ABRASIVE METAL CUTTING

These operations employ a cutting edge of controlled geometry, and although temperature influences are possible, the consensus seems to be that mechanical effects are the predominant cause of residual stresses. Henriksen conducted planing tests on a range of plane carbon steels and from his findings concluded that the maximum surface stresses were predominatly tensile. Colwell investigated the effect of milling and shaping operations and found the residual surface stresses to be compressive in nature. From this and other work he concluded that either type

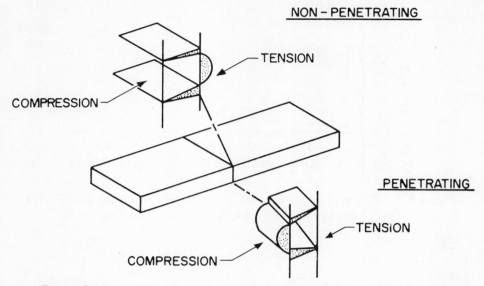

Figure 8–6a. Residual stress distributions caused by penetrating and
non-penetrating rolling of flat strip stock (Reference 1).

of stress can result. Apparently, the geometry and degree of sharpness of the cutting tool, as well as lubrication, size of cut, and overall rigidity of the machining
setup all exert some influence upon the type of stress that results. Regardless of
the end condition, the depth of stress penetration is relatively shallow with critical
stress levels seldom exceeding 0.010 inches.

g. ABRASIVE METAL CUTTING

In recent years the major emphasis of residual stress studies in the area of
metal cutting has been devoted to abrasive operations. A logical answer to the
apparent overemphasis on this area is that a great many of today's machined prod-

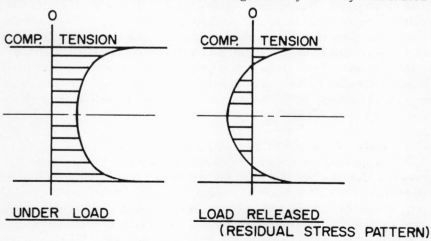

Figure 8–6b. Stress distributions caused by penetrating rolling.

ucts require the degree of precision and surface finish that can be attained only through abrasive techniques.

These operations involve the use of hard abrasive particles that serve as cutting edges having uncontrolled geometry. In addition, the workpiece is subjected to more severe thermal influences as compared to non-abrasive types of operations. Practically all of the investigations reported pertain to restricted test conditions. Tentative general conclusions appear to be the following:

1. Stress penetration at the surface is quite shallow, and critical stresses seldom exceed several thousandths of an inch.
2. Predominance of the thermal influence usually produces tensile stresses. This would be characteristic of commercial conditions that are considered to be "heavy" cuts.
3. Compressive surface stresses can result when cutting conditions are "light" by commercial standards.
4. Peak stresses are usually greater than those that result from non-abrasive operations.

Tarasov, Hyler, and Letner reported that stresses resulting from the grinding of a ball bearing grade of steel reduced the fatigue limit as much as 13 per cent but could increase the limit by 38 per cent depending upon the grinding conditions. Apparently, other investigators feel the detrimental aspects of these findings are conservative and may prove misleading for the general grinding situation. Letner, Colwell, Sinnott, and Tobin; Halverstadt; and Clorite and Reed reported findings for different work materials and the results substantiate the general conclusions mentioned previously. Variations of measured stress distributions are pronounced and, as yet, unexplained. It is of interest to note that tensile residual stresses in excess of 200,000 psi and compressive stresses greater than 100,000 psi have been reported.

h. SUMMARY OF EFFECTS OF PROCESSING METHODS

The variety of metal processing methods suggests that considerable variation is possible in the stresses trapped in the surface layers of a part. The table below illustrates that several factors are involved in the introduction of residual stresses during various processing operations.

Types of Residual Stress Introduced by Processing Operations

Residual Stress Introduced or Altered By	Temp. Difference	Phase Transform.	Cold Plastic Flow	Warpage	Altered Chemistry
Heat Treatment (quenching and tempering)	Yes	Yes	No	No	No
Case Hardening (carburizing and nitriding)	Yes	Yes	No	No	Yes
Induction Hardening	Yes	Yes	No	No	No
Machining	Possibly	Unknown	Yes	Yes	No
Grinding	Yes	Unknown	Yes	Yes	No

Types of Residual Stress Introduced by Processing Operations (Continued)

Residual Stress Introduced or Altered By	Temp. Difference	Phase Transform.	Cold Plastic Flow	Warpage	Altered Chemistry
Cold Working (shot peening, surface rolling, tumbling, lapping, blast cleaning)	No	No	Yes	Yes	No
Straightening	No	No	Yes	No	No

8.3 Effects of Residual Stresses

Due to such factors as residual stress gradients and fading of residual stresses, practical difficulties arise when handling residual stresses by direct addition to stresses caused by external loading. For this reason it is recommended that for most situations residual stresses be taken into account in determining the *strength* of a part. This procedure will be discussed in detail in Chapter 13.

Figure 8-7 illustrates the principle by which residual stresses modify the ability of a part to carry external loads. Figure 8-7a shows a residual stress pattern resulting from a process, such as carburizing or shot peening, which places the outer surface in residual compression. Superposition of bending stresses (Figure 8-7b) onto the residual stress pattern produces the combined stress gradient of Figure 8-7c. If this part is subjected to reversed bending, the fatigue strength of the part will be increased by virtue of the residual stresses, because of the reduction of surface tensile stresses.

The effect of residual stresses varies with material hardness and with the presence of stress raisers. In general, soft materials with no stress raisers experience almost complete fading of residual stresses during operation under conditions of reversed loading. On the other hand, notched parts made of very hard materials retain almost all of their residual stress. This qualitative relationship is represented in the table below. The dividing line between hard and soft materials is considered to be in the general region of 250 BHN.

TABLE 8-1

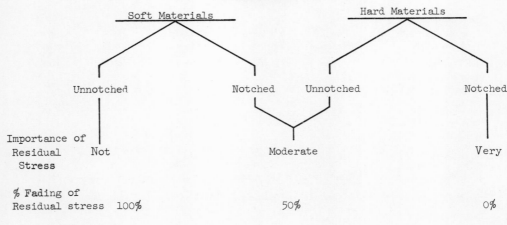

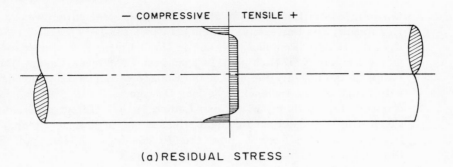

(a) RESIDUAL STRESS

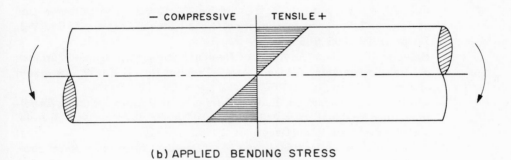

(b) APPLIED BENDING STRESS

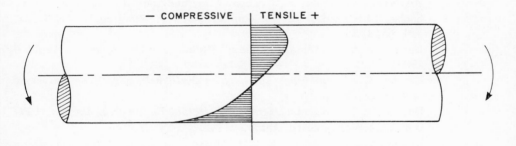

(c) RESIDUAL STRESS PLUS APPLIED BENDING STRESS

Figure 8–7. Stress gradient resulting from residual stress plus bending.

References

1. *Cold Working of Metals*, The American Society for Metals, Cleveland, Ohio, pp. 34, 41, 48, 1949.
2. *Metals Handbook*, 1955 Supplement, pp. 89, 96, 120.
3. Letner, H. R., "Residual Grinding Stresses in Hardened Steel," *Trans. ASME*, Vol. 77, No. 7, pp. 1089-1098 (October 1955).
4. Henriksen, E. K., "Residual Stresses in Machined Surfaces," *ASME Preprint* No. 50-SA-27 (April 24, 1950).

5. Colwell, L. V., "Machinability Studies of X4340 Steel at High Strength," *ERI Report*, The University of Michigan, No. 2133-1-F (January, 1954).
6. Colwell, L. V., "Residual Stresses in Metal Cutting," Lectures given at the University of Michigan, 1958 Summer Conference Course, Published by the Industry Program of the College of Engineering under the title "Engineering Approach to Surface Damage."
7. Tarasov, L. P., Hyler, W. S., and Letner, H. R., "Effect of Grinding Conditions and Resultant Residual Stresses on the Fatigue Strength of Hardened Steel," Reprint from the *Proceedings*, *ASTM*, Vol. 57, Philadelphia, 1957.
8. Letner, H. R., "Grinding and Lapping Stresses in Manganese Oil-Hardening Tool Steel," *Trans. ASME*, Vol. 75, 1953.
9. Colwell, L. V., Sinnott, M. J., and Tobin, J. C., "The Determination of Residual Stresses in Hardened Ground Steel," *Trans. ASME*, Vol. 77, pp. 1099-1105, 1955.
10. Halverstadt, R. D., "Analysis of Residual Stresses in Ground Surfaces of High Temperature Alloys," *ASME Preprint* No. 57-SA-62, Presented at San Francisco (June, 1957).
11. Clorite, P. A. and Reed, E. C., "Influence of Various Grinding Conditions Upon Residual Stresses in Titanium," *ASME Preprint* No. 56-A-44, presented at New York (December, 1956).
12. ASM Committee on Residual Stresses, "Residual Stresses," *Metal Progress* (August 15, 1955).
13. Horger, O. J., "Residual Stresses," *Handbook of Experimental Stress Analysis* by Hetényi, M., London, Wiley and Sons, Inc., 1950.
14. Sachs, S., "Control of Residual Stresses In Practice," *SAE Trans.*, Vol. 63, 1955.
15. Barrett, C. S., "Internal Stresses," *Metals and Alloys*, Vol. 5 (October, 1934).
16. Lipson, C., *Engineering Approach to Surface Damage*, The University of Michigan Press, 1958.
17. Horger, O. J., "Residual Stresses," *Metals Engineering Design*, ASME Handbook, McGraw-Hill, 1953.
18. Lipson, C., "Failure of Tractor Wheels," a report of the John Deere Waterloo Tractor Works (December, 1952).
19. Mattson, R. L., "Effects of Residual Stress on Fatigue Life of Metals," *SAE Trans.*, Vol. 62, 1954.
20. A.S.M. Committee on Residual Stresses, "Residual Stresses," *Metal Progress* (August 15, 1955).
21. Baldwin, W. M., "Residual Stresses in Metals," ASTM Edgar Marburg Lecture, 1949.
22. "Reducing Residual Stresses," from "Engineering Abstracts," *Product Engineering* (November, 1951).

PART II

Consideration of Strength

Chapter 9

GENERAL CONSIDERATIONS OF STRENGTH

9.1 Significant Strength

In general, the term strength implies the ability of a material to resist external loading. Since external loads may be expressed in terms of stresses, strength can be defined as the maximum stress which a material can sustain. By *significant strength* (allowable stress) we mean the maximum stress which a material can sustain in the form of the fabricated part for the loading conditions under consideration.

Significant strength is obviously the strength characteristic of the material which will be exceeded if the part is overloaded to failure. For example, the significant strength associated with a part susceptible to failure due to general yielding is the yield strength of the material as it exists at the location of potential failure. The significant strength associated with a gear tooth susceptible to a fatigue fracture at the tooth fillet is the bending endurance of the material at the point of potential crack origin. In determining this value, due consideration must be given to such factors as surface finish and surface treatment, size effect, exact nature of loading, fatigue life required, etc.

Conventional design practice employs one of two criteria for determining the significant strength. The first is derived from experience with successful and unsuccessful designs and, accordingly, significant strength is taken as the maximum stress which the parts are known to sustain without failure. These values will usually be found in design codes, and their reliability depends on individual interpretation and experience. In some instances, significant strength may be expressed in terms of the magnitude of externally applied load necessary for failure. An example of this practice is the frequently used wear capacity of gear teeth, expressed in terms of the externally applied dynamic load in pounds.

The second criterion uses for significant strength a value which is related to the ultimate strength or the yield point of the material. The reason for using ultimate strength as the basis for the derivation of the significant strength is that it is one of the most readily measured quantities. It represents the optimum strength that the material can exhibit, and it is generally related to all other measurable quantities pertaining to strength.

It has been realized by designers and metallurgists that the ultimate strength by itself could not serve as the correct index of strength, because the strength of the member varies with such factors as the condition of loading, surface finish, etc. In view of insufficient knowledge, and for the sake of simplicity, it was found convenient to group all of these effects under a common index termed "factor of safety." This factor was then divided into the ultimate strength, and the resultant ratio was tacitly accepted as the significant strength (also termed design stress).

In view of the fact that design practices are predicated on the absence of failure, the significant strength thus derived was usually on the conservative side. The result was that for severe service conditions the significant strength represented values which were approximately correct, but which were decidedly on the conservative side for a more favorable set of conditions.

A more rational approach would still employ ultimate strength as the basis for the derivation of the significant strength. However, instead of an indiscriminate grouping of all the factors affecting the ultimate strength into one index, it would attempt to evaluate, quantitatively, the effect of each individual factor pertaining to the part and the conditions under consideration. The result would be a value for the significant strength that would be strictly applicable to the part under consideration and to the set of loading conditions to which the part would be subjected in service. This is the approach used in this book.

The principal factors affecting strength, and which must be considered in determining the significant strength are:

1. Life expectancy.
2. Type of loading (axial, bending, torsional, or a combination).
3. Size effect.
4. Surface finish.
5. Surface treatment.
6. Notch effects.
7. Mode of loading (static, completely reversed dynamic, or a combination).

These factors are discussed in detail in the following chapters. It will be noted that many other factors commonly included in the study of materials, such as the chemical composition, notched-bar impact strength, per cent elongation, and hardenability, are not included in the above classification. The principal reasons for the omission of these factors are that, at least in the case of steel, they have a minor effect on the strength of fabricated members. Also, they are expressed in units which render them difficult to use in design.

For example, consider the effects of per cent elongation, which is conventionally used to denote the ductility of the material. This quantity is evaluated in connection with the yield point and tensile strength determination, and many specifications classify materials according to certain required elongations. The basis for these specifications is an assumption that ductility is associated with toughness and that a high degree of ductility is required to allow the part to deform under load, so that fracture may be prevented. Thus, 20 per cent elongation is a common requirement for conventional steels, even though most manufactured members could never endure such a large deformation and still be able to function satisfactorily in service. One or two per cent elongation is probably all that is required of most parts, with the possible exception of bolted members. In the case of notched parts subjected to fatigue loading, a certain amount of ductility is required so that the effect of stress concentration may be diminished. Even in this case, however, only about five per cent elongation is required. Furthermore, the resultant deformation involves only a highly localized region and consequently is not governed by the conventionally determined values of the per cent elongation.

Another factor which frequently enters into the discussion of the strength of steels is hardenability. This is an index of the ability of steel to harden throughout. In the case of parts subjected to an axial loading, the ability of a member to resist an external load will be governed both by the strength of the surface and by the strength of the core. A steel of a higher hardenability will provide an obvious advantage. The majority of load-carrying members are subjected, in service, to bending or torsional loads, resulting in a stress which is maximum at the surface and zero at the neutral axis. In these cases, high hardness in the core is not an essential requirement, and steels of different hardenabilities may exhibit the same service strength. Further discussion of the relative effectiveness of the surface and core hardness will be found later in article two of Chapter 13. It is recognized that some parts require a steel of high hardenability in order to control distortion and residual stresses due to quenching.

9.2 Selection of Material

The selection of the correct material is a factor which contributes greatly to the success of a designed structure or machine member. Some of the more important factors to be considered when selecting materials are listed below.

a. STRENGTH

Generally, the most important criterion to be considered in selecting a material is the requirement of strength. The strength of a material is its capacity to resist the action of applied forces. Unfortunately, the strength of a material cannot be represented by a single number because its ability to resist the actions of loads depends upon the nature of these loads and on the environment of the material. However, enough data and information have been obtained to enable a designer to calculate with reasonable accuracy the strength of a material under various loading and environmental conditions. This topic will be discussed in detail in the subsequent articles and chapters of this book.

b. ELASTIC DEFLECTION AND STABILITY

The second criterion to be considered is the stiffness or rigidity of the part. Most materials possess an elastic limit, which is the maximum stress to which a test specimen may be subjected without permanent deformation. The specimen returns to its original size if subjected to stresses less than the elastic limit. Below the elastic limit, stress is proportional to strain, and the proportionality constant is called the modulus of elasticity. For simple tension and compression,

$$\sigma = E \epsilon \tag{9.1}$$

where

$$\sigma = \text{stress (psi)}$$
$$E = \text{modulus of elasticity (psi)}$$
$$\epsilon = \text{strain (in./in.)}$$

In terms of total deformation, where $\delta = \epsilon L$

$$\sigma = \frac{E\delta}{L} \qquad\qquad (9.2)$$

where

δ = deformation (in.)

L = total length undergoing the deformation (in.)

From these equations it is apparent that for a given stress, deformation is inversely proportional to the modulus of elasticity. Therefore, the modulus of elasticity is a direct measure of stiffness or rigidity. Stiffness is an important criterion in many designs, such as those of machine tools for accurate work (lathes, milling machines, etc.), and rotor shafts in motors, generators, and turbines. Many failures of gears, bearings, and the like stem from lack of stiffness of the parts, their housings, or some other part of the whole assembly. Correction for this deficiency is usually a matter of design, rather than a change in materials. Merely changing from one alloy to another of the same base metal will not increase the modulus. Buckling considerations are important in the design of compression members. Examples are engine connecting rods, struts, etc.

A more detailed treatment of stiffness and stability is contained in Part IV.

c. WEAR

Wherever the material is subjected to the action of rubbing contact with another member, problems of wear must be considered. Gears, cams, pistons, bearings, etc. afford common examples.

d. ENVIRONMENT

It is very important when selecting a material to consider the effect of temperature and corrosion upon the material properties.

Many materials are temperature-sensitive, so that properties existing at room temperature may be vastly different at other temperatures. Yield strength, tensile strength, and impact strength vary for different operating temperatures. High temperatures cause the phenomena of creep. Notch sensitivity may increase suddenly at subnormal temperatures. In steels, this condition may occur above room temperature. At some elevated temperature, yield strength may fall greatly, although generally it decreases rather gradually. Thus, the material properties must be known corresponding to the operating temperature ranges involved.

Any environment that promotes corrosion, either by liquids or gases, requires a specific choice of material to defeat the specific corrodent, or a modification of the environment to render it noncorrosive. It has been found that metals exposed to corrosive atmospheres have reduced endurance limits. High strength steels have a corrosion fatigue resistance close to that of plain mild steels. Low alloy steels have about the same resistance to corrosion fatigue as unalloyed steels. High chromium steels, which have improved corrosion resistance, have improved corrosion fatigue resistance. Also, stress corrosion cracking has been observed in almost all metal systems. Yet for each metal, specific environments are required. Iron and steel alloys are subject to rapid stress corrosion cracking in some nitrate solutions and also to caustic embrittlement. From the corrosion standpoint, suitable materials can sometimes be chosen on the basis of prior knowledge and experience. Most often, and particularly when new processes are involved, corrosion tests are required.

e. PRODUCTION

The choice of a material may be based on the ease with which it can be given its finished form, rather than on its properties. Many materials may have properties suitable for the intended use but may still have different forming characteristics. The choice of processing methods is largely predicated on how many duplicated pieces are to be produced and whether or not savings will amortize the cost of dies or other special equipment.

Machinability, formability, and weldability are important factors in processing. Large improvements in any of these factors, however, is at the expense of maximum strength. None of these features can be precisely evaluated from tensile data; therefore, specific tests are required, duplicating the actual processing conditions.

f. AVAILABILITY

The supply of a material is a significant factor when parts are to be produced on a mass production basis. The quantity of material available, the supplier of the material, and other possible sources of material in case of emergency, should be considered, especially when working with the uncommon materials. Changing the material from which a part is to be produced often requires a new design and new processing methods.

g. COST

When selecting a material which possesses the necessary properties, cost is always of primary concern. Material selection can influence the cost in two ways. First is the initial cost of the material. Second is the cost involved in processing the material. Processing methods such as brazing, extruding, electroforming, forging, sand casting, precision casting, centrifugal casting, and forming have a wide range of relative costs. The method of processing selected depends to a great extent on the material; thus, the selection of material may greatly affect the cost of production.

9.3 Properties of Materials

The following are definitions of some of the more important material properties. They correspond to the definitions given by the American Society for Testing and Materials.

a. **Ultimate Tensile Strength (S_u).** The maximum tensile stress which a material is capable of developing. Tensile strength is calculated from the maximum load carried during a tension test using the original cross-sectional area of the specimen.

$$s_u = \frac{P_{max}}{A}$$

b. **Ultimate Compressive Strength (S_{uc}).** The maximum compressive stress which a material is capable of developing, based on the original cross-sectional area. In the case of a material which fails in compression by a shattering fracture, the compressive strength has a very definite value. In the case of materials which do not fail in compression by a shattering fracture, the value obtained for compressive strength is an arbitrary value depending upon the degree of distortion. This is regarded as indicating complete failure of the material.

c. **Ultimate Shear Strength (S_{us}).** The maximum shearing stress which a material is capable of developing, based on the original cross-sectional area.

d. **Yield Strength (S_y).** The greatest stress which a material is capable of developing without exceeding a specified small amount of permanent strain, generally 0.2 per cent.

e. **Proportional Limit.** The greatest stress which a material is capable of developing without any deviation from proportionality of stress to strain (Hooke's Law).

f. **Elastic Limit.** The greatest stress which a material is capable of developing without any permanent strain remaining upon complete release of the stress.

g. **Hardness.** The measure of a material's resistance to indentation. A common criterion is the Brinell hardness number (BHN), increasing numbers indicating increasing hardness. This hardness number, BHN, is approximately related to the ultimate tensile strength of steel as follows:

$$S_u = 500 \times BHN \text{ psi} \qquad (9.3)$$

(for steel when $200 < BHN < 350$)

This approximation should be used only if more reliable test data are unavailable. The relationship between three commonly used hardness scales is plotted in Figure 9-1.

h. **Percentage Elongation.** The extension in the vicinity of the fracture of a tensile specimen, expressed as a percentage of the original gage length; for example, 20 per cent in two inches.

$$\% \text{ Elong.} = \frac{\Delta L}{L} \times 100 \qquad (9.4)$$

i. **Percentage Reduction of Area.** The smallest area at the point of rupture of a tensile speciment divided by the original area.

$$\% \text{ R.A.} = \frac{A_{rupture}}{A_{original}} \times 100 \qquad (9.5)$$

j. **Endurance Limit (S_n').** The maximum completely reversed stress which may be repeated an indefinite number of times on a polished standard specimen in bending without causing failure.

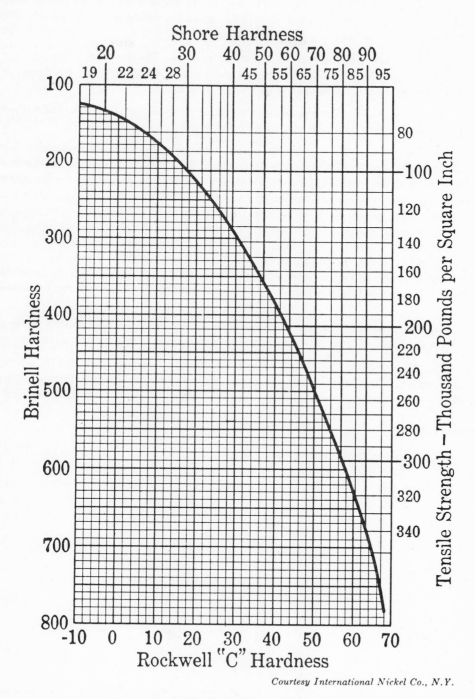

Courtesy *International Nickel Co., N.Y.*

Figure 9–1. Relation of hardness numbers.

k. **Endurance Strength** (S_n). The maximum completely reversed stress which an actual part can withstand for a specified number of times without failure. The loading may be either bending, torsional, or axial.

l. **Stiffness.** The ability to resist deformation. The linear stiffness characteristic of a material is measured by the modulus of elasticity, E; the torsional stiffness characteristic is measured by shear modulus, G.

m. **Toughness.** The capacity of material to withstand a shock load without breaking. The impact strength evaluates toughness.

n. **Ductility.** That property which permits permanent deformation before fracture in tension. Ductility is the opposite of *brittleness*. There is no absolute measure of ductility, but the percentage elongation and the percentage reduction of area are used as indices; the higher these indices, the more ductile the material is said to be. For purposes of definition, it is frequently assumed that the dividing line between ductile and brittle materials is in the range of 2 to 5 percent elongation in two inches. For example, steels having less than 2 percent elongation and a hardness of over 400 BHN are commonly considered brittle. Steels having over 5 percent elongation and a hardness less than 400 BHN are usually regarded as ductile. Steels meeting neither set of criteria cannot be clearly classified either way.

o. **Elasticity.** The ability of a material to be deformed and to return to the original shape. Stress is proportional to strain only during elastic deformation.

p. **Plasticity.** The ability of a material to be deformed plastically without rupture. In a plastic deformation, the material does not return to its original shape, but rather absorbs the energy of deformation internally (thereby resulting in heat).

References

1. Lipson, Noll, and Clock, *Stress and Strength of Manufactured Parts*, McGraw-Hill, 1950.
2. *Metals Handbooks*, Vol. 1, 8th Ed., American Society for Metals, 1961.

Chapter 10

STATIC AND IMPACT STRENGTH

Many parts in service are subjected to either a dead load or to a load which in the useful life of the part is repeated only a small number of cycles, less than 1000. Members loaded in this manner are normally considered to be under a condition of static loading, and the corresponding significant static strength should be used for design purposes.

10.1 Simple Loading

Simple loading may be considered as loading which imposes stresses identical in character with those produced by standard material tests. Strength values for simple loading are directly determined from test results; hence, no consideration of a failure theory is involved. For example, the strength in direct tension and compression is determined directly from the standard tensile and compression tests. These same test results apply directly to bending, because bending loads produce uniaxial tension and compression which have maximum values in the outer fibres. Likewise, if torsion test results are available, the strength values for pure torsional loading are determined directly.

In contrast with simple loading is the case of general loading which is discussed in the next article. A generally loaded part, for example, might be subjected to a combination of axial, bending, and torsional loads. Such a loading would produce a general state of biaxial stress which would not correspond to the stress state existing in any standard test. In order to apply standard test results to a condition of general loading it is necessary to utilize a theory of failure.

For the case of simple static loading, a decision must be made as to whether the yield strength, ultimate strength, or impact strength of the material will be taken as the significant strength. Which one of these is used for the criterion of strength depends upon the speed of loading, type of material, and allowable deformation.

a. ULTIMATE STRENGTH

The use of ultimate strength in designing for static loads utilizes the maximum strength of the material. When designed under these conditions, a member exhibits a stress which is often greater than the yield strength of the material, thus causing the material to be in the plastic range and to be permanently deformed. Therefore, when a design is based upon S_u, the member should be such that permanent deformation will not be harmful. Failure under these conditions will usually appear as a complete fracture of the member. The ultimate strength is always used as the basis of design for brittle materials which exhibit very little yielding, such as cast irons. The common shear pin is an example of a ductile part designed on the basis of ultimate strength.

The relationship between hardness and tensile strength of ferrous materials is shown in Figure 10-1. It will be noted that the relationship for steel is represented by a band that includes test data on alloy and plain carbon steels. That is, for a given hardness the tensile strength will be essentially the same, regardless of the composition of the steel and its processing. The center line of the band reveals that the tensile strength is approximately equal to 500 times the Brinell Hardness Number. When dealing with ductile materials such as steel or aluminum, the ultimate strength in tension is approximately equal to the ultimate strength in compression, while for gray cast iron the ultimate strength in compression is approximately three to five times greater than the ultimate strength in tension. For some design calculations it is necessary to use a guaranteed minimum ultimate tensile strength. The ASTM class number for cast iron is equal to the minimum tensile strength in ksi.

b. YIELD STRENGTH

Under many conditions of static loading the permanent distortion of a member would not be acceptable due to tolerance and space requirements. For these conditions of static loading, the yield point or yield strength of the material will be taken as the significant strength. This type of failure is recognizable by the yielding of a considerable portion of the member.

Figure 10-2 shows the relationship between the yield point of steel and the tensile strength or equivalent Brinell Hardness. For high strength steels ($S_u >$ 200,000 psi), the yield point is approximately $0.9S_u$, while for low strength steels the yield point can be as low as $0.6S_u$.

c. IMPACT STRENGTH

In the design of structures and machine parts for static loading, accelerations of all mass elements are assumed to be zero. Material properties such as yield strength and ultimate strength are taken to correspond to values obtained in laboratory tests conducted at slow speeds. When the structures or machine parts are components of machines that run smoothly at a constant speed as, for example, a turbine generator, then the designer must cope with the additional problem of fatigue of metals. However, even here speed has been shown not to be a factor except insofar as the total number of loading cycles is concerned.

It has been found that in designing for impact loading, stress concentration should be kept to an absolute minimum, and that a maximum volume of material should be stressed to the highest existing level. In actual practice, stress raisers (stress concentrations) are usually present. Therefore, to reduce the effect of stress raisers, the material should have sufficient ductility to permit the redistribution of stresses in the vicinity of the stress raiser. Also, the maximum stress varies directly with the square root of the modulus of elasticity. Therefore, it is wise to use a material with low modulus of elasticity provided the yield strength is adequate.

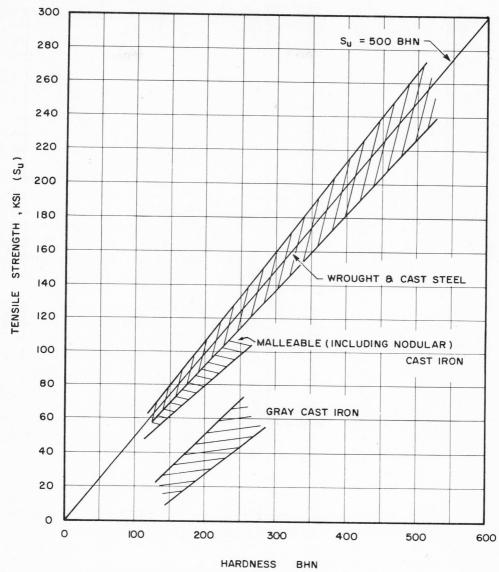

Figure 10–1. Tensile strength vs. hardness, ferrous metals.

Laboratory tests have shown that the speed of loading, or more specifically the rate of strain, has a marked effect on the physical properties of materials. Tests, conducted upon mild steels, have shown that the yield strength increases continuously with the rate of strain, whereas the ultimate shows a decrease for the lowest rates (below the strain rates encountered in impact) and an increase for the higher rates (Figure 10-3).

As a consequence of these test data, and in the absence of knowledge of the actual strain rate that will exist, the use of the static properties of the material for designing parts for impact loads is a satisfactory and conservative approach.

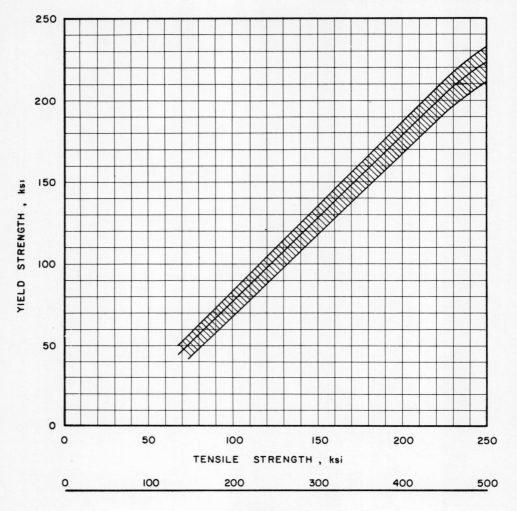

Figure 10-2. Yield strength of wrought steel.

10.2 General Loading, Theories of Failure

When considering the strength of a material subjected to general loading (loading different from that corresponding to available material strength test data), it is necessary to apply a theory of failure. The process of formulating and applying a failure theory consists of two basic steps:

1. A theory is postulated to explain the failure of a standard test specimen. For example, a tensile specimen apparently yields when some capacity of the material has been exceeded. According to three well-known theories the critical capacity of the material is:

   a. capacity to withstand normal stress (maximum normal stress theory),

   b. capacity to withstand shear stress (maximum shear stress theory), and

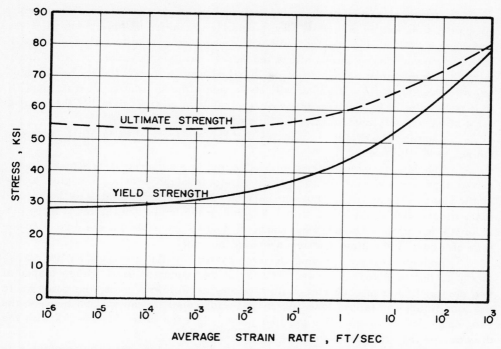

Figure 10–3. Effect of strain rate on physical properties of mild steel.

    c. capacity to absorb distortion energy (maximum distortion energy theory).

2. The results of the standard test are used to establish the magnitude of the capacity chosen. Thus, if the standard tensile test indicates a yield strength of 100 ksi, the above failure theories would predict that the same material, subjected to any combination of loading, would always yield when:

    a. the maximum normal stress reached the level corresponding to 100 ksi uniaxial tension; namely, 100 ksi (maximum normal stress theory)

    b. the maximum shear stress reached the level corresponding to 100 ksi uniaxial tension; namely, 50 ksi (maximum shear stress theory), or

    c. the level of distortion energy reached that which exists at 100 ksi uniaxial tension (distortion energy theory).

       A brief discussion of each of the above mentioned failure theories is given below.

a. MAXIMUM NORMAL STRESS THEORY

       This theory, sometimes called Rankine's Theory, takes maximum stress as the criterion of failure. The theory states that failure takes place whenever one of the principal stresses, irrespective of the others, reaches the value of the yield point as determined in a simple tensile test. According to this theory, shear has no effect on failure, since, when principal stresses are acting, the shear is zero.

Thus, suppose a specimen, the yield point of which in tension is 35 ksi and in compression 45 ksi, is subjected simultaneously to tension and compression. Then, according to this theory yielding will occur whenever a tensile stress reaches 35 ksi or whenever a compressive stress reaches 45 ksi, whichever occurs first. Stated in more general terms, if a three-dimensional element is subjected to three principal stresses σ_1, σ_2, σ_3, yielding will be caused either by the maximum stress σ_1, if it is tensile, or by the minimum stress σ_3, if it is compressive, but the intermediate stress σ_2 will have no effect on failure.

Experimental evidence indicates that this theory applies to brittle materials but not to ductile ones.

Consider, for example, cast iron subjected to a simple tensile stress. Theory shows that the maximum tensile stress exists in a plane at right angles to the applied load and consequently the specimen should fail at right angles to the applied load, irrespective of the shear stress diagonal to the load. This is found to be true in brittle materials. On the other hand, in ductile materials failure occurs in the form of a cone, indicating maximum shear as the cause.

Another example, proving the applicability of the maximum normal stress theory to brittle materials, is that of a reinforced concrete beam. When loaded at two points, $L/3$ from each end, failure occurs as follows: under the point where the load is applied failure takes place on the diagonal; in the section between the two loads, failure occurs in a vertical plane. In each case this checks with the direction of the principal plane.

Thus, the maximum stress theory appears to be generally applicable to brittle materials but not to ductile ones. Another disadvantage of this theory is its failure to explain the behavior of both brittle and ductile materials under hydrostatic pressure. Under hydrostatic pressure the part is subjected to compressive stresses and consequently failure should occur at right angles to the applied loads. Actually, specimens subjected to a hydrostatic pressure from all sides do not fail at all.

b. MAXIMUM SHEAR STRESS THEORY

The maximum shear stress theory is widely used by engineers. It states that failure takes place whenever the shear stress reaches the value of the shear, at yielding, in a simple tension test. This is known as Guest's Law.

The maximum shear theory can be applied satisfactorily to ductile materials but not to brittle ones. According to basic stress theory, in a specimen loaded in simple tension, maximum shear occurs in a 45° plane; according to the maximum shear theory, failure should then occur in this plane. Experience shows that this is true for ductile materials, for a ductile specimen will fail in a characteristic cone fracture, in a plane approximately 45° to the direction of loading. This theory however does not apply to brittle materials, for a brittle specimen when subjected to a tensile load will fail in a transverse plane instead of on a 45° diagonal.

Similarly, in torsion it will be found that the maximum shear theory is applicable to ductile materials but not to brittle ones. General theory shows that a specimen, subjected to torsional loads, has maximum shear in a plane of the longitudinal axis of the specimen and in a plane transverse to it, while maximum tension is in a plane 45° to it. Thus, according to the maximum shear theory, we would expect the specimen to fail in a longitudinal or in a transverse plane. Ductile materials do so, brittle ones do not. The latter fail in a 45° diagonal plane.

Torsional failures are of a particular interest to the engineer because of a general misconception involved in the appearance of torsional cracks. It is quite common, for example, for an engineer presented with a transverse fracture in a cylindrical shaft, to attribute the failure to a bending load because "torsion always produces helical breaks." This misconception arises out of the common observation that manufactured members subjected to torsional loads, such as crankshafts, for example, do fail on a diagonal. Crankshafts, however, are notched parts, on account of the presence of transverse oil holes, and the mode of failure in notched specimens is much affected by the state of stress produced by the notch.

Apparently, in ductile parts subjected to torsional loads, we are faced with two fundamentally different types of fracture: (1) helical, in the direction of maximum tension, (2) transverse or axial, along the line of maximum shear. Attempts have been made in the past to explain these failures in terms of hardness, softer materials producing transverse or axial fractures, hard materials producing helical failures. Another explanation is in terms of sound metals, free from inclusions, exhibiting the transverse and axial breaks. But neither interpretation can be accepted as a satisfactory criterion of torsional failure.

Understanding the differentiation between these two types of failure can be effected by a consideration of the pertinent stress magnitudes and stress directions. If a part is weak in shear, it will fail along the plane of maximum shear giving a transverse or axial fracture, and if weak in tension, it will fail in the direction of the maximum tensile stress, causing a helical break. In a plane shaft, the maximum shearing stress is equal to the maximum tension and since ductile materials are weaker in shear, failure will occur transversely or axially.

In a notched shaft, however, fracture will be of a different character. If a hole, such as an oil hole in a crankshaft, is drilled radially, the maximum tensile stress may be four times the maximum shearing stress and since ductile materials are only twice as strong in tension as in shear, failure will occur in tension in a 45° plane.

Thus, the maximum shear theory, in contrast to the maximum stress theory, appears to be applicable to ductile materials but not to brittle ones. It will also be recalled that the maximum stress theory failed to explain why materials do not fail under a hydrostatic pressure. The maximum shear theory explains this satisfactorily. When a specimen is subjected to a hydrostatic pressure, equal compressive forces are exerted on all sides and therefore, in accordance with general theory, the shear stress are zero. According to the maximum shear theory, if shear stresses are zero, failure cannot take place.

c. *MAXIMUM DISTORTION ENERGY THEORY*

According to this theory, also referred to as the Von Mises-Hencky Theory, static yielding takes place whenever the three principal stresses are such that the following equation is satisfied:

$$(\sigma_1 - \sigma_2)^2 + (\sigma_1 - \sigma_3)^2 + (\sigma_2 - \sigma_3)^2 = 2S_y^{\,2} \qquad (10.1)$$

For the general case of biaxial loading, involving stresses σ_x, σ_y, and τ_{xy}, the maximum distortion energy theory predicts yielding when Equation (10.2) is satisfied.

$$\sigma_x{}^2 + \sigma_y{}^2 - \sigma_x\sigma_y + 3\tau_{xy} = S_y{}^2 \tag{10.2}$$

The distortion energy theory is recommended for ductile materials since it predicts yielding with a high degree of accuracy. Where only a reasonably close and conservative estimate is required, the maximum shear stress theory is often preferred in practice. The maximum shear stress predicts yielding at loads from 0 to 15 percent lower than those predicted by the maximum distortion energy theory. The 15 per cent discrepancy exists in the case of pure torsion which is illustrated in the following article.

10.3 Sample Problems Illustrating Failure Theories

Problem 1

The standard tensile test indicates that a given steel has a tensile yield strength of 100 ksi. What value of pure torsional stress would be expected to cause yielding?

a. Maximum Normal Stress Theory. According to this theory, the answer is $\tau = TR/J = 100$ ksi, as illustrated by the Mohr circles below:

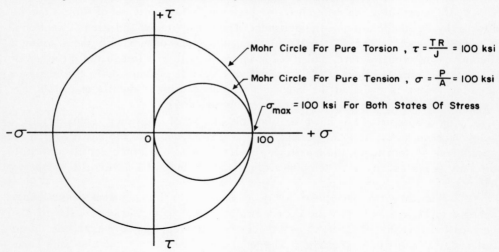

Figure 10–4.

Equation (10.3) provides an alternate solution:

$$\sigma_1 = \frac{\sigma_x + \sigma_y}{2} + \sqrt{\tau_{xy}{}^2 + \frac{(\sigma_x - \sigma_y)^2}{2}} \tag{10.3}$$

For pure torsion, $\sigma_x = \sigma_y = 0$, and $\tau_{xy} = \tau$. We wish to determine what value of τ will give $\sigma_1 = 100$ ksi. Substituting in Equation (10.3) we have:

$$100 \text{ ksi} = 0 + \sqrt{\tau^2}, \text{ or } \underline{\tau = 100 \text{ ksi}}$$

b. Maximum Shear Stress Theory. According to this theory, the answer is $\tau = TR/J = 50$ ksi, as illustrated by the Mohr circles in Figure 10-5.

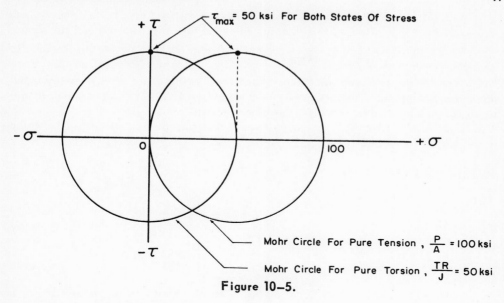

Figure 10-5.

An alternate analytical solution is provided by Equation (10.4):

$$\tau_{max} = \sqrt{\tau_{xy}^2 + \left(\frac{\sigma_x - \sigma_y}{2}\right)^2} \qquad (10.4)$$

Again substituting, $\sigma_x = \sigma_y = 0$, and $\tau_{xy} = \tau$, we solve the equation to determine the value of τ which makes τ_{max} equal to the value of τ_{max} in the tensile yield test; namely, 50 ksi. Obviously, the answer is $\tau = 50\ ksi$.

c. **Maximum Distortion Energy Theory.** This theory cannot be represented by Mohr's circles; hence, Equation (10.2) will be applied. Making the same substitutions of $\sigma_x = \sigma_y = 0$ and $\tau_{xy} = \tau$ to represent the case of pure torsion, we have:

$$0 + 3\tau^2 = S_y^2 = (100\ ksi)^2$$

$$\tau = 57.7\ ksi$$

The value predicted by the distortion energy theory checks well with experimental results for ductile materials. Note that this theory predicts that the yield strength is 15 per cent higher than the value predicted by the maximum shear stress theory.

Problem 2

A material is to be selected for the bar subjected to combined loading in the sample problem of article 5.3. What should be the tensile yield strength of the material if the given stresses are to be just sufficient to cause initial yielding?

a. **Maximum Normal Stress Theory.** Figure 5-9 shows that the maximum normal stress is 22.9 ksi. Hence, this theory indicates that the material should have a tensile yield strength of 22.9 ksi.

b. Maximum Shear Stress Theory. Figure 5-9 shows that the maximum shear stress is 13.7 ksi. Hence, this theory indicates that the material should have a tensile yield strength of 27.4 ksi. (A uniaxial stress of 27.4 ksi results in a maximum shear stress of 13.7 ksi.)

c. Maximum Distortion Energy Theory. The distortion energy theory equations can be applied here in any one of several ways. First, since the principal stresses are known, Equation (10.1) may be applied:

$$(\sigma_1 - \sigma_2)^2 + (\sigma_1 - \sigma_3)^2 + (\sigma_2 - \sigma_3)^2 = 2S_y^2$$

$$(22.9 + 4.5)^2 + (22.9 - 0)^2 + (-4.5 - 0)^2 = 2S_y^2$$

$$750 + 525 + 20 = 2S_y^2$$

$$1295 = 2S_y^2$$

$$S_y = 25.4 \; ksi$$

As an alternate solution, use Equation (10.2) together with stress values shown in Figure 5-8 for element A:

$$\sigma_x^2 + \sigma_y^2 - \sigma_x\sigma_y + 3\tau_{xy} = S_y^2$$

$$(18.3)^2 + 0 - 0 + 3(10.2)^2 = S_y^2$$

$$335 + 312 = S_y^2$$

$$647 = S_y^2$$

$$S_y = 25.4 \; ksi$$

Problem 1, involving a state of pure torsion, represents the condition of maximum discrepancy between the three failure theories. Problem 2, involving a state of stress roughly approximating uniaxial tension, represents a state of stress for which the discrepancy is small (for pure uniaxial tension the three theories are, of course, in exact agreement). If the material selected for problem 2 is ductile, the distortion energy theory result would undoubtedly check closest with actual test results.

References

1. Lipson, Noll, and Clock, *Stress and Strength of Manufactured Parts,* McGraw-Hill, 1950.
2. Lipson, C. and Thiel, D. H., *Applications of Stress Analysis,* University of Michigan, 1959.
3. Grover, H. J., Gordon, S. A., and Jackson, L. R., *Fatigue of Metals and Structures,* U. S. Government Printing Office, 1960.
4. Lipson, C., *Five Theories of Static Failure Explained and Compared,* Product Engineering (June, 1947).

Chapter 11

FATIGUE STRENGTH

When failure of a moving machine element occurs, it is usually due to so-called fatigue. Fatigue failure occurs because, at some point, repeated stress in a member exceeds the endurance strength of the material. In the case of alternating loading, where the load is repeated a large number of times, failure occurs as a brittle fracture without any evidence of yielding. The failure usually originates in the formation of a crack at a localized point on the surface. Under successive loading, the crack propagates through the section, until the remaining portion is not sufficiently strong to sustain even a single load application, and instantaneous failure occurs. The surface of the zone, through which the crack propagates itself, exhibits a typical brittle fracture and is termed a fatigue zone. The appearance is usually smooth and velvety, due to the successive pressing and rubbing of the cracked faces. In contrast, the instantaneous zone is coarse and crystalline, due to the rapid rate at which failure occurs.

Since machine parts do fail by fatigue, it is logical to base their design on their endurance strengths, rather than on their yield or ultimate strengths, especially in the case of new parts in new machines where there is no analogous experience to provide a guide for design. When the design is made on the basis of the nominal average computed stress (P/A, Mc/I, TR/J) and the factor of safety is based on the yield or ultimate strength, no proportionate account is taken of the effects of the surface condition, flaws in the material, discontinuties in the surface, life expectancy of the member, or conditions of loading. To cover these unaccounted-for eventualities, the designer chooses a large and ordinarily conservative factor of safety. Yet it often happens that, even though the designer thought he was being very conservative, extreme conditions result in unexpected failure. Thus, a generous factor of safety based on the traditional yield or ultimate strength is largely a factor of ignorance. Designs which account for the actual service conditions and the shape of the part are more desirable. With knowledge of fatigue strengths increasing during recent years, designers have been rapidly accepting this point of view.

11.1 Endurance Limit

When designing for fatigue loading, the foremost criterion is the endurance limit of the material. This is the strength possessed by a test specimen subjected to an infinite number of cycles of load fluctuation. To find an endurance limit, a test specimen is placed in a machine, loaded as a beam, and then rotated. The load produces a tensile stress on one side of the beam and a compressive stress on the other side. After a 180° rotation, the fibre that was in tension is now in compression; another 180° rotation brings the stress in this fibre back to tension. Thus, in every revolution, the stress is completely reversed. Since it is convenient to think of the normal stress (tension and compression) algebraically, compressive stress will be taken as a negative stress. That is, the largest compressive stress is the minimum stress σ_{min}, and the largest tensile stress is the maximum stress σ_{max}. For complete reversal, σ_{max} is numerically the same as σ_{min}.

The endurance limit $S_n{}'$ of a material is the maximum completely reversed bending stress which may be repeated an infinite number of times (greater than 10 million cycles for steel) on a polished standard test specimen, without causing failure. Ten million cycles has been chosen for steel because it was found that in virtually all cases, if a steel part can withstand this number of cycles without failure, it will last indefinitely. Experimentally, it has been found that the closest correlation with static properties exists between endurance limit and ultimate strength. For steels having up to 200,000 psi tensile strength, the fatigue ratio of endurance limit to ultimate strength is approximately 0.50. In equation form,

$$S_n{}' = 0.50 \, S_u \tag{11.1}$$

where $S_n{}'$ is the endurance limit for infinite life of a polished unnotched specimen subjected to completely reversed cycles of stress imposed by bending.

In gray iron, the endurance limit is between 35 and 50 per cent of the tensile strength. The 35 per cent applies to a very large section whereas the 50 per cent would apply to smaller sections. For most sections, an arbitrary figure of 40 per cent of the tensile strength can safely be used. For aluminum and magnesium, the endurance limit is approximately 30 to 40 per cent of the tensile strength. Relationships between tensile strength and endurance limit for several metals are graphically illustrated in Figures 11-1, 11-2, 11-3, and 11-4. Since non-ferrous materials do not possess a true endurance limit, it is customary to use the endurance strength at 10^8 or 5×10^8 cycles as a substitute.

In actual practice, machine members differ greatly from standard polished test specimens and are very seldom under conditions of completely reversed bending. Also, many parts are not required to run indefinitely. In order to determine fatigue strengths under various conditions of alternating loading, the endurance limit must be corrected for type of loading, size, surface, and life. In this manner an endurance strength S_n, or significant strength, is determined which is applicable to the particular machine member and service conditions involved. These correction factors will be developed in the following sections. An example of fatigue loading is provided by a railroad axle shaft. The shaft is loaded as a simple supported beam with the top of the shaft being stressed in compression and the bottom in tension. Since the wheels are rigidly fastened to the shaft, the shaft rotates with the wheels as the car moves. During each rotation, a point on the shaft is subjected to a compressive stress when it is on the top and a tensile stress when it is on the bottom. Thus, during each revolution the stress varies from a maximum compression to a maximum tension and back to a maximum compression; that is, a complete reversal of stress is accomplished during each revolution. This reversal of stress will

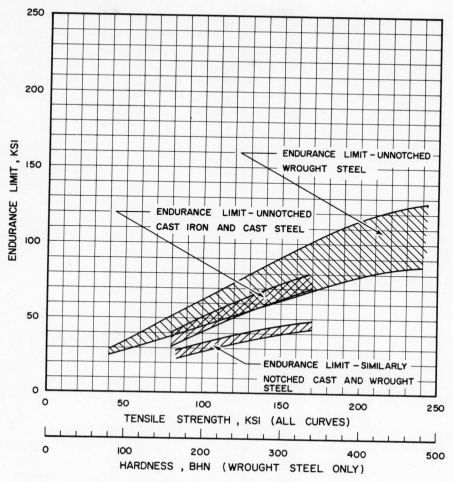

Figure 11-1. Endurance limit of ferrous metals.

eventually cause failure by fatiguing the steel if the stress range is great enough and if it is applied a sufficient number of times.

11.2 S-N Curve

Figure 11-5 illustrates a generalized plot of endurance strength versus number of cycles for standard steel R. R. Moore samples. These samples are 0.3 inch diameter, mirror polished, free of geometric stress raisers, and they are subjected to pure reversed (rotating) bending. A considerable scatter exists among tests for various steels, and even among tests of presumably identical steels. The extent of this scatter is illustrated by Figure 11-6. The generalized curve given in Figure 11-5 provides a practical and conservative approximation which may be used in the absence of specific test information on the exact steel involved.

Note that for one million or more cycles the strength is equal to the endurance limit, and that for less than one million cycles the fatigue strength varies

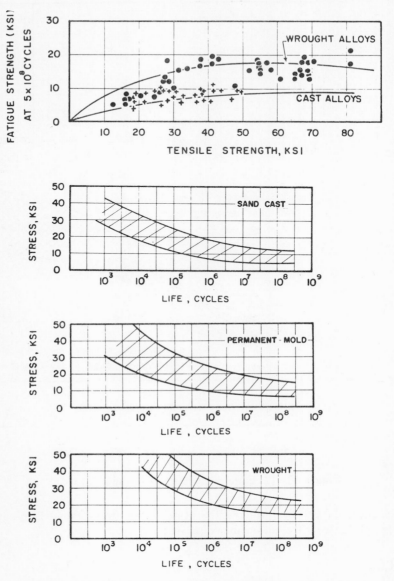

Figure 11–2. Fatigue strength of aluminum alloys.[2]

linearly with life when plotted on log-log coordinates. Loads applied less than 100 cycles may be treated as static loads, as stated in Chapter 10.

A significant observation is that by using Equation (11.1) the complete S-N for any steel curve can be approximated from only a knowledge of the ultimate strength. By using the relationship between Brinnel hardness number and tensile strength given in the last chapter (S_u = 500 BHN), the S-N curve for any steel can be approximated if only the hardness is known. It should be emphasized that the empirical relationships between hardness, tensile strength, and endurance limit are

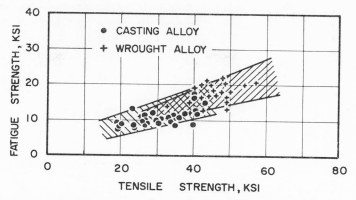

Figure 11–3. Fatigue strength of magnesium alloys (10^8 cycle life).[2]

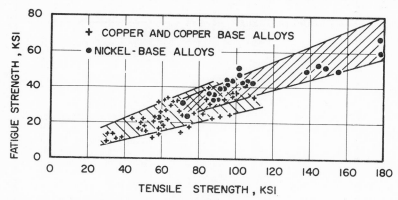

Figure 11–4. Fatigue strength of copper alloys and nickel alloys (10^8 cycle life).[2]

valid only for steels which gain their hardness through good commercial heat treating procedures, and which do not exceed hardness values permitting adequate relieving of quenching stresses. This latter limitation is illustrated for several steels in Figure 11-7. Figure 11-8 shows the order of magnitude of variation in endurance limit among steels having the same hardness but varying percentages of martensite in the as quenched structure.

An S-N curve constructed in accordance with Figure 11-5 provides an approximation of the strength corresponding to any desired life, but is severely restricted by the following conditions:

1. completely reversed bending load
2. 0.3 inch diameter size
3. mirror polished surface, and
4. freedom from any geometric stress raisers.

The next four articles will deal with procedures for modifying the basic S-N curve so as to take into account each of the above items.

S-N curves for cast iron also conform reasonably well to a straight line relationship on log-log coordinates between 10^3 and 10^6 cycles. Representative S-N curves for steel, cast iron, and aluminum are given in Chapter 21.

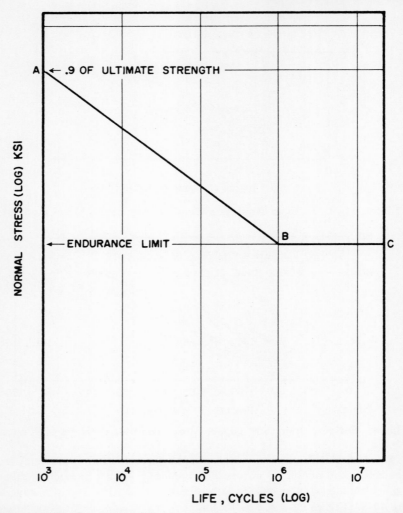

Figure 11-5. Generalized S-N curve for steel, reversed bending loads.

11.3 Type of Loading

The three major types of fluctuating loading encountered in designing members are axial, bending, and torsion. Since the endurance limit is commonly determined from specimens loaded in bending, no correction factor is necessary for the bending load. Hence:

$$C_{load} \text{ (reversed bending)} = 1.0$$

However, it has been found that the endurance strength of polished specimens subjected to reversed axial loading is less than the endurance limit determined using a bending load. Although there is a great amount of scatter among the data available, a reasonable and conservative assumption appears to be that the endur-

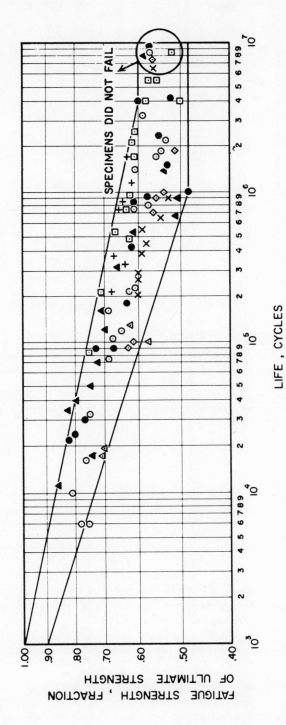

Figure 11-6. Fatigue strength vs. life, unnotched polished specimens, wrought steel, reversed bending loads.

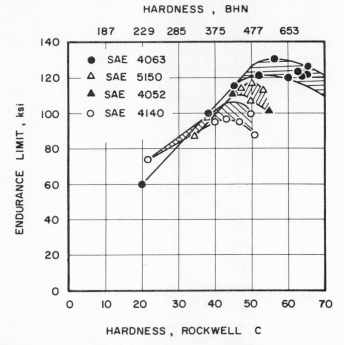

Figure 11-7. Endurance limit of specimens tempered to various hardness.[11]

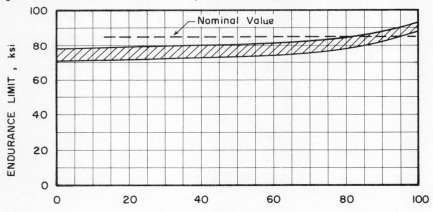

Figure 11-8. Endurance limit vs. per cent "as quenched" martensite in specimens tempered to 340 BHN.[11]

ance limit for reversed axial loads is 15 per cent less than the value for reversed bending, thus:

$$C_{load} \text{ (reversed axial load)} = 0.85$$

The reasons why the axial endurance limit is not as high as the bending endurance limit probably include: (1) the difficulty of applying axial loads with no eccentricity, and (2) the zero stress gradient which causes the entire volume of material to be subjected to maximum stress.

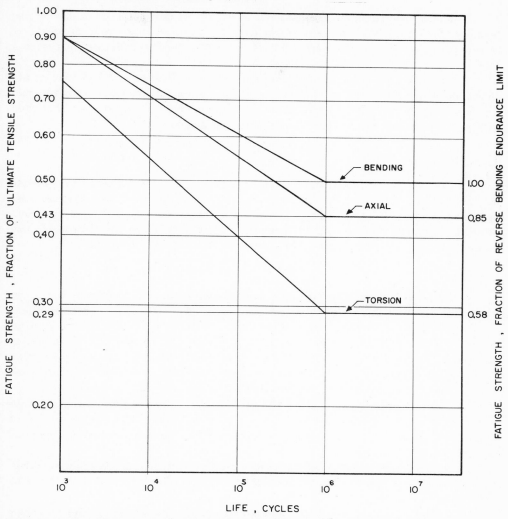

Figure 11–9. Generalized steel S–N curves reversed axial, bending, and torsional loading.

Fatigue tests in torsion on steel show a torsional endurance limit of a polished specimen to be approximately 58 per cent of the endurance limit in bending, thereby indicating good agreement with the distortion energy theory.

$$C_{load} \text{ (reversed torsion)} = 0.58$$

The influence of type of loading on the 10^3 cycle point of the S-N curve is as follows:

a. For reversed bending, use $0.9S_u$.

b. For reversed axial load, use $0.9S_u$.

c. For reversed torsion, use $0.9S_{us}$.

Where specific data for S_{us} is not available, it is recommended that S_{us} be taken as $0.82 \, S_u$. This figure is compatible with results of a study of 35 steels reported by T. J. Dolan in Chapter 6.2 of the ASME Handbook *Metals Engineering Design*.

Generalized S-N curves for steel subjected to all three types of loading are shown in Figure 11-9. In plotting the curves for torsional loading it was assumed that $S_{us} = 0.82 \, S_u$. Although the load factors given above are most commonly used with steel, they may be used for ductile metals in general.

11.4 Size Effect

For bending and torsional loading, the endurance strength tends to decrease as size increases. Wire has a higher endurance limit than that of a standard test specimen (nominal 0.3 in. diameter). For sizes larger than the standard specimen, strength decreases approximately 15 per cent up to 1/2 in. diameter, after which and up to about 2 in. it varies little. Thus, between 1/2 in. and 2 in. size, let

$$C_{size} = 0.85 \text{ (bending and torsion)}$$

Large specimens tend to have much lower endurance strengths, but since large-scale testing is costly, there are not enough data for a firm generalization. For very large parts, the endurance strength may be reduced by 25 per cent or more below the endurance limit of test specimens. Figure 11-10 illustrates the effect of size on the endurance limit of steel for small sizes. It seems likely that the reason size has a negligible influence in axial loading (i.e., $C_{size} = 1.0$ for axial loading) is associated with the zero stress gradient of all size parts.

The influence of size on the 10^3 cycle point of the S-N curve is considerably less than at the 10^6 cycle point and is commonly neglected. Whenever possible, of course, the value of S_u or S_{us} should be obtained from test samples of the approximate size range involved.

Although the size correction factors plotted in Figure 11-10 apply specifically to steel, the best available information indicates that they may be applied to other metals generally.

Figure 11-11 represents an attempt to correlate size effect with hardness for steel parts. These curves involve the Neuber notch sensitivity constant for steels of various hardness, and are based on material contained in Reference 8. Size factors represented in Figure 11-11 are higher, and hence less conservative, than those shown in Figure 11-10. For present usage, it is suggested that a size factor of 0.85 be used for bending and torsional loads in the range of 1/2 to 2 inches unless additional test data are at hand to support higher values in the direction of those given in Figure 11-11.

11.5 Surface Effect

The condition of the surface should always be taken into account when the design is based on fatigue. For the purpose of discussion of the effect of surface

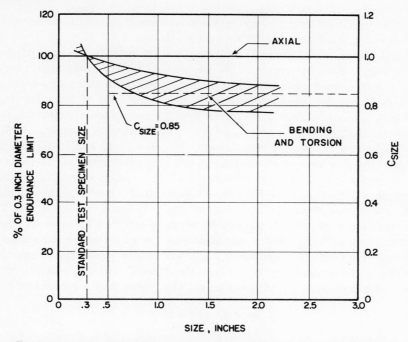

Figure 11-10. Size effect — bending, axial, and torsional loads.

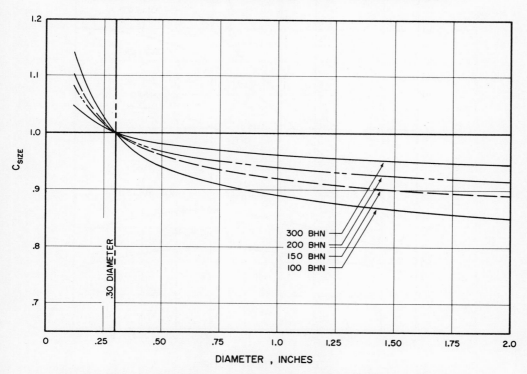

Figure 11-11. Size effect — bending and torsional loads — steel parts.

finish on the significant strength, surfaces will be classified into five broad categories: polished, ground, machined, hot-rolled, and as-forged.

The reason for this classification is that, at least in the case of steel, the fatigue strength depends very much on the surface finish, being higher for smooth surfaces than for rough surfaces. For example, while the endurance limit of well-polished parts can be taken approximately as 50 per cent of the ultimate, in the case of as-forged surfaces it can be less than 10 per cent. Intermediate surfaces, such as hot-rolled, turned machined, etc. are characterized by endurance-limit values between 10 and 50 per cent of the ultimate. Figures 11-12 and 11-13 illustrate the influence of the five surface categories on the endurance limit of steels of various tensile strengths. The endurance strength at 10^6 cycles is multiplied by factor C_{surf} obtained from Figure 11-13. The strength at 10^3 cycles is not significantly affected by surface finish.

The above categories of surface finish were selected because they represent the most common surfaces used in manufacture. The meaning and the scope of each category is defined and discussed below as to how it affects the significant strength.

The polished category represents the "ideal" surface, and is the surface applied to standard fatigue test specimens. This curve thus represents the limiting

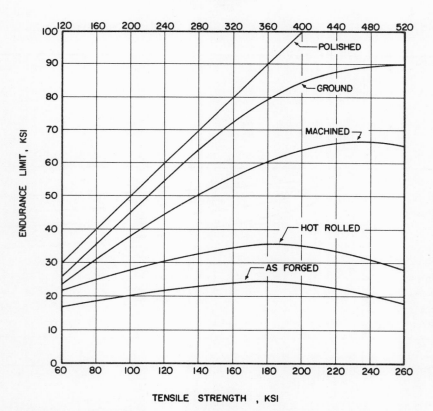

Figure 11-12. Effect of surface finish on endurance limit of steel.

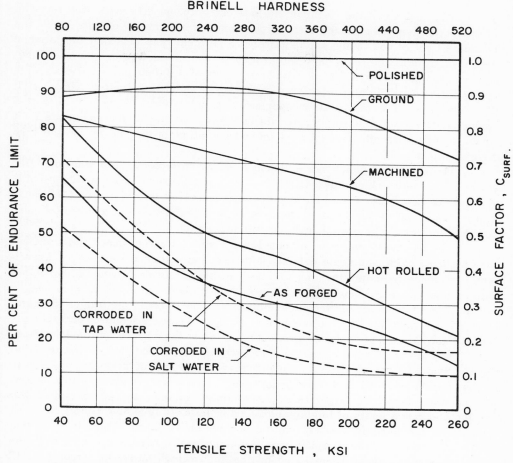

Figure 11–13. Reduction of endurance strength due to surface finish.

strength attainable as far as surface effect is concerned. In only rare instances would the cost of applying this careful polishing treatment be justified for commercial parts.

The ground surface category includes all types of surface finish which do not affect the endurance limit by more than 10 per cent. Laboratory tests have shown little variation in the endurance limit between ground, commercially polished, and superfinished soft steel specimens. Also, the variation in the endurance limit between specimens finished with fine and coarse emery paper was three per cent for a steel of 118,000 psi tensile strength and 11 per cent for a steel of 138,000 psi strength.

Further investigations found no significant difference between ground and commercially polished specimens of low strength steel. In view of this evidence, all data from commercially polished, ground, honed, lapped, and superfinished specimens were included in the ground surface category and plotted against the tensile strength as shown in Figure 11-12. These methods of finishing give a surface with a maximum profilometer reading of 100 microinches.

With respect to the machined surface category, no difference was found in endurance limit between rough and finish machined specimens of soft steel, the endurance limit of both being approximately 25 per cent less than that for polished specimens. Additional tests have shown a 28 per cent reduction in endurance limit from a 0.004 in. deep tool mark with specimens of 150,000 psi tensile strength steel. Other investigators reported a decrease in endurance limit of 20 per cent with a wide, shallow tool mark in specimens of soft steel. Since only a limited amount of data were available under this category, the plot of the endurance limit versus tensile strength necessitated an extrapolation of the curve for the high strength steels.

The hot-rolled class was included to cover surface conditions encountered on hot-rolled parts which have slight surface irregularities; some included oxide and scale defects, with partial surface decarburization. It is reported that the range of stress is 55 per cent less for spring steel plates (455BHN) with a hot-rolled surface than for those with a machined and polished surface.

The as-forged category included parts with larger surface irregularities; some included oxide and scale defects, with total surface decarburization. Experimental evidence indicates that the low fatigue strength of as-forged and hot-rolled parts is due to the combined effect of surface decarburization and surface irregularities. The more severe are these characteristics, the lower is the fatigue strength.

Thus, controlled forging operations produce a small amount of decarburization and correspondingly smaller differences between the surface and interior hardness. They are also characterized by less pronounced surface pits and fewer inclusions and surface irregularities. Standard large-scale manufacturing processes produce a more pronounced decarburized layer and more surface defects. As a result, the endurance limits of large-scale manufactured forgings are appreciably lower than the endurance limits of forgings produced under more favorable conditions.

The forged surface effect plotted in Figures 11-12 and 11-13 is conservative. Controlled favorable forging conditions can easily permit as-forged surfaces to be as strong as those represented by the "hot-rolled" curves of Figures 11-12 and 11-13. A similar approach has been adopted in plotting the curves for other surfaces. For example, a carefully machined surface can approach the "ground" curve, and a carefully ground surface can approach the "polished" curve. All of the S-N curves and Goodman diagrams for steel in Chapters 21 and 22 are based on the conservative surface factor curves of Figure 11-13.

The curves "corroded in salt water" and "corroded in tap water" included in Figure 11-13 illustrate the order of magnitude of reduction in fatigue strength caused by these factors. Obviously, many factors such as steel composition, duration of exposure, temperature, etc. will influence the exact extent of weakening in each specific case.

At the present time, data are not available for determining surface correction factors for materials other than steel. The common practice is to ignore the surface effect for these materials. Except for extremely non-notch sensitive materials such as cast iron, this practice undoubtedly results in some error. Hence, the designer would be well advised to be slightly more generous in the selection of a safety factor for cases involving poor surface finishes.

The effect of surface finish on parts subjected to 1000 or fewer load cycles has been found negligible. Hence, in estimating S-N diagrams for steels of various surface finishes, the surface correction is applied to the 10^6 cycle point, no correction is made at the 10^3 cycle point, and a straight line may still be used to connect these two points on a log-log plot. This procedure is illustrated in the S-N curves for steel shown in Chapter 21.

11.6 Fatigue Strength Reduction Factors, K_f vs. K_t

A notch, or stress raiser, in a part subjected to fatigue loading can be regarded as a factor causing a local increase in stress or as a factor reducing strength. For example, a notch resulting in a factor of 2 can be thought of as doubling the stress or as halving the strength. In either case the effect is to reduce the magnitude of external load causing failure by a factor of 2.

If all parts were made of materials which were completely homogeneous (even on a microscopic scale, i.e., there could be no grains) and had surface finishes which were perfectly polished, the effect of a notch would be to increase the stress by the factor K_t, discussed in Chapter 6. Since actual materials are not perfectly homogeneous and actual surfaces are seldom perfectly polished, there exist internal and surface stress raisers in notch-free parts. For this reason, the addition of a notch to an actual part generally produces a smaller effect than would be predicted from the theoretical stress concentration factor, K_t. The extent to which a notch reduces the endurance limit of a part is referred to as the fatigue stress concentration factor, or the fatigue strength reduction factor of the notch, and is designated by the symbol K_f. Thus:

$$K_f = \frac{\text{endurance limit of specimen without the notch}}{\text{endurance limit of specimen with the notch}}$$

When comparative endurance limit tests are conducted for the purpose of evaluating K_f, it is understood (unless specifically stated to the contrary) that both sets of samples have the same effective section so that the test evaluates only the effect of the stress concentration and does not include an effect due to a reduction in section caused by cutting the notch.

General curves relating K_f and K_t for ferrous materials are contained in Figure 11-14. These curves serve to provide a rough method of obtaining K_f when K_t is known; however, more accurate means of determining K_f for steel will be given in the next article.

Figure 11-14 indicates that coarse grained steels, such as normalized and annealed carbon steels, are relatively insensitive to notches, while fine grain, heat treated steels are much more notch-sensitive. In Figure 11-14, "quenched-and-drawn" is meant to include any steel which is given heat treatment to increase its hardness above that of the as-received state. Annealing is meant to include normalizing and all other processes which use a slow cool, with the exception of tempering. The dividing line between quenched-and-drawn steels, thus defined, and the annealed steels is approximately 200 BHN.

Of particular interest in Figure 11-14 are the limiting values of K_f which are shown. The significance of this point is illustrated by the following example. It has been reported that in the case of threads the theoretical stress concentration factor K_t reaches a value of 11. This does not mean that the presence of a thread results in an elevenfold (or 91 per cent) reduction in the strength of a threaded mem-

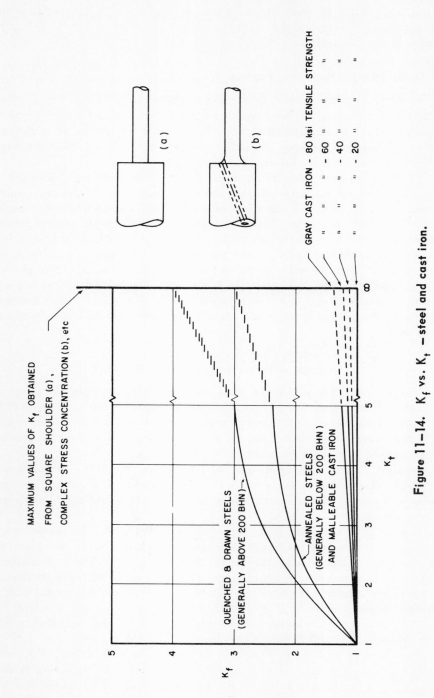

Figure 11–14. K_f vs. K_t — steel and cast iron.

ber. It will be noted from Figure 11-14 that for this case K_f is in the order of 2.7 for annealed steels and 3.3 for quenched-and-drawn. Therefore, the reduction in strength resulting from the presence of threads will be about 70 per cent for quenched-and-drawn steels and 63 per cent for annealed steels, instead of 91 per cent.

Cast irons have very little or no notch sensitivity due to graphite inclusions which exist in the finished metal and which have the effect of stress raisers. Figure 11-14 illustrates that low strength cast iron is not affected by stress concentrations while high strength cast iron has a maximum stress concentration factor K_f of 1.4.

Figure 11-15 illustrates relationships between K_f and K_t for non-ferrous materials. These curves are based on considerably less experimental data than are curves used for steel.

Values of K_f for use in design are preferably obtained from one of the two methods described in the next article.

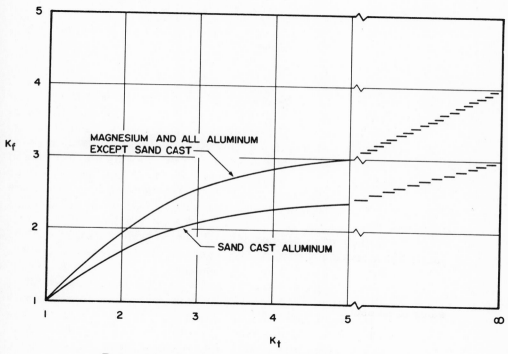

Figure 11–15. K_f vs. K_t – non-ferrous metals.

11.7 Refined Methods for Estimating K_f

a. DIRECT TEST INVOLVING ACTUAL SURFACE

The most accurate method of obtaining K_f is from test data involving the same material, the same notch geometry, and the same surface finish as the actual part. This experimental procedure yields a combination notch and surface factor. Hence, when values of K_f are obtained from this procedure, no additional correction for surface should be made.

Common examples of stress raisers handled in this manner are thread and keyways, tabulated in Figure 20-67. Surface finishing procedures for threads and keyways are generally standardized, thus making this approach practical. Furthermore, the making of fatigue samples with threads or keyways which are finished with the careful polish associated with standard fatigue test specimens would be virtually impossible.

b. CALCULATION FROM K_t

When calculating K_f from K_t for steel parts, the generally accepted practice involves making a correction for the notch sensitivity, q, of the material, where q is defined by the following equation:

$$q = \frac{K_f - 1}{K_t - 1} \tag{11.2}$$

Thus, when both K_t and q have been determined, K_f can be computed from Equation (11.3), below:

$$K_f = 1 + (K_t - 1) q \tag{11.3}$$

A completely homogeneous material would have a notch sensitivity of 1 for all notches. All actual materials are nonhomogeneous to some extent. There appears to be reasonably good experimental evidence that actual materials are relatively insensitive to notches of size sufficiently small as to approach the size of the material grain structure. Thus, hardened, fine grain steels are sensitive to much smaller notches than are soft, coarse grained steels. Figure 11-16 contains curves relating notch sensitivity to steel hardness and notch radius. These are average curves and assume normal grain size for steels heat treated to the hardness values represented.

Values of K_f obtained from Equation (11.3) are probably somewhat too high for parts not finished with the equivalent of a highly polished surface. In the case of ordinary machined parts, for example, the endurance limit has already been reduced by a surface factor (Figure 11-13) accounting for the stress concentration effect of the surface irregularities. A notch added to such a surface acts very much like the notch sensitivity (q) factor. The reduction in fatigue strength caused by a notch is greatest in the case of an otherwise "perfect" material, completely free of either internal or surface irregularities. Both internal irregularities (measured by q) and surface irregularities (measured by C_{surf}) cause a weakening of the basic unnotched sample and both serve to reduce the additional damage which can be done by a notch.

As a means of correcting the fatigue strength reduction factor for the surface effect, it is suggested that the following equation be used in preference to the more common Equation (11.3):

$$K_f = 1 + (K_t - 1)q \cdot C_{surf} \tag{11.4}$$

In the above equation, q is obtained from Figure 11-16; C_{surf} from Figure 11-13.

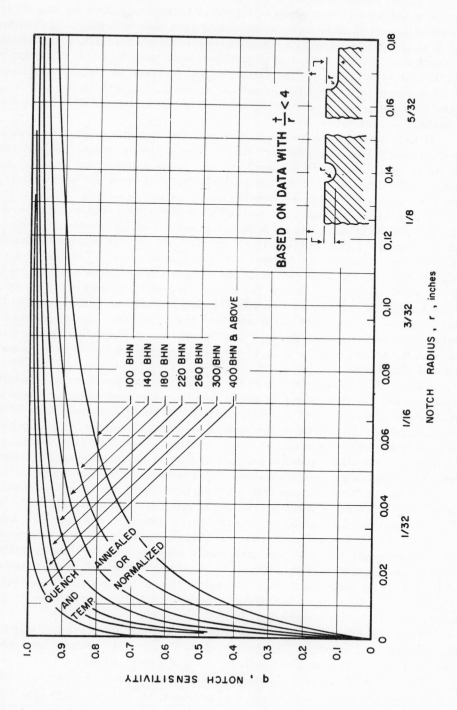

Figure 11–16. Notch sensitivity curves. [5]

A pitfall exists in using Equation (11.4) for as-forged and hot-rolled surfaces. The surface constant given in Figure 11-13 for these surfaces reflects the combined influence of surface roughness and surface decarburization. In Equation (11.4) it is desired that the C_{surf} term represent surface roughness only. In the absence of more specific data it is suggested that in using Equation (11.4) for as-forged and hot-rolled surfaces, the value of C_{surf} be taken for machined surfaces. This procedure assumes that the decarburizing effect accounts for the difference between machined surfaces and hot-rolled or as-forged surfaces. This assumption is undoubtedly conservative.

In many cases, machine members do not contain just a single stress raiser but possess many discontinuities such that the stress pattern is very involved. The total stress concentration factor resulting from such a large number of notches cannot be related to the individual stress concentration factors due to the effect of stress relieving caused by the relationship among the stress raisers.

Figure 11-14 illustrates one case of a complex stress concentration involving a fillet and an intersecting oil hole. A geometric stress concentration factor could be determined from both the fillet and the hole and the product of the two taken as the resultant geometric stress concentration factor K_t. Then, after determining the material notch sensitivity q, the fatigue stress concentration factor K_f could be calculated and applied to the nominal stress to determine the maximum existing stress. If the member were then tested, it would be discovered that the actual effect of the combined notch was less than computed. In the absence of specific information, a factor $K_f = 4$ can be used on steel members having many notches or discontinuities. K_f should never be larger than 4 and in most cases it will not be greater than 3.0.

Figure 11-16 illustrates that as the strength or hardness increases, material become more notch-sensitive and K_f approaches K_t. Most high hardness steels exhibit this phenomenon of high notch sensitivity and resulting large values of K_f, thus causing large reductions in the endurance limit. Therefore, it is often not advantageous to use high strength steels for members possessing large stress concentrations. On the other hand, low strength steels are not so notch-sensitive, with the result that their endurance limits are not reduced to such a large degree.

The discussion of fatigue strength reduction factors (or fatigue stress concentration factors) thus far has been concerned with the infinite life end of the S-N curve. This involves 10^6 cycles or more for ferrous materials, and is usually taken arbitrarily at 10^8 or 5×10^8 cycles for non ferrous materials. The influence of a notch on the strength of a steel part subjected to not more than 1000 load cycles has generally been found negligible. Hence, in correcting a steel S-N curve to reflect the fatigue strength reduction caused by a notch, the 10^6 cycle strength is divided by K_f, the 10^3 cycle point is not altered, and a straight line can still be used to connect these two points on a log-log plot.

Notch sensitivity relationships have not been as clearly established for materials other than steel. At the present time, Figure 11-15 probably represents the most satisfactory means of converting K_t to K_f for these materials.

The effect of stress concentration does not in general become negligible below 1000 cycles in the case of non-ferrous materials. Figure 11-17 illustrates specific test results showing the variation in the fatigue stress concentration factor with life for aluminum.

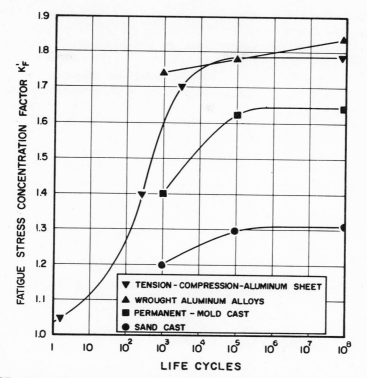

Figure 11–17. Fatigue stress concentration factors — finite life — aluminum alloys.[2]

11.8 Sample Problem

The shaft sketched in Figure 11-18 is machined from a steel of 160 BHN and is subjected to completely reversed torsional loads. Plot the appropriate S-N curve indicating the relationship between expected life and magnitude of load for this part.

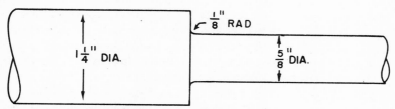

Figure 11–18. Shaft in sample problem.

1. From the 160 BHN hardness value, we estimate:

S_u = 80 ksi $[S_u \approx 500$ BHN from Equation (9.3)$]$

S_n' (bending) = 40 ksi [from Equation (11.1)]

S_n' (torsion) = .58 (40 ksi) = 23 ksi (article 11.3)

S_{us} = .82 S_u = 66 ksi (article 11.3)

2. The basic S-N curve for reversed torsional loading (of polished 0.3 in. diameter samples) is a line between 0.9 S_{us} = 59 ksi at 10^3 cycles, and 23 ksi at 10^6 cycles. Note that this agrees with the polished curve for torsional loading plotted in Figure 21-1.

3. Figure 11-13 shows C_{surf} = .78. Applying this correction to the 10^6 point, drops it to (23) (.78) = 18 ksi. This agrees with the machined torsion curve in Figure 21-1.

4. Two more corrections must be applied to the 10^6 cycle point, C_{size} and K_f. C_{size} = .85 (article 11.4). K_f will now be estimated.

    a. K_t = 1.26 (Figure 20-3)

    b. q   = .95 (Figure 11-16)

    c. C_{surf} = .78 (Figure 11-13)

    d. K_f = $1 + (K_t - 1) q C_{surf}$ [Equation (11-4)]

       K_f = $1 + (.26) (.95) (.78) = 1.193$; use $K_f = 1.2$

5. The desired S-N curve is a straight line connecting 59 ksi at 10^3 cycles and 18(.85) (1/1.2) = 12.8 ksi (round off to 13 ksi) at 10^6 cycles.

6. The final curve is shown in Figure 11-19.

11.9 Goodman Diagrams

Up to this point, fatigue strength has been considered only with respect to completely reversed loading. The majority of practical situations involve a combination of alternating load and static load, as shown graphically in Figure 11-20. Note that the terms "mean," "variable" or "alternating," "maximum," and "minimum," as applied to load and stress cycles are defined in this figure. These definitions are in accordance with the nomenclature recommended in Reference 9.

A typical example of combined mean and variable loading is afforded by the valve springs of an internal combustion engine. The valve spring is preloaded in assembly to hold the valve on the seat. During operation, as the valve is opened the spring is given greater loading due to the additional deflection. Thus, the loading cycle goes from a low magnitude to a higher magnitude and then back to the low magnitude. That is, the stress resulting from this combination of loads may be broken down into a steady component that raises or lowers the general stress level and an alternating component that tends to fatigue the metal.

In the case of combined static and alternating loading some value between the endurance strength and the yield strength of the material is taken as the significant strength (allowable stress). Several methods have been proposed to determine the significant strength for the various combinations of static and alternating load.

The first method used for determining the significant strength for this type of loading employed the original Goodman diagram, as illustrated in Figure 11-21. This diagram applied only to steel parts requiring infinite life. In constructing the diagram, it is assumed that the endurance limit for completely reversed stress is one-third the tensile strength, and the range of stress that can be superimposed on a given steady stress is given by a vertical line drawn at the appropriate location in the triangular area, CBD.

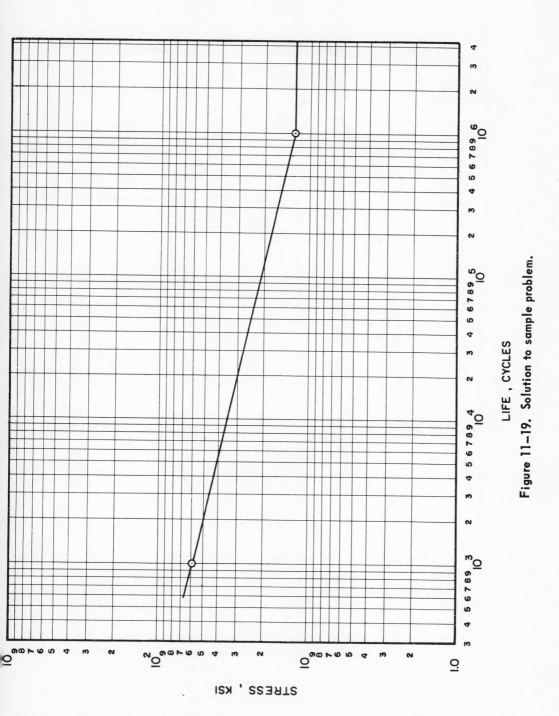

LIFE , CYCLES

Figure 11-19. Solution to sample problem.

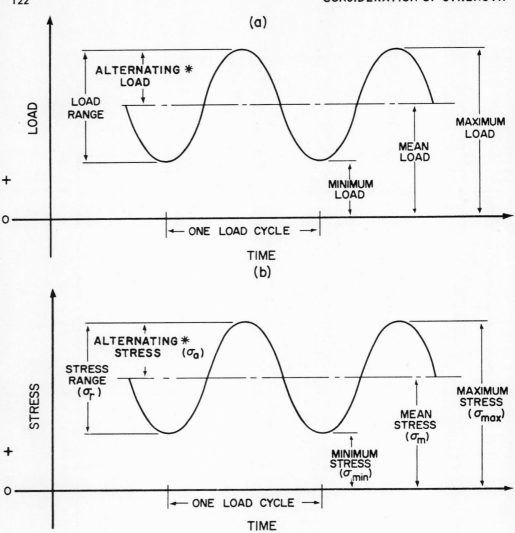

* Also frequently referred to as "variable" load or stress.

Figure 11–20. Fatigue load and stress nomenclature.

    A commonly used method of determining the significant strength for this type of loading now employs the so-called modified Goodman diagram, Figure 11-22. In this diagram stress (either maximum or minimum) is plotted on the ordinate and the mean stress on the abscissa, using the same scale on both axes. The significant strength S_n for a completely alternating load (endurance limit modified for load, surface, size, and life) is laid off on the zero mean-stress ordinate for both tension (F) and compression (E). A straight line called the Goodman line drawn between S_n (points E and F) and the intersection of the ultimate strength lines (point D) gives the allowable stress or significant strength for any value of mean stress. For example, if a particular loading produces a mean stress Z, then the

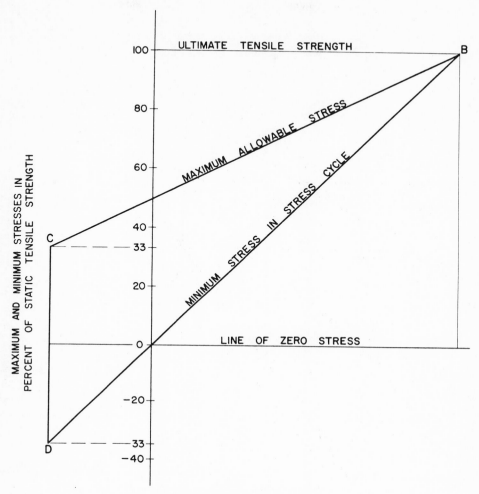

Figure 11-21. Original Goodman diagram.

maximum allowable stress would be designated by C', the minimum allowable stress by A', and the maximum allowable stress range by the difference between C' and A'. Thus, the diagram represents the significant strength of this material for any fluctuating loading (combined static and alternating loading), and is corrected for size effect, surface finish, type of loading, and life expectancy.

Experimental tests show that the diagram in Figure 11-22 does not hold true for specimens subjected to compressive stresses. From the limited number of tests which have been conducted on compression specimens, it has been found that the alternating stress range remains essentially constant at the value of the endurance strength as the mean stress increases (Figure 11-25). Thus, the Goodman diagram of Figure 11-22 can now be completed on the compression side by extending lines from the two values of endurance strength (points E and F) at zero mean stress, parallel to the steady stress line. This then gives the constant alternating stress range in compression.

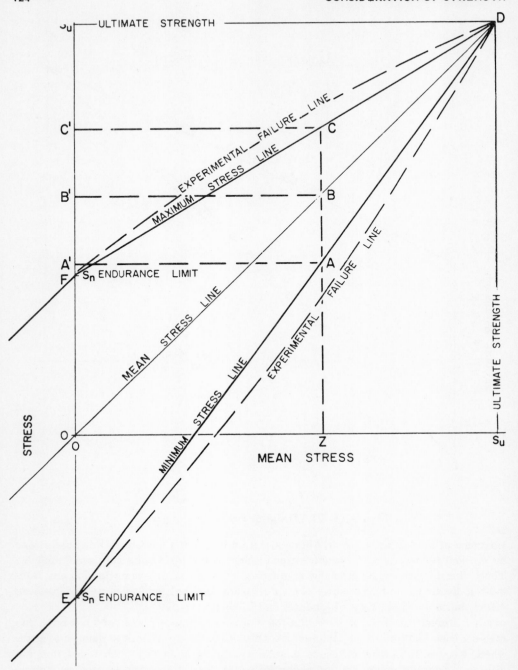

Figure 11–22. Modified Goodman diagram – wrought steel.

For materials having appreciably different strengths in tension and compression, the Goodman diagram for axial loading will reflect this difference. The most important example is cast iron. For this reason the Goodman diagrams given in Chapter 22 for axial loading of cast iron are arranged in two groups: (1) Figure 22-56 which shows the entire diagram including both tensile and compressive mean stresses, and (2) Figure 22-57 which shows the tensile side magnified to a more useable scale. Note that due to the extremely low notch sensitivity of cast iron, surface finish is unimportant from the fatigue standpoint. Hence, a single curve is adequate to represent all surfaces.

Since the Goodman line is drawn through the point representing static loading equal to the ultimate strength, the right-hand portion of the diagram implies that it is permissible for stress peaks to exceed the yield strength. While it is true that operation under these conditions of stress will not result in fatigue fracture, it is usually desirable to limit the peak stress to the yield strength to preclude any possibility of yielding. For this reason, a dotted line representing the average yield strength is shown on the Goodman diagrams in Chapter 22 of this book. The reason for drawing the line dotted so as to merely call attention to this consideration is twofold: (1) In the case of steel, different materials within the same hardness range have somewhat different yield strengths; hence, when this consideration is involved, it is best to check the yield strength for the particular steel being considered, (2) there is some evidence indicating that stress fluctuations of the order of 500 cycles per minute and above permit stress peaks to exceed the static yield strength without evidence of yielding. The reason for this apparently is that before sufficient time has elapsed for yielding to take place, the cycle is safely past the peak stress. Since only limited data are currently available concerning this phenomenon, conservative practice is to avoid stress peaks exceeding the yield strength.

The modification of the Goodman diagram so as to preclude yielding is illustrated in more detail in Figure 11-23. On this diagram, it will be noted that for the case of alternating loading only (zero mean stress) the endurance strength of the material is taken as the significant strength (point A on the ordinate). When the loading is combined static and alternating (mean stress between points O and L) the significant strength is defined by the sloping line AB. For combined loads giving mean stresses between L and M, the significant stress is represented by the yield point.

The modified Goodman diagram has three important advantages over the original Goodman diagram: (1) It makes no assumption as to the endurance limit since actual experimental values are plotted, (2) it can be used for both finite and infinite life, (3) it properly reflects the yielding criterion of failure.

In this book, the modified form of the Goodman diagram (Figure 11-22 or 11-23) will be used throughout.

Since for non-ferrous alloys no definite endurance limits exist, endurance limits for these materials are usually defined as the strength at 5×10^8 cycles of load fluctuation.

The construction and use of Goodman diagrams will be illustrated by the examples in article 11.11.

Figure 11-20 shows that the general case of fluctuating stress can be characterized by five quantities; mean stress, alternating (or variable) stress, maximum stress, minimum stress, and stress range. Note that any two of these five serve to define the fluctuating stress. From a knowledge of any two, the other three can readily be computed. Hence, in plotting diagrams to represent all possible proportions of fluctuating stress, any two of these quantities can be used as coordinates.

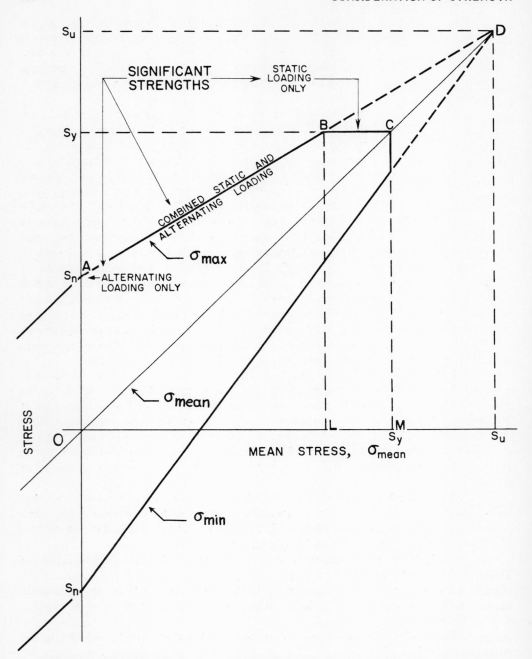

Figure 11–23. Modified Goodman diagram for design limited by yield strength.

In Figure 11-22, mean stress and maximum stress are used to define the upper Goodman line (labeled "maximum stress line"). The lower Goodman line (labeled "minimum stress line") uses as coordinates mean stress and minimum stress. Either of these two lines completely defines the limiting values of fluctuating stress. The second line is totally unnecessary, but is added merely as a convenience in visualizing stress ranges (vertical distances between the two Goodman lines) which may be superimposed upon various mean stresses.

An alternate form of fluctuating stress diagram which is also in common use in illustrated in Figure 11-24. This figure corresponds exactly to Figure 11-23. In both figures note that (1) points C and D represent stresses corresponding to static yielding and static ultimate fracture respectively, (2) point A represents the endurance strength for completely reversed stress, (3) straight line AD represents the modified Goodman criterion of fatigue fracture, and (4) straight line BC represents all fluctuating stress having a maximum stress equal to the yield strength. Any fatigue problem solved with one diagram can be solved just as easily with the other diagram, and the answers will always agree exactly.

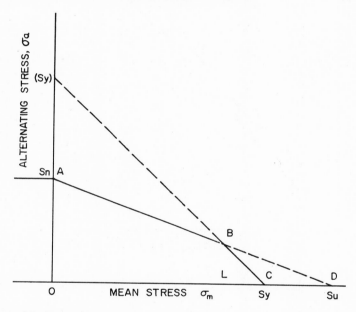

Figure 11–24. Alternate form of Goodman diagram – wrought steel.

Figure 11-25 shows the alternate form of the Goodman diagram with generalized coordinates. This figure illustrates the fact that the Goodman line is on the conservative side for wrought steel parts. Cast materials usually fracture at slightly lower stress than those predicted by the Goodman criterion.

The possibility of yielding failures resulting from peak stress in excess of yield strength was analyzed [10] by means of the alternate form of Goodman diagram illustrated in Figures 11-24 and 11-25. Figures 11-26 and 11-27 present curves for low strength and high strength steels respectively. Note that in both figures, combinations of mean stress and variable stress falling above and to the right of the 45° line indicate peak stresses in excess of the yield strength, the curves bring out the fact that steels having a low ratio of yield strength to endurance limit (hence, a low ratio of yield strength to tensile strength) are more prone to yielding type failures.

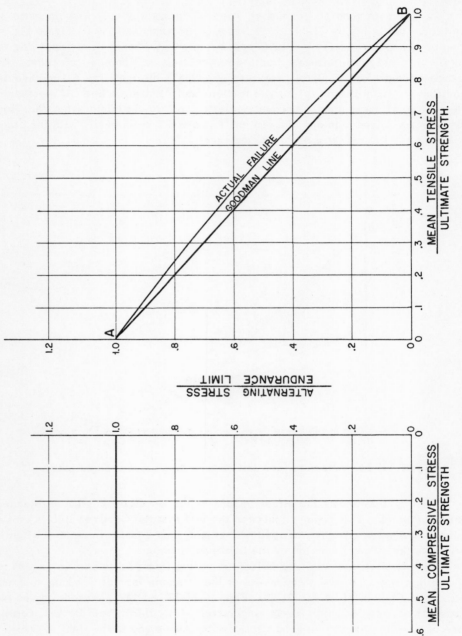

Figure 11–25. Alternate form of Goodman diagram.

11.10 Mean Stresses Which Do Not Decrease Allowable Variable Stress

There are a few exceptions to the usual rule that the presence of a mean stress decreases the ability of a material to withstand variable stress. The most important example is that of an axial compressive mean stress. As shown on all of the axial loading Goodman diagrams for steel in Chapter 22, the allowable stress range is the same for a compressive mean stress as for zero mean stress. The compressive mean stress can be increased without reduction of variable stress at least until the compressive peak stress reaches the compressive yield strength (and possibly beyond this point, as discussed above).

A second case where a mean stress does not reduce the magnitude of allowable variable stress is torsional loading of members free of stress raisers. Experimental evidence has indicated that for polished notch-free cylindrical specimens of ductile metals, the maximum alternating stress that may be superimposed on any given steady stress without causing fatigue failure is independent of the magnitude

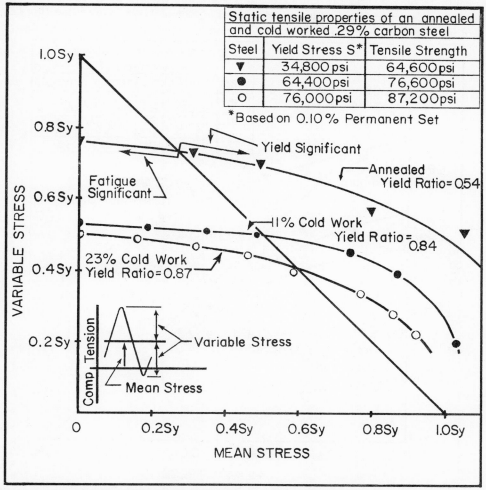

Static tensile properties of an annealed and cold worked .29% carbon steel		
Steel	Yield Stress S*	Tensile Strength
▼	34,800 psi	64,600 psi
●	64,400 psi	76,600 psi
O	76,000 psi	87,200 psi

*Based on 0.10% Permanent Set

Figure 11–26. Effect of stress range on mode of failure for low-strength steels.[10]

of mean stress, provided the maximum stress does not exceed the torsional yield strength.   Since virtually all actual parts subjected to torsional loading contain stress raisers of some kind, the above phenomenon is of little practical importance. For this reason the Goodman diagrams for torsional loading drawn in Chapter 22 are of the conventional form, which agrees well with tests of notched torsion members.

11.11 Sample Problems

1. Goodman Diagram — Infinite Life

For the sample problem given in article 11.8, construct a Goodman diagram giving an estimate of the maximum magnitude of alternating stress which could be superimposed upon various values of mean stress without causing eventual fatigue failure.

Solution.   As determined in article 11.8, the estimated torsional ultimate strength is 66 ksi, and the estimated torsional endurance limit is 13 ksi. These two points determine the Goodman line plotted in Figure 11-28. (Note that this line is in agreement with machined surface Goodman line in Figure 22-37 except that in

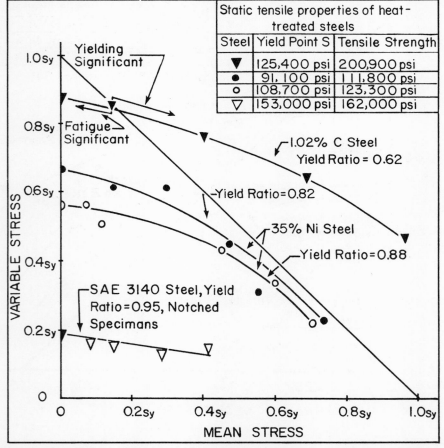

Figure 11–27. Effect of stress range on mode of failure for high-strength steels. [10]

the present problem the fatigue strength reduction factor due to the fillet has been applied to the zero mean-stress fatigue strength.)

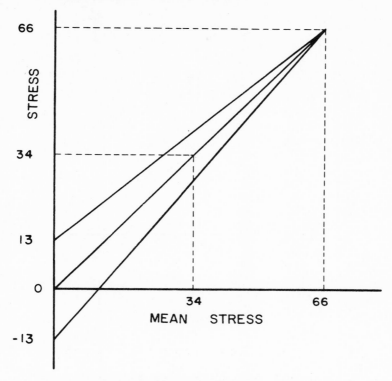

Figure 11–28. Goodman diagram for sample problem.

Figure 10-2 gives an average yield strength for 160 BHN steel as about 72 per cent of the ultimate strength, or 58 ksi. The shear yield strength will be close to 58 per cent of the tensile yield strength (in accordance with the maximum distortion energy theory), or 34 ksi. This value is used in drawing the dotted line in Figure 11-28.

2. Goodman Diagram – Finite Life

Repeat the first problem except draw the diagram for a finite life of 10^5 load cycles.

Solution. The only change from the previous solution is that the strength at zero mean stress is greater, because failure after 10^5 cycles is now regarded as acceptable. The magnitude of this strength is read from the S-N curve in Figure 11-19 as 21 ksi. The Goodman diagram is drawn in Figure 11-29. Note that this problem could not have been solved without first plotting the S-N curve.

3. Find Allowable τ_v for Given τ_m

Again referring to the shaft in Figure 11-18, suppose that a mean torsional stress of 10 ksi exists ($\tau_m = T_m R/J$). What is the greatest value of variable stress ($\tau_v = T_v R/J$) that can be superimposed without causing eventual failure?

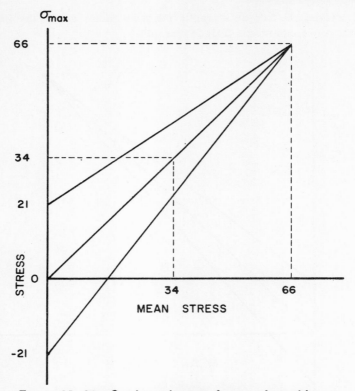

Figure 11–29. Goodman diagram for sample problem.

Solution. Figure 11-30 (which contains the same Goodman line as Figure 11-29) shows the answer to be 18 ksi. (Note that since the strength reduction factor, K_f, has been incorporated into the Goodman diagram, K_f should *not* be used in the stress calculations.)

11.12 Combined Loading

When steel is subjected to combinations of completely reversed bending and completely reversed torsion, failure occurs in general agreement with the maximum distortion energy theory, as illustrated in Figure 11-31. It seems reasonable to assume that other ductile metals also follow the relationship in Figure 11-31.

Extremely limited test data are available concerning the general state of combined mean stress superimposed upon combined variable stress. Pending further research in this area, the following rules of procedure are recommended:

1. Combine all of the variable components of stress using the distortion energy theory, as suggested by the data represented in Figure 11-31.
2. Neglect any compressive mean loads so long as they do not result in compressive peak stresses exceeding the compressive yield strength.
3. Combine bending, tensile, and torsional components of mean stress in accordance with the distortion energy theory.

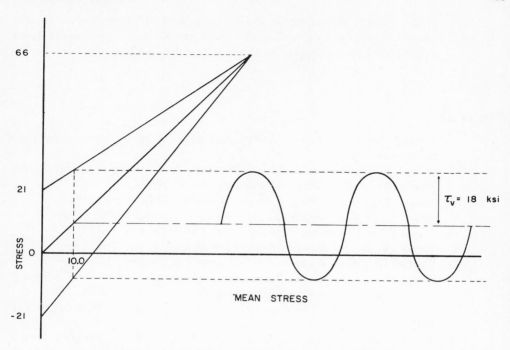

Figure 11–30. Goodman diagram for sample problem.

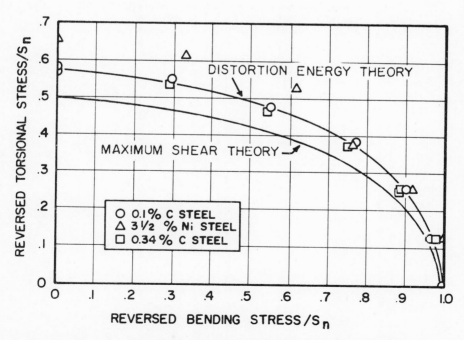

Figure 11–31. Failure theories for combined alternating stresses.[3]

4. Steps 1 and 3 will result in the determination of an equivalent tensile variable stress and an equivalent tensile mean stress. Represent these equivalent stresses in the usual manner on the Goodman diagram.

References

1. Lipson, Noll, and Clock, *Stress and Strength of Manufactured Parts*, McGraw-Hill, 1950.
2. Grover, H. J., Gordon, S. A., and Jackson, L. R., *Fatigue of Metals and Structures*, U. S. Government Printing Office, 1960.
3. *Metals Engineering Design*, ASME Handbook, McGraw-Hill, 1953.
4. Lessells, J. M., *Strength and Resistance of Metals*, Wiley, 1954.
5. Sines, G. and Waisman, J. L., *Metal Fatigue*, McGraw-Hill, 1959.
6. Murray, W. M., *Fatigue and Fracture of Metals*, Wiley, 1952.
7. Pope, J. A., *Metal Fatigue*, Chapman and Hall, 1959.
8. Kuhn, P. and Hardrath, H. F., *An Engineering Method for Estimating Notch-Size Effect in Fatigue Tests on Steel*, NACA TN 2805, 1952.
9. *Manual on Fatigue Testing*, ASTM, Special Technical Publication 91, 1949.
10. Smith, J. O., "Symposium on the Significance of the Tension Test," *Proc. ASTM*, Vol. 40, 1940.
11. Garwood, M.F., Zurburg, H.H., and Erickson, M.A., *Interpretation of Tests and Correlation with Service*, American Society of Metals, 1950.
12. *Steel Castings Handbook*, Steel Founders Society of America, Third Ed., 1960.

Chapter 12

FATIGUE DAMAGE

If an actual part is always subjected to stresses below the endurance limit, or if it is subjected to repetitions of one particular stress cycle in the finite life range, the procedures discussed in the last chapter are adequate. Many parts, however, are subjected to a variety of stress cycles within the finite life range. A stress cycle within the finite range (i.e., a stress cycle above the original endurance limit of the material) is called an *overstress*. When parts are subjected to overstress, such questions arise as: (1) what effect does a given number of cycles at a particular overstress have upon the ability of the part to withstand successfully repeated cycles at or below the endurance limit, and (2) how can the cumulative fatigue damage caused by a variety of overstress cycles be evaluated? These and related points are discussed in this chapter.

12.1 Damage Line

Figure 12-1 illustrates the probable damage line for a particular steel, together with the conventional S-N curve for the same steel. Note that the finite life portion of the S-N curve is not a straight line in this case as the ordinate is plotted to a linear scale.

The damage line indicates the approximate number of times that a given overstress can be applied to the material without causing "damage," in the sense of lowering the original endurance limit. For example, the damage line curve in Figure 12-1 indicates that if test samples were subjected to a reversed bending stress of 140 ksi for fewer than about 50,000 cycles, these parts would still be capable of operating at the original endurance limit (114 ksi) indefinitely without failure. If the test part were subjected to more than about 50,000 cycles at 140 ksi, they would no longer be able to withstand an indefinite number of 115 ksi cycles. If the test parts were subjected to somewhere in the region of 75,000 cycles at 140 ksi, the original S-N curve indicates that failure would be expected.

As an example of the usefulness of the damage line concept, consider a vehicle suspension part having fatigue strength characteristics represented by Figure 12-1. Let this part be subjected to a rapid accumulation of stress cycles in the range of 110 to 115 ksi, and to occasional overstresses of about 140 ksi. In estimating the life of this part, the damage line indicates that failure may occur shortly after 50,000 cycles of overstress rather than waiting until 75,000 cycles have been accumulated. It is important to recognize that an appreciable scatter

135

band exists around both the S-N curve and the damage line, so that the above illustration indicates orders of magnitude only.

Different materials have different damage line characteristics, some being
much flatter. For example, a particular steel with an S-N curve similar to Figure
12-1 might have a damage line such that 10,000 or 20,000 cycles of 140 ksi stress
would result in "damage." The type of damage indicated by the damage line cannot
be visually detected; hence, subsequent tests at the original endurance limit must
be run in order to ascertain whether or not damage has occurred.

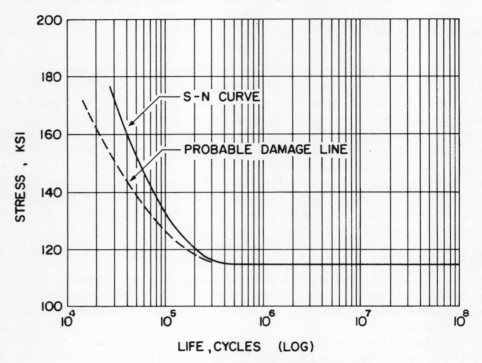

Figure 12—1. Probable damage line.

12.2 Understressing

The operation of parts for extended periods at stresses just under the endurance limit increases the endurance limit of the part. This process is called
understressing. To obtain the greatest benefit from understressing, parts should be
run for something like one- to ten-million cycles at perhaps 90 percent of the endurance limit, followed by similar runs at increased small increments of stress. This
process is called "coaxing." By coaxing, the endurance limit of steel samples has
been increased by 20 to 30 per cent. Since this treatment requires many millions of
accurately controlled stress cycles, its application has been confined largely to
laboratory experiment.

Evidence has indicated that understressing can be used to compensate for
the detrimental effects caused by overstressing. This compensating effect is sometimes referred to as "healing."

12.3 Cumulative Damage

Suppose that a part is operated under conditions resulting in a variety of overstress cycles each hour. It is desired to estimate the life under these conditions. Miner's rule (Reference 2) suggests that the life can be estimated by merely adding up the percentage of the life which is consumed by each overstress cycle. For example, using the S-N curve in Figure 12-1, Miner's rule implies that 1/75,000 of life is used up by each 140 ksi stress cycle, 1/40,000 by each 160 ksi cycles, 1/200,000 by each 120 ksi cycle, etc. If, during one hour's operation there are overstress cycles which consume 1/50 of the life, then, according to Miner's rule, the life of the part would be 50 hours.

Miner's rule may be expressed in equation form as follows:

$$\Sigma \left(\frac{n_1}{N_1} + \frac{n_2}{N_2} + \ldots \right) = 1 \tag{12.1}$$

Terms n_1, n_2, etc. represent the number of cycles at specific overstress levels; and N_1, N_2, etc. represent the life (in cycles) at these levels of overstress. as taken from the S-N curve. Failure is predicted when sufficient time has elapsed for the summation to be equal to unity.

Unfortunately, test results indicate the Miner's rule predicts the life of a part in only a very approximate manner. Such factors as the order in which the severe and moderate overstress cycles are applied appear to have an influence on cumulative damage. Reference 4 cites tests during which failure occurred when Equation (12.1) indicated that between 18 and 2300 per cent of the life had been consumed. However, these results are probably extreme. Miner's original tests indicated failure after a computed 61 to 145 per cent of life was consumed, with the average being 98 per cent. In any event, Miner's rule appears to be as satisfactory a method for computing cumulative damage as is currently available.

References

1. Grover, H. J., Gordon, S. A., and Jackson, L. R., *Fatigue of Metals and Structures*, U. S. Government Printing Office, 1960.
2. Miner, M. A., "Cumulative Damage in Fatigue," Journal *of Applied Mechanics*, Vol. 12 September 1945.
3. Miner, M. A., "Estimation of Fatigue Life with Particular Emphasis on Cumulative Damage," Chap. 12 of Sines, G. and Waisman, J. L., *Metal Fatigue*, McGraw-Hill, 1959.
4. Dolan, T. J., Richart, F. E., and Work, C. E., "Influence of Fluctuations in Stress Amplitude on the Fatigue of Metals," *Proceedings*, ASTM, Vol. 49, 1949.

Chapter 13

SURFACE TREATMENT, CORROSION

Since most fatigue failures originate at the surface of the part, the condition of the surface is of particular importance. In many instances, substantial improvements in fatigue strength can be obtained by subjecting the part to a surface treatment specifically selected for its beneficial effect upon fatigue strength.

There are generally three factors to be considered in connection with surface effects: (1) the existence of stress raisers resulting from surface roughness, (2) a difference in actual strength between the surface material and the core material, and (3) residual stresses.

In practice, it is seldom important or possible to determine the relative magnitude of the above three factors in considering the characteristics of a particular surface. In article 11.5, for example, factors were considered pertaining to the overall influence of various commercially produced surfaces. A ground or machined surface involves a certain degree of surface roughness. The surface layers may receive some cold working, and residual stresses may be present. The as-forged and hot-rolled surface factors reflect some surface weakening due to decarburization. In like manner, the present chapter is concerned with the overall influence of surface treatments which are applied for such purposes as increasing resistance to corrosion, wear, and fatigue.

The commonly used processes whose effect on strength have been studied are:

Cold working (shot peening, cold rolling, stretching).

Surface hardening (carburizing, nitriding, cyaniding, flame hardening, induction hardening).

Plating (chromium, zinc, cadmium).

13.1 Cold Working

In cold working, the material is strained beyond the yield point and caused to flow plastically. This plastic flow increases the strength of the steel, but utilizes a portion of its ductility. Therefore, if strain hardening is carried to excess, the ductility is exhausted and cracks result. Heating after cold working tends to relieve the effects of cold working. The higher the temperature, the greater the relief, although a temperature of 825°F relieved the entire effect in one case.

The most commonly used methods of cold working are cold rolling, stretching, and shot peening. Cold rolling, as the name implies, is accomplished by compressing the outer surface of the material under rolls, as performed in rolling sheet stock, screw threads, etc. Cold stretching is straining the metal above the yield point. Shot peening is accomplished by subjecting the member to a blast of chilled iron or steel shot from a rotating wheel or from a nozzle. Of these, shot peening and cold rolling have been widely used to increase fatigue strength.

As to the effect of shot peening on the fatigue strength, the following general trend can be noted from the reported test values given in Table 13-1. The effect varies with the surface of the member before the process is applied. Thus, in the case of unnotched specimens, the increase in the fatigue strength for polished specimens seldom exceeds 20 per cent, and in many cases it is less than 10 per cent. For hot-rolled specimens the corresponding increase is 30 to 50 per cent, and for as-forged parts, 100 per cent. This general trend is also apparent in the case of notched specimens, although the per cent improvement is higher. Figure 13-1 shows that the fatigue strength increases as the peening time increases. However, a point is reached where further peening does not increase the fatigue strength. Figure 13-2 illustrates the percentage increase that can be obtained in fatigue strength by shot peening various surfaces. Figure 13-3 shows that shot peening causes a greater increase in the fatigue strength of high strength steels than it does in low strength

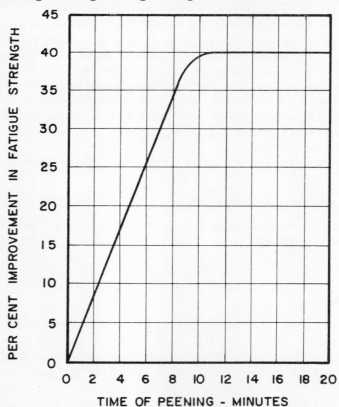

Figure 13-1. Effect of shot peening — representative steel part.[8]

TABLE 13-1

Effect of Shot Peening on Endurance Limit — Specific Test Values[1]

Material	Specimen	Treatment Prior to Shot Peening	Surface Prior to Shot Peening	Percentage Increase in Endurance Limit
SAE 1020 Steel	Plate	As-rolled	Polished	9
SAE 1045 Steel	Plate	Normalized	Polished	11
SAE 1050 Steel	Plate	As-rolled	Polished	22
SAE S4340 Steel	Standard	Quenched-and-drawn	Polished	18
Ni-Cr-Mo Steel	Standard	Carburized	Polished	4
Alloy Steel	Bar	Hardened	Polished	2
Alloy Steel	Bar	Hardened	Machined	23
SAE 1020 Steel	Plate	As-rolled	Hot-rolled	34
SAE 1045 Steel	Plate	Induction hardened	Not-rolled	50
Rail Steel	Rail	As-rolled	Hot-rolled	32
0.65 C Steel	Wire	As-drawn	Hot-rolled	42
SAE 1095 Steel	Wire	As-drawn	Hot-rolled	50
Ni-Cr-Mo Steel	Standard	Carburized	Hot-rolled	23
NE 9470 Steel	Standard	Carburized	Hot-rolled	50
NE 9240 Steel	Standard	Carburized	Hot-rolled	53
NE 8650 Steel	Axle	Quenched-and-tempered	As-forged	100
NE 8650 Steel	Axle	Normalized-and-tempered	As-forged	54
NE 8650 Steel	Flat bar	Quenched-and-tempered	Severely ground	90
4340 Steel	Shaft	Quenched-and-tempered	Chrome plating*	90
Phosphor bronze	Coil spring			40
Beryllium copper	Coil spring			80
S-816(Co-Cr-Ni Base)	Coil spring			80
18-8 Stainless	Coil spring			70
13-2 Stainless	Coil spring			50

* Shot peening performed before chrome plating.

steels. It has also been found that spontaneous cracking of metal resulting from the combined effect of high stress and corrosive attack can be inhibited by shot peening. Table 13-2 illustrates that cold rolling of machined surfaces can increase the endurance strength from 20 to more than 100 per cent of the original endurance strength.

Figure 13-4 illustrates improvements in fatigue strength made by pressing the edges of transverse holes in steel shafts.

13.2 Surface Hardening — Carburizing

Surface hardening is a process which increases the hardness of the surface to a depth ranging from a few thousandths of an inch to 1/4 in. or more. This localized hardening results in a composite structure: a hard surface layer commonly known as the case, and a softer interior known as the core. Although the hardening

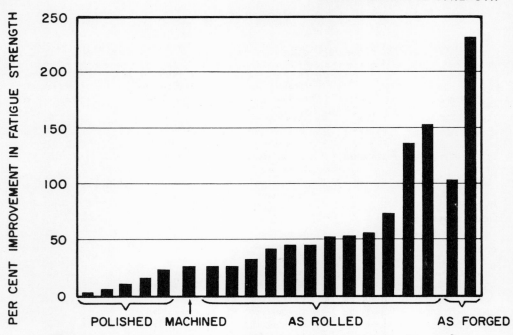

Figure 13–2. Effect of surface prior to shot peening – steel parts.[8]

TABLE 13-2

Effect of Cold Rolling and Cold Stretching on Endurance Limit –
Specific Test Values[1]

Material	Specimen	Treatment Prior to Cold Working	Surface Prior to Cold Working	Percentage Increase in Endurance Limit
		Cold rolling		
SAE 1045	Bar	Normalized	Polished	6
SAE 1045	Bored	Quenched-and-tempered	Polished	52
SAE 1045	Bored	Quenched-and-tempered	Polished	33
SAE 1045	Bar	Normalized	Machined	27
SAE 1045		Notched	Machined	120
SAE 1045		Notched	Machined	52
SAE 1050	Press fit	Normalized	Machined	150
3.1 Ni	Press fit	Normalized	Machined	100
0.35 C	Thread	Quenched-and-tempered	Machined	33
0.20 C	Bars	Hot-rolled	Hot-rolled	67
Alloy steel	Shaft with fillet	Normalized-and-tempered	Polished	68
Alloy steel	Shaft with fillet	Normalized-and-tempered	Polished	56
Alloy steel	Shaft with fillet	Quenched-and-tempered	Polished	30

Material	Specimen	Treatment Prior to Cold Working	Surface Prior to Cold Working	Percentage Increase in Endurance Limit
		Cold stretching		
	Wire	Patented	Polished	42
0.49 C	Bar	As-rolled	Machined	35
0.18 C	Standard	As-rolled	Hot-rolled	35
	Wire	Patented	Hot-rolled	42

is usually applied to provide a long wearing surface, the process affects the strength of the part, particularly under fatigue loading.

In estimating the signifcant strength for surface treated parts the obvious question arises: What hardness (case or core) should be used to determine significant strength?

Although the actual hardness distribution over the cross-section does not consist of two levels (uniform high hardness in the case, with a drop to a lower uniform hardness in the core), this may be used as a conservative assumption in

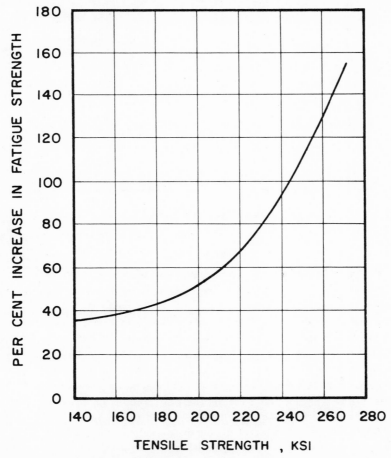

Figure 13-3. Effect of shot peening on various strength steels.[8]

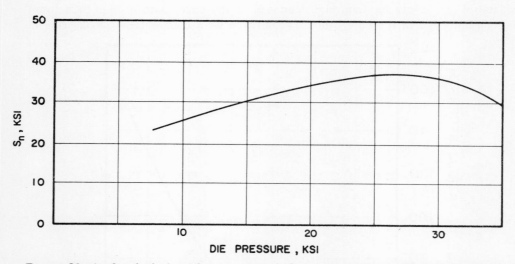

DIE SHAPE			
PRESSING LOAD (LBS)	0	44,100	66,150
ENDURANCE LIMIT (PSI)	22,100	30,400	18,800
IMPROVEMENT %	0	+ 38,5	− 14

Figure 13–4. Steel shaft with transverse hole – fatigue strength improvement due to pressing edge of hole with die.

practical design.   Since significant strength (allowable stress) is proportional to hardness, once the hardness distribution is established, the distribution of allowable stresses is known.

The first step in determining whether the case or the core hardness should be used in determining allowable stresses for surface treated parts is to superimpose applied stresses on the allowable stresses.   This is illustrated in Figures 13-5 and 13-6, where it will be noted that failure will occur in the case or in the core depending on the type of loading and the absence or presence of a notch. This in turn determines whether the case or the core should be used in estimating the allowable stresses for a particular surface treated part.   Thus, for example, in the case of an unnotched bar subjected to bending loading, the hardness of the core is the criterion of the significant strength, whereas for a bar with a severe notch the hardness of the case should be used in determining the allowable stress.   It is ob-

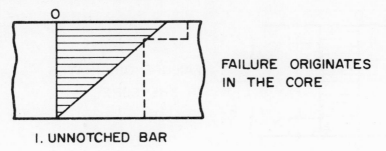

FAILURE ORIGINATES
IN THE CORE

I. UNNOTCHED BAR

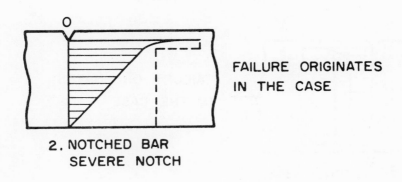

FAILURE ORIGINATES
IN THE CASE

2. NOTCHED BAR
SEVERE NOTCH

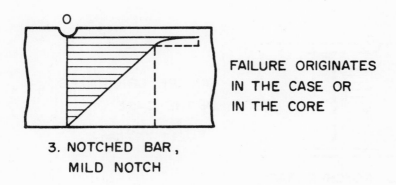

FAILURE ORIGINATES
IN THE CASE OR
IN THE CORE

3. NOTCHED BAR,
MILD NOTCH

——— APPLIED STRESS

– – – – ALLOWABLE STRESS AS DETERMINED FROM HARDNESS

Figure 13-5. Failure of surface-treated parts under bending or torsional loads.

vious that the significant stress (applied stress to be compared with the significant
strength) will also be different for the two cases. In the case of the unnotched bar
(failure in the core) it will be the stress at the point corresponding approximately to

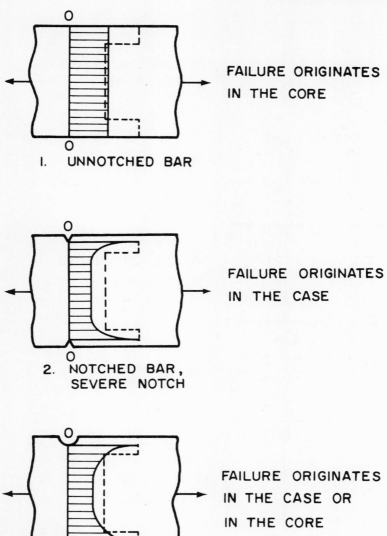

1. UNNOTCHED BAR

2. NOTCHED BAR,
   SEVERE NOTCH

3. NOTCHED BAR,
   MILD NOTCH

FAILURE ORIGINATES
IN THE CORE

FAILURE ORIGINATES
IN THE CASE

FAILURE ORIGINATES
IN THE CASE OR
IN THE CORE

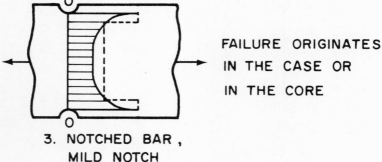

────── APPLIED STRESS

── ── ── ── ALLOWABLE STRESS AS DETERMINED FROM HARDNESS

Figure 13-6. Failure of surface-treated parts under axial loads.

the junction of the case and core. This is obviously lower than the corresponding nominal surface stress as computed from the conventional equations Mc/I or Tc/J.

In the case of a bar with a severe notch, the significant stress will be obtained by multiplying the nominal stress at the base of the notch by the fatigue stress concentration factor.

The type of gradient curves which should be used for the studies repre - sented by Figures 13-5 and 13-6 are illustrated by Figures 6-5 through 6-7.

Table 13-3 illustrates the correlation between calculated and actual endurance limits of unnotched bars loaded in reversed bending. The computed values are based on the following assumptions:

1. Core tensile strength = 500 BHN; $S_n' = S_u/2$; hence $S_n' = 250$ BHN.
2. No correction need be made for the size of the .25 inch specimens.
3. No "surface" correction need be made, as the failure originates below the surface. This amounts to assuming that conditions relating to fatigue fracture below the surface are comparable with conditions at a carefully polished surface.
4. The "square cornered" strength distribution curves as shown in Figures 13-5 and 13-6 are sufficiently accurate for this purpose.

TABLE 13-3

Fatigue Strength of Carburized Unnotched Specimens [1]

Steel	Diameter of Test Specimen in.	Case Depth in.	Hardness Case, R_c	Hardness Core, BHN	Endurance Limit Determined from Test psi	Endurance Limit Estimated from Core Hardness psi
SAE 2330	0.25	0.041	61	495	157,000	184,000
SAE 2330	0.25	0.030	63	514	147,000	169,000
SAE 2330	0.25	0.031	61	514	113,000	171,000
SAE 2315	0.25	0.041	60	341	120,000	127,000
SAE 2315	0.25	0.041	60	341	108,000	127,000
SAE 2315	0.25	0.041	60	302	105,000	112,000
SAE 2315	0.25	0.042	60	197	101,000	74,000
SAE 2315	0.25	0.032	60	197	98,500	66,000

The calculation associated with the first line of Table 13-3 is given below and illustrated in Figure 13-7.

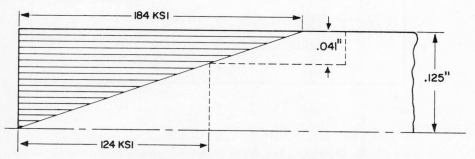

Figure 13-7. Illustration of line 1, Table 13-3.

1. Computed endurance limit at core-case junction = 250 × BHN = 250 (495) = 124 ksi.
2. Surface stress corresponding to 124 ksi junction stress =

$$124 \text{ ksi } \frac{.125''}{.125'' - .041''} = 184 \text{ ksi.}$$

On the basis of the foregoing discussion it is apparent that notched parts will be particularly benefited by a deep case. This point is illustrated in a quantitative way in Figure 13-8.

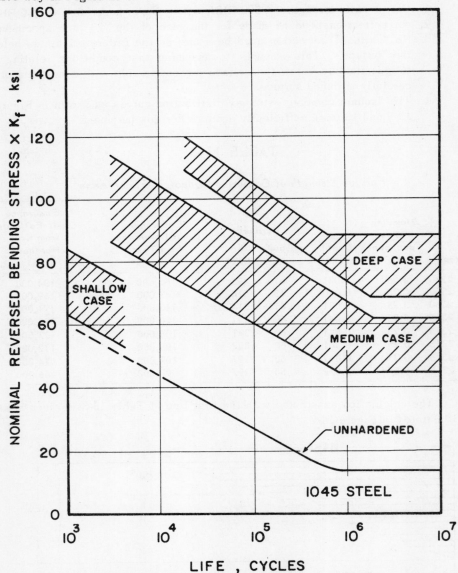

Figure 13–8. Effect of case depth on fatigue strength of notched SAE 1045 steel bars.[2]

13.3 Surface Hardening — Induction and Flame Hardening

Presumably the same considerations will apply to induction-hardened or flame-hardened parts. However, because of the nature of the processing there is between the case and core a transformation zone that is essentially in a normalized or annealed state and its hardness may be less than the hardness of the core. Consequently, in conservative design the hardness of the transformation zone rather than the hardness of the core should be used in instances where the core hardness would otherwise be critical, that is, for unnotched or mildly notched specimens. In

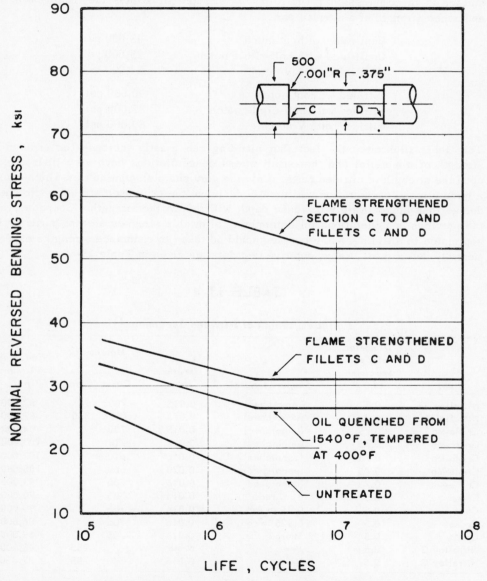

Figure 13-9. Effect of flame strengthening on notched SAE 1045 steel bars.[2]

the presence of sharp notches the criterion of significant strength will be the hardness of the case, as for carburized parts. The effect of flame strengthening on the endurance strength is illustrated in Figure 13-9.

13.4 Surface Hardening — Nitriding

In the case of nitriding, tests have indicated that the endurance limit is unaffected by surface finish for unnotched or moderately notched specimens. Also, improved fatigue characteristics of all nitrided steels result because a nitrided surface is in compression. The following example illustrates the improvement in endurance strength of a nitrided part.

Unnitrided without notch	45,000 psi
Unnitrided with half-circle notch	25,000 psi
Unnitrided with V notch	24,000 psi
Nitrided without notch	90,000 psi
Nitrided with half-circle notch	87,000 psi
Nitrided with V notch	80,000 psi

This table illustrates the fact that nitriding can greatly increase the endurance strength of a material and that small stress concentrations have very little effect upon the strength of nitrided parts. Only the very sharp discontinuities which cause a large stress concentration will greatly decrease the endurance strength. Notches deeper than approximately 0.7 case depth will reduce the strength. Consequently, the previous considerations for determining allowable stresses are not particularly applicable to nitriding, and recourse should be taken to endurance strengths experimentally determined. Representative test data are given in Table 13-4.

TABLE 13-4

Fatigue Strength of Nitrided Specimens[1]

Steel	Diameter of Test Specimen in.	Shape of Notch	Case Depth in.	Hardness BHN Case	Hardness BHN Core	Endurance Limit psi
Nitralloy G	0.3	(unnotched)	0.015	730	285	82,000
Nitralloy G	0.3	(unnotched)	0.015	760	360	87,000
Cr-Mo-Mn	0.75	(unnotched)	0.015	700		104,000
Cr-Mo-Mn	0.75	(unnotched)	0.019	710		103,000
Cr-Mo-Mn	0.75	(unnotched)	0.016	610		102,000
Cr-Mo-Mn	0.75	(unnotched)	0.020	680		100,000
Cr-Mo-Mn	0.75	(unnotched)	0.016	700		93,000
Cr-Mo	0.5	3 in. rad.	0.014	705		90,000
Cr-Mo	0.5	0.25 in rad.	0.014	705		90,000
Cr-Mo	0.5	0.125 in rad.	0.014	705		86,000
Cr-Mo	0.5	Sharp	0.014	705		69,000
Nitralloy G	0.5	Vee	None		285	43,000
Nitralloy G	0.5	Vee	0.015	740	285	82,000

13.5 Plating — Corrosion

Since platings are commonly applied to metal surfaces in order to combat corrosion, and since both corrosion and the plating itself influence fatigue strength, these items are considered together in this article.

The most obvious damaging effect of corrosion is that of roughening of the surface and, eventually, reduction of section. A more serious effect, known as *corrosion fatigue*, occurs when fatigue loading exists simultaneously with corrosion. During the latter process, the corrosive medium attacks the walls and base of the initial fatigue crack. This causes the corroded particles to break loose and lodge in the crack so as to form a wedge which intensifies the stresses at the base of the crack during a portion of the load cycle and tends to press the fractured surfaces together.

Figure 13-10 illustrates S-N curves for corroded and non-corroded unclad aluminum samples. The corroded samples were prepared by immersing them in salt water for 18 hours before testing.

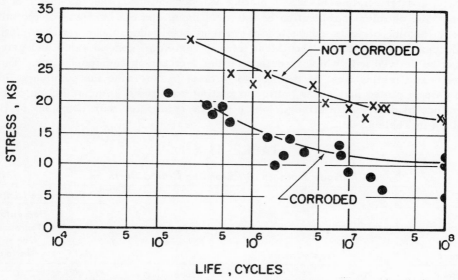

LIFE , CYCLES

Figure 13-10. Effect of corrosion on S-N curve of aluminum.[2]

The extent of damage caused by corrosion is affected by such factors as speed of testing, rest periods, atmospheric conditions, etc. Corrosion can be controlled by the use of protective non-metallic coatings such as paints, lacquers, and plastic films; or by metallic plating. It has been found that softer electroplating processes such as zinc, lead, and copper have no detrimental effect on the fatigue strength of steel when tested in air. However, when the tests were conducted in fresh water the plated specimens showed an increase in strength over the bare steel. This would indicate that soft platings offer advantages in cases of fatigue loading on members subjected to corrosion. The data of Table 13-5 illustrate this fact.

The above statements do not apply to hard platings, such as chrome or nickel, when these are deposited in a highly stressed condition or when the conditions of plating are such as to produce hydrogen embrittlement.

TABLE 13-5

Effect of Fresh Water Corrosion on Endurance Limit

Condition	Endurance Limit in Air psi	Endurance Limit in Fresh Water psi	Percentage Decrease Due to Corrosion
Uncoated	31,000	15,500	50
Copper plated	28,000	28,000	0
Nickel plated	23,500	23,500	0
Chromium plated	33,000	33,000	0

The general effect of chromium plating on the fatigue strength of steel is to reduce the endurance limit; under particularly unfavorable conditions it has been reduced to 35 per cent of the value for the unplated steel. The extent to which the endurance limit may be reduced in any particular chrome plated part depends upon the plating process and the steel base. Some important factors are the current density, and temperature at which plating is accomplished, the thickness of the plating, the chemical composition of the steel base, and the hardness of the steel base. Results of tests conducted on various steels and under variable plating conditions do not follow a consistent trend. Therefore, general rules and values cannot be derived with which to determine the decrease in endurance limit. Thus, experimental testing must be resorted to in order to determine the endurance limit of a chrome plated part under particular plating conditions. An indication of the magnitude of decrease in strength which may be associated with chromium plating is given in Table 13-6.

TABLE 13-6

Fatigue Strength of Chromium Plated Parts

Steel	Treatment	Plating Thickness in.	Endurance Limit psi	Percentage Decrease Due to Plating
Cr-Mo-V		None	74,000	0
Cr-Mo-V	Plated 15 hr.	0.0015	68,000	8
Cr-Mo-V	Plated 8 hr.	0.006	64,000	14
Cr-Mo-V	Plated 8 hr., tempered 250°C	0.008	31,000	58
Cr-Mo-V	Plated 1 hr., tempered 250°C	0.0015	62,000	16
SAE 6130	Normalized, not plated	None	33,000	0
SAE 6130	Normalized, plated	0.00018	30,000	9
SAE 6130	Normalized, plated	0.0045	32,000	3
SAE 6130	Quenched-and-drawn, not plated	None	65,500	0
SAE 6130	Quenched-and-drawn, plated	0.00015	38,000	57
SAE 6130	Quenched-and-drawn, plated	0.0045	41,000	38

References

1. Lipson, Noll, and Clock, *Stress and Strength of Manufactured Parts*, McGraw-Hill, 1950.
2. Grover, H. J., Gordon, S. A., and Jackson, L. R., *Fatigue of Metals and Structures*, U.S. Government Printing Office, 1960.
3. *Metals Engineering Design*, ASME Handbook, McGraw-Hill, 1953.
4. Lessells, J. M., *Strength and Resistance of Metals*, Wiley, 1954.
5. Sines, G. and Waisman, J. L., *Metal Fatigue*, McGraw-Hill, 1959.
6. Murray, W. M., *Fatigue and Fracture of Metals*, Wiley, 1952.
7. Pope, J. A., *Metal Fatigue*, Chapman and Hall, 1959.
8. Lipson, C., "More Realistic Measure of Shot-Peening Effectiveness," *Steel* (Aug. 6, 1951).

Chapter 14

SURFACE FATIGUE STRENGTH

In Chapter 11 it was pointed out that steels have S-N curves of the general type illustrated in Figure 11-5. The fundamental characteristic of the steel S-N curve is that the life of the material increases as the level of reversed stress is reduced. Upon reducing the stress to the endurance limit, the life suddenly increases to "infinity." This means that if a steel can successfully withstand one million to ten million applications of a given stress, it can withstand a billion, 100 billion, or any number of stress applications without failure.

Unfortunately, even steel does not display this characteristic with regard to contact stresses. It is well known, for example, that ball and roller bearings must be designed with regard to actual life requirements (usually many millions or billions of cycles) and that they cannot be designed for "infinite life."

The relationship between Hertz contact stresses, as computed from the Chapter 7 equations, and life has been the subject of several investigations which have been reported in the literature. A summary of the results obtained by various investigators is given in Figure 14-1. These S-N curves indicate a continuous decrease in strength as life increases, up to as many as 10^{10} cycles. Note that this represents a life of 1000 to 10,000 times the life at the knee of the steel S-N curve for bending, torsional, or axial loading.

All of the curves in Figure 14-1 are plotted on the basis of 90 per cent of the samples tested having lives in excess of the curve values, while 10 per cent have lives less than the plotted values. The gears tested represent high quality manufacture and case hardened steel of approximately 60 Rockwell C hardness. The bearings tested represent commercial bearing manufacturing practice and 52100 steel. Further information pertaining to the curves in Figure 14-1 is contained in Table 14-1. The values of Hertz contact stress represented correspond to the maximum compressive stress under the load. The factors due to sliding and thermal considerations, which are discussed in Chapter 7, were not taken into account.

It appears significant that with only two exceptions, the slopes of all curves are fairly uniform, regardless of whether gears, bearings, or guided test rollers were used in the tests.

Figure 14-2 has been prepared as a general summary of the data presented in Figure 14-1 in order to show the order of magnitude of allowable contact stresses for gears and bearings. The curves shown were selected as follows:

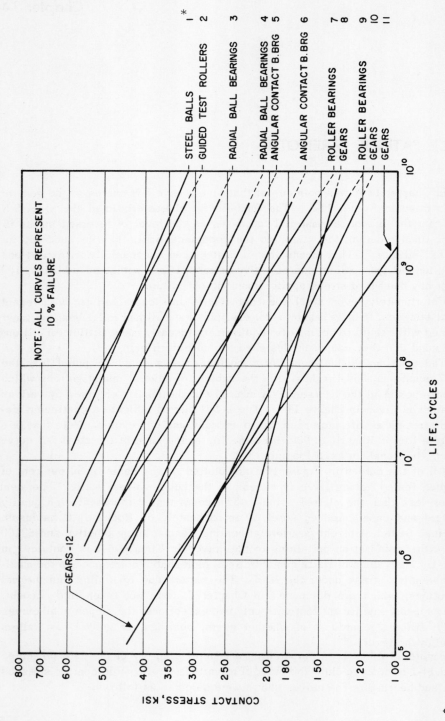

Figure 14—1. S-N curves for contact stresses — steel members.

* Numbers refer to references given in Table 14—1.

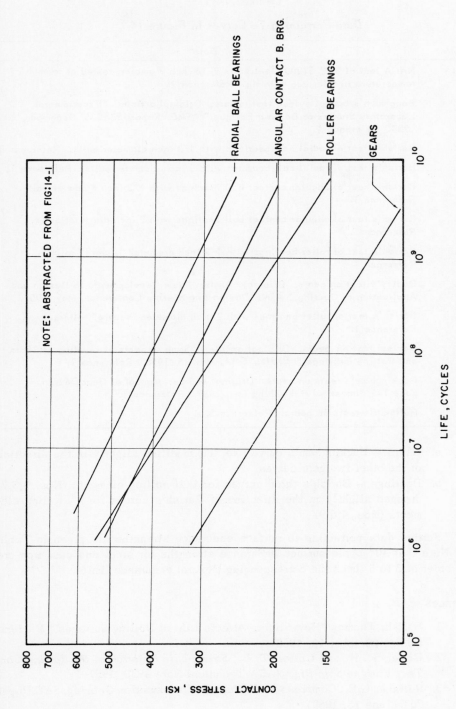

Figure 14–2. S-N curves for contact stresses — gears and anti-friction bearings.

TABLE 14-1

Data Pertaining To Curves In Figure 14-1

Curve No.	Data
1.	NACA test of SAE 51200 steel balls 9/16 inch diameter, tested at room temperature in a fatigue spin rig. Reference 2.
2.	Baughman's test of guided test rollers. Original article: "Experimental Laboratory Studies of Bearing Fatigue," *ASME*, Report 58A235, December, 1958. Reference 1.
3.	Barish's test of radial ball bearings with 1/2 inch diameter balls. Reference 1.
4.	Barish's test of radial ball bearings with 2 inch diameter balls. Reference 1.
5.	Barish's test of angular contact ball bearings with 1/2 inch diameter balls. Reference 1.
6.	Barish's test of angular contact ball bearings with 2 inch diameter balls. Reference 1.
7.	Barish's test of roller bearings with 1/2 inch diameter "square" rollers. Reference 1.
8.	Dudley's test on gears. Original article: "New Developments in Design and Application of Gearing," *ASME Design Engineering Conference*, May, 1957.
9.	Barish's test of roller bearings with 2 inch diameter "square" rollers. Reference 1.
10.	Davies' test on gears. Original article: "Some Aspects of Loading of Gears and Rolling Bearings," *British GMA*, May 15, 1956. Reference 1.
11.	Buckingham's tests on gears. Original source: *Manual of Gear Design*, page 145, Industrial Publishing Co., 1957. Reference 1.
12.	Huffaker's tests on gears. Reference 3.

a. Gears — Buckingham's curve (No. 11) modified slightly in the direction of the other two gear curves.

b. Bearings — Barish's three curves for 1/2" rolling elements (Nos. 3,5,7) dropped slightly in the direction of Barish's curves for 2" rolling elements (Nos. 4,6,9).

Further data pertaining to surface endurance strengths are given in Table 14-2. Note that 10^8 cycle surface endurance strengths for steel and cast iron are of the order of 3 to 5 times the corresponding flexural endurance limits.

References

1. Barish, Thomas "How Sliding Affects Life of Rolling Surfaces," *Machine Design* (October 13, 1960).
2. Butler, R. H. and Carter, T. L., *Stress-Life Relation of the Rolling-Contact Fatigue Spin Rig*, NACA Technical Note 3930, 1957.
3. Huffaker G.E., *Compressive Failure in Transmission Gearing*, SAE Paper 76T (June 15, 1959).
4. Buckingham, Earl, *Analytical Mechanics of Gears*, McGraw-Hill, 1949.

TABLE 14-2
Surface Endurance Limits

Drive Roll	Driven Roll	Ultimate Strength Tension psi	Ultimate Strength Comp.* psi	Elastic Limit psi	Brinell Hardness	Flexural Endurance Limit psi	Surface Endurance Strength @ 108 Cycles psi	Surf. End. Strength / Flex. End. Limit
Hardened and Ground Steel	Cast iron with steel scrap, as cast	35,200	120,000	15,000	223	21,000	87,000	4.14
	Cast iron with steel scrap, heat treated	45,950	138,000	35,750	255	25,000	87,000	3.48
	Nickel cast iron, as cast	35,400	121,000	12,600	217	16,000	69,200	4.31
	Nickel cast iron, heat treated, drawn	41,700 / --	131,000 / --	24,000 / --	246 / 375	21,000* / --	75,800 / 81,900	3.71 / --
	Nickel cast iron, heat treated	46,500	138,000	25,000	287	19,000	107,300 / 92,900	5.62 / 4.88
	Nickel chrome-cast iron, as cast, heat treated	39,000 / 44,700	125,000 / 134,000	15,100 / 31,600	234 / 243	18,000* / --	72,400 / 72,400	4.02 / --
	Moly. cast iron, as cast, heat treated	-- / 49,200	-- / 137,500	-- / 22,400	-- / 290	-- / 22,000	82,000 / 113,700	-- / 5.16
SAE 2515 Steel, Carburized	SAE 2515 Steel carburized Case Depth .030" .040" .060"	core: 180,000	--	core: 163,000	core: 363 case: 600	90,000*	247,400** 294,600** 207,200**	2.75 3.27 2.30
SAE 1040 Steel, Induction-Hardened	SAE 1040 Steel, Induction-hardened	core: 85,000*	--	core: 71,000*	core:170* case:500*	42,000*	237,000	5.93

* Estimated values, data primarily from Reference 4.

** Rolling plus 10 per cent sliding (all other values in the column are for pure rolling).

PART III

Balancing Strength and Stress

Chapter 15

FACTORS OF SAFETY

The adequacy of a given design from a structural standpoint obviously requires that the part be strong enough for the anticipated service conditions. That is, in order to avoid failure, the stress imposed on the part by the operating loads must be less than the strength of the material. At the same time, the imposed stress must not be too much less than the strength if the design is to be practical. Thus, a satisfactory design must be characterized by a proper balance between the significant stress and significant strength. This balance must be expressed in terms of an index which is readily understood and convenient to establish. It has been the general practice to express this balance by the so called "factor of safety." This term arose from the practice of designing on the basis of the ultimate strength and was defined by the equation.

$$N = \frac{S_u}{\sigma} \tag{15.1}$$

where
$$N = \text{factory of safety}$$
$$S_u = \text{ultimate strength}$$
$$\sigma = \text{design stress}$$

Apparently, the factor of safety was meant to account for all the variables which were known to affect the stress and strength of the member, such as the mode of loading, surface finish, stress concentration, etc.

The utilization of a factor of safety of this nature has justification when its value is based on considerable experience with parts not too different from the one under consideration. However, when substantial changes in the geometry, the processing, or the functioning of the part are contemplated, a major error may result if the old factor of safety is projected to the new set of conditions.

A more reliable method of predicting the balance between stress and strength for a member with which the designer has little or no experience requires that all the factors affecting the stress and strength be considered individually. (See Parts I and II.) The balance between the two would then be expressed in terms of a factor of safety which will be smaller than the conventional factor of safety, as the latter is basically a "factor of ignorance," to allow for such factors as surface finish, mode of loading, etc. This "new" factor of safety will be smaller since it needs to account only for occasional overloading, production and service variations, etc.

163

15.1 Empirical Concepts

In present usage, the concept of factor of safety varies greatly throughout the field of machine design. Some of these variations will be discussed briefly in order to develop the correct of applying safety factors.

a. TERMINOLOGY

The factor of safety is called by many names, all of which have essentially the same meaning. Some of the most common usages are listed below:

$$\text{Factor of safety} = \frac{\text{strength}}{\text{stress}} \qquad\qquad\qquad (a)$$

$$\text{Design factor} = \frac{\text{strength}}{\text{design stress}} \qquad\qquad (b)$$

$$\qquad\qquad\qquad\qquad\qquad\qquad\qquad\qquad (15.2)$$

$$\text{Factor of utilization} = \frac{\text{stress}}{\text{strength}} = \frac{1}{\text{F.S.}} \qquad (c)$$

$$\text{Margin of safety} = \frac{\text{strength} - \text{stress}}{\text{stress}} = \text{F.S.} - 1 \qquad (d)$$

Recently, a new concept has been introduced called a "functional reserve factor" in order to link factor of safety with the strength of a particular part. Functional reserve factor is defined as the ratio of the magnitude of a variable producing failure to the value of the variable at operating conditions. Some of the forms in which it has been suggested to use this factor are power reserve factor, torque reserve factor, material reserve factor, surface reserve factor, fillet radius reserve factor, part dimension reserve factor, etc. For example, the torque reserve factor for an existing part might be defined as the ratio of some future torque requirement that would produce failure to the present torque. This functional reserve factor would enable the designer to know immediately at some future date if a particular part can safely withstand a given increase in torque.

Thus, it is quite apparent that the concept of functional reserve factor, if ever fully developed and accepted, could become a very important tool in machine design. Any variable, which could possibly cause failure, could be expressed in terms of a reserve factor, the relationship stating the change that the variable could undergo before failure would occur. A designer could, therefore, compare the critical reserve factors to determine whether a part could withstand any contemplated changes. This concept is still in the formative stages.

b. NUMERICAL VALUES

In the past, many representative safety factors have been developed, based upon the ultimate or yield strength, to apply for various kinds of loading. Most of these factors were obtained through experience on members which exhibited no failure when designed from these conventionally large safety factors. However, these large factors were obtained by lumping together all the effects of loading and service conditions about which very little was known. Consequently, these factors often resulted in gross overdesign. Tables 15-1 and 15-2 are representative of conventional safety factors used in practice. Table 15-1 lists values from *Machinery's Handbook*. As these tables illustrate, safety factors range in magnitude from about 4 to 20. Any machine member designed with such a large factor of safety could not have been completely analyzed to determine the strength of the member or the stresses imposed from the loading conditions. If this had been done, a smaller safety factor should have been used. Thus, large safety factors should not be used in machine design where the loads fluctuate in a definite manner. The methods to be used are developed in the following articles.

TABLE 15-1

Factors of Safety

Kind of Load	Steel Based on S_u	Cast Iron Based on S_u
Dead load	5	6
Repeated one direction gradual (mild shock)	6	10
Repeated reversed direction gradual (mild shock)	8	15
Shock	12	20

TABLE 15-2

Factors of Safety (Based on Ultimate Strength)

Shock loads	10
Fluid tight joints	6
Live loads	6
Variable loads	4
Ordinary work	4
Dead load	4

15.2 Significant Factors of Safety

A more meaningful concept of the factor of safety is expressed by the following equation:

$$\text{Factor of safety} = \frac{\text{Significant strength}}{\text{Significant stress}} \tag{15.3}$$

The significant strength and significant stress are normally determined in accordance with the methods given in Parts I and II. However, it is not necessary that stress and strength be expressed in terms of psi. The stress and strength can be expressed in terms of load applied and load capacity respectively, in which case they could be expressed in terms of force, torque, or bending moment. For example, in gears the strength, as determined from the Lewis equation, is expressed in terms of the tooth strength F_s which is the maximum allowable force in pounds which could be applied to the tooth without causing fracture. The stress in pounds is the dynamic load, F_d, as determined from the transmitted horsepower corrected for impact, tooth profile errors, etc. Thus, safety factor is a unitless ratio of strength to stress and can be determined without always converting to psi.

a. ALLOWANCE FOR UNAVOIDABLE VARIATIONS

In the ideal case, a safety factor equal to 1 would mean that the maximum stress and part strength would be exactly equal and the design would be perfect. In actual practice, the safety factor must be greater than 1; that is, the design must be overbalanced in favor of strength. This overbalance is necessitated by the limitation of the theoretical stress equations, experimental errors in stress measurement, production variations in the geometry of the part, and all other factors which may adversely affect the estimated significant stress. In addition, unknown factors which affect the significant strength must be provided for in the safety factor. These include material and processing tolerances causing surface variations, etc.

The decision as to whether a given safety factor is adequate must be determined for each design since each member is essentially an individual problem. Consequently, the safety factor must be based on judgment and experience, with the consideration of such factors as the consequence of failure and economical production. When the unknown factors affecting the significant stress and significant strength can be reduced to a minimum, a safety factor as low as 1.3 may represent adequate insurance against failure. At the other extreme, if the factors affecting significant stress and significant strength are not too well defined, a safety factor of 2 should be applied. Generally,

$$1.3 \leq \text{Safety Factor} \leq 2.0$$

Since the significant safety factor is arrived at through the consideration of the principal variables affecting the stress and strength of a member, it is not necessary to assign to it the high values associated with the conventional factor of safety.

b. PROVISION FOR OVERLOAD

Another consideration often taken into account when a designer chooses a factor of safety is the magnitude and frequency of overloading. Many designs are determined from stresses imposed under general operating conditions, and the infrequent overloads are accounted for by using a larger factor of safety. The method of determining the magnitude of overload that can be withstood can be illustrated by the following example. Suppose a machine member was being designed for general operating conditions for which all the effects upon stress and strength were known so that the minimum safety factor of 1.3 could be used. However, the operating conditions were also such that the member was subjected to infrequent overloading. Therefore, the safety factor was increased to 2.0 to prevent failure. This allows the determination of the amount of overload in relation to the original design load as expressed below:

$$\text{per cent overload } = \frac{N_2 - N_1}{N_2} \times 100$$

where N_1 = safety factor neglecting overload

               N_2 = safety factor accounting for overload

In the example,

$$\text{per cent overload } = \frac{2 - 1.3}{1.3} \times 100 = 54 \text{ per cent}$$

Thus, a 54 per cent overload could be sustained without failure.

Safety factors in the region of 2 are usually used for moderate overloads. If the overloads are so severe that safety factors larger than 2 are required, the overloading effect should be included in the stress analysis.

c. PROVISION FOR INCREASED CAPACITY

It is often desirable to increase the power rating of an existing machine without completely redesigning it. Obviously, if the machine is originally designed with a minimum safety factor of 1.3, it could not withstand the increased stresses caused by increasing the load; at some point the machine would fail. However, if, when the original machine was being designed, it was forseen that in the future the capacity would possibly be increased, the machine could have been overdesigned by using a safety factor larger than the one deemed necessary under the existing loading conditions. Thus, it is often cheaper to overdesign a machine for a limited time rather than design a new but similar machine at some future date in order to get a larger output. The new machine would probably be less economical than overdesigning the original machine since it is costly to arrive at the new design, to set up new methods of production, and to conduct experimental tests.

15.3 Determination of Significant Factors of Safety

From the previous definition it is apparent that the significant safety factor is determined from the consideration of the stress and strength analyses. However, the manner in which these two analyses are compared depends upon the pattern of loading and the stresses resulting therefrom. Four different patterns of stresses will be considered and the method of determining the factor of safety for each case will be explained.

Conventionally, factor of safety is determined by constructing the Goodman diagram to represent the strength of the member. The various stress components (σ_{max}, σ_{mean}, σ_{min}, $\sigma_{variable}$) are then superimposed upon the strength diagram and the safety factor determined. For example, Figure 15-1 illustrates the Goodman diagram which represents the strength of some member, the stength being determined for the actual service conditions involved. Figure 15-1 also illustrates the stress to which the part is subjected. If the mean stress were plotted on the Goodman diagram, the Point A would be determined on the steady stress line. If the variable component of stress was also plotted, the points B_1 and C_1 would be de-

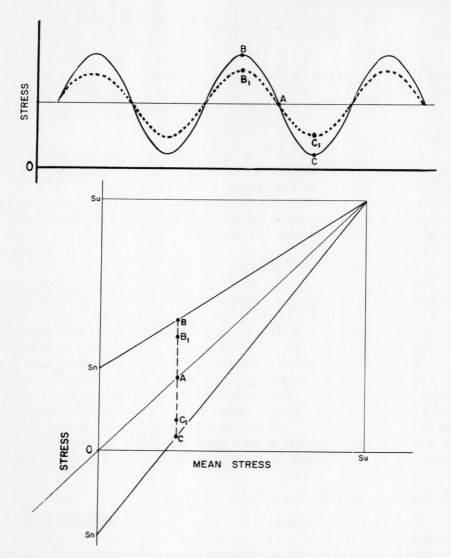

Figure 15-1. Conventional method of determining factor of safety.

determined. Thus, the stress would fluctuate between B_1 and C_1. The Goodman diagram reveals that at this particular preload or mean stress, the fluctuating stress could reach a magnitude of AB (or the stress range could reach a magnitude CB) before failure would occur. Thus, the factor of safety for this case could be expressed as the allowable variable stress AB divided by the actual variable stress AB_1 (or allowable stress range CB divided by actual stress range $C_1 B_1$).

However, this procedure is not applicable to all cases of fluctuating loads. Therefore, four methods of determining factors of safety will be developed. Each of these four cases depends upon the physical significance of the stresses involved The four cases correspond to situations in which

1. The minimum stress remains unchanged during overloads.
2. The mean stress remains unchanged during overloads.
3. The maximum stress remains unchanged during overloads.
4. The variable stress remains unchanged during overloads.

Case 1. Constant Preload, Variable Stress Completely Additive to Preload

Consider first the special condition of no preload (zero minimum stress). Figure 15-2 illustrates the stress pattern for this type of loading where the external load fluctuates from zero to a maximum and then back to zero. The nominal loading is represented by stress fluctuations from C_1 to B_1. As the magnitude of external loading is increased, the maximum stress increases from B_1 to B_2, and finally to B.

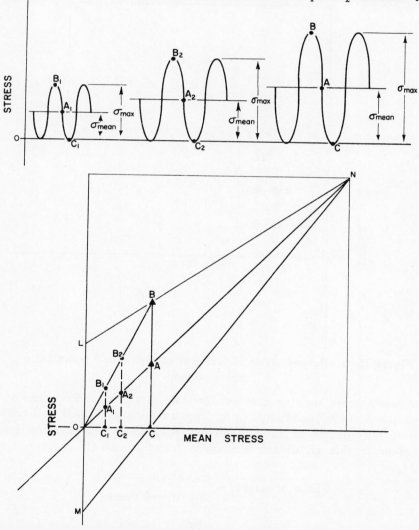

Figure 15—2. Method of determining factor of safety, case I (constant σ_{min}), zero preload.

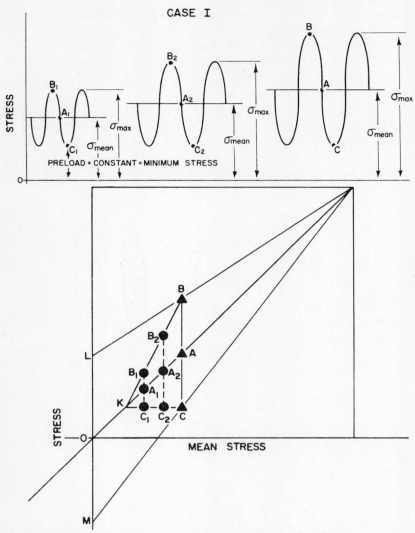

Figure 15–3. Determination of factor of safety, case I (constant σ_{min}), finite preload.

The minimum stress remains constant (points C_1, C_2, C). The mean stress increases from A_1 to A_2, and finally to A. Stress fluctuation from C to B corresponds exactly to the strength of the material, as indicated by the Goodman line. The safety factor for this application is computed from Equation (15.3) thus:

$$\text{Factor of safety} = \frac{\text{Significant strength}}{\text{Significant stress}} \qquad (15.3)$$

$$= \frac{BC}{B_1 C_1} \left(\text{or } \frac{AB}{A_1 B_1} \right)$$

Figure 15-3 illustrates the general condition of Case 1; namely, that of a constant preload (other than zero) plus a repeated stress varying from zero to a maximum. The constant preload stress acting without a fluctuating stress is represented by point K, the nominal stress fluctuation is from C_1 to B_1, and the overload stress fluctuation corresponding to incipient eventual failure is from C to B. Hence, the safety factor is BC/B_1C_1.

Note that in both Figures 15-2 and 15-3, line CB is readily determined by projecting horizontally from C_1 to the lower Goodman line, thereby locating point C; and by projecting vertically from C to the upper Goodman line to locate point B.

The bolts holding down the cylinder head of an engine can be considered as an illustration of Case 1. The bolts are initially tightened to a given preload. The repeated load imposed upon the bolt by combustion chamber pressure variations is superimposed upon this preload. With reference to Figure 15-3, stress $C = C_1 = C_2$ would represent the bolt preload stress; B_1C_1 would represent the stress fluctuation caused by normal combustion chamber pressure fluctuations which would occur if the maximum combustion chamber pressure were increased to the point of exhausting the safety factor (i.e., the point where significant stress = significant strength). The safety factor in this case would indicate the gas pressure functional reserve factor.

Case 2.   Constant Preload, Variable Stress Completely Reversed Around the Preload

If a member has a constant preload and a fluctuating external load which both supports and opposes the preload, a stress pattern is set up as shown in Figure 15-4. If the magnitude of the external load is changed, σ_{max} and σ_{min} will also change but σ_{mean} will remain constant. Thus, the factor of safety will be based on this criterion.

Figure 15-4 illustrates the fact that when the stress range is increased to CB, the full strength of the material is utilized. The safety factor is thus the allowable stress range (significant strength) divided by the actual stress range (significant stress), or:

$$\text{Factor of safety } = \frac{BC}{B_1 \, C_1}$$

An example of Case 2 would be vibrating weight supported by a spring. The static weight of the spring would provide the constant preload or mean stress. Normal vibration would provide the stress range B_1C_1. The maximum vibration which could occur without premature spring failure would cause stress range BC.

Note that Case 2 corresponds to the "conventional" method of determining the safety factor, shown in Figure 15-1.

Case 3.   Constant Preload, Variable Stress Completely Subtractive from Preload

If a member is subjected to a constant preload and a fluctuating external load which opposes the preload, the pattern of loading or stresses will be as illustrated in Figure 15-5. The constant preload in the absence of any fluctuating stress is represented by point K. The maximum stress will remain constant while the σ_{mean} and σ_{min} both will be susceptible to change.

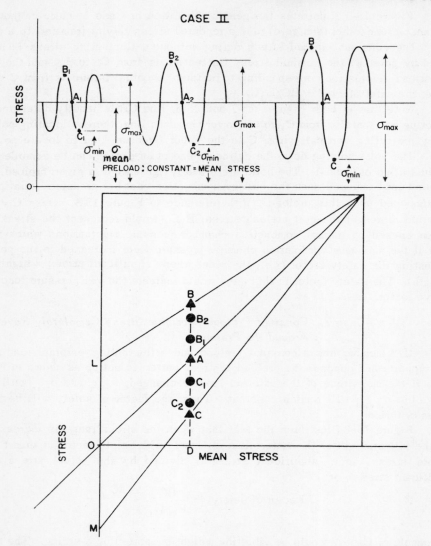

Figure 15—4. Determination of factor of safety, case 2 (constant σ_{min}).

The stress range corresponding to the strength of the material is determined by projecting horizontally from B_1 to the Goodman line, thereby locating point B. Vertical projection from B to the lower Goodman line establishes point C. The safety factor is the ratio of significant strength to stress, or BC/B_1C_1.

Case 4. Constant Fluctuating Stress, Variable Preload

If loading conditions were imposed which allowed the mean load or stress to be changed but which caused the external fluctuating load range to remain constant, a stress pattern would be set up as shown in Figure 15-6. The constant stress range, in the absence of any mean stress, is indicated by K'K". Normal operating stress range B_1C_1 involves the superposition of mean stress D_1.

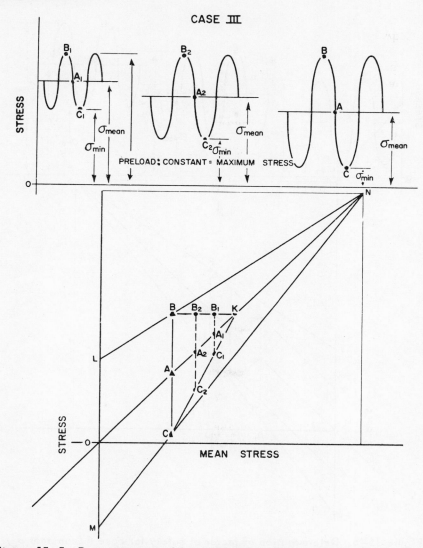

Figure 15–5. Determination of factor of safety for case 3 (constant σ_{max}).

The maximum preload stress which would not result in premature failure is D. Note that points B and C (and also K'K") are located by projecting at 45° from points B_1 and C_1. The safety factor in this case is the ratio between the maximum allowed mean stress (significant strength) OD to the actual mean stress (significant strength) OD to the actual mean stress (significant stress) OD_1.

The bolts holding down the cylinder head of an engine which served to illustrate Case 2 can also be used to illustrate Case 4. Case 4 would correspond to the situation in which the cylinder pressure cycle was considered fixed, and the initial tightening of the bolt was considered to be subject to production or servicing variations. Nominal stress range $B_1 C_1$ of Figure 15-6 corresponds to the normal initial bolt tension plus normal gas pressure fluctuations. Stress range BC corre-

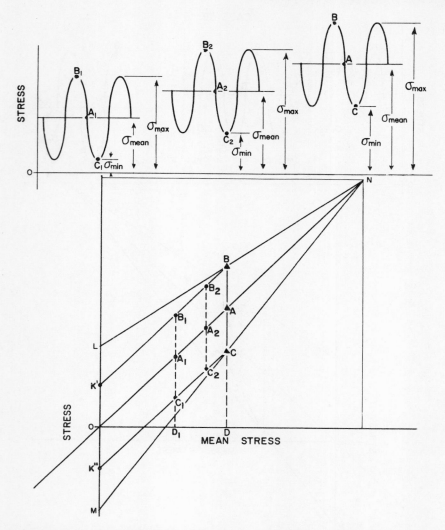

Figure 15–6. Determination of factor of safety for case 4 (constant σ_v).

sponds to the same gas pressure fluctuations, together with the maximum initial bolt overstressing which would not cause eventual failure. In this case, the safety factor would indicate the bolt overtightening functional reserve factor.

Figure 15-7 has been prepared to illustrate the comparison of the four methods of computing factor of safety. In each case, the same Goodman diagram has been shown, and in each case the same nominal stress variation B_1C_1 has been drawn. If overloads are such that the minimum stress remains constant, Case 1 applies, and the safety factor is shown to be 1.6. If the application were such that overloads would result in no change in mean stress, Case 2 would apply, and the safety factor would be 1.9. Similarly, the factors of safety for Cases 3 and 4 are shown to be 2.6 and 1.8. Thus, for any particular application, the value of the

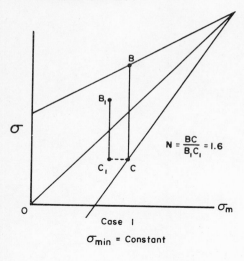

$$N = \frac{BC}{B_1 C_1} = 1.6$$

Case 1

σ_{min} = Constant

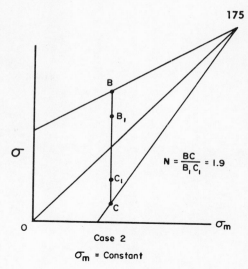

$$N = \frac{BC}{B_1 C_1} = 1.9$$

Case 2

σ_m = Constant

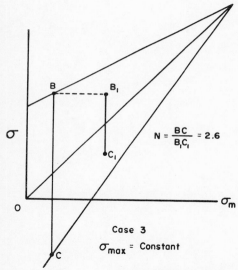

$$N = \frac{BC}{B_1 C_1} = 2.6$$

Case 3

σ_{max} = Constant

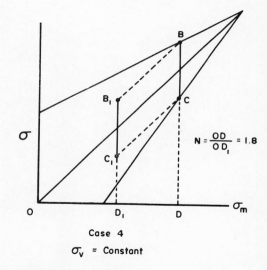

$$N = \frac{OD}{OD_1} = 1.8$$

Case 4

σ_v = Constant

Figure 15–7. Comparison of four safety factors.

significant factor of safety depends upon the assumed manner in which the loading would be increased to cause failure.

References

1. Lipson, Noll, and Clock, *Stress and Strength of Manufactured Parts*, McGraw-Hill, 1950.
2. *Machinery's Handbook*, The Industrial Press, 1953.
3. Lipson, C. and Thiel, D. H., *Applications of Stress Analysis*, University of Michigan, 1959.

Chapter 16

APPEARANCE OF FATIGUE FRACTURES

When the significant stress imposed upon a part exceeds the corresponding infinite life significant strength, a fatigue fracture will occur. The appearance of the fatigue fracture is indicative of the nature and magnitude of the stress/strength imbalance which resulted in failure.

16.1 Bending Fracture

Fatigue failures caused by bending loads result in fracture faces composed of two zones: (1) a smooth, velvety, dull *fatigue* zone, which may or may not show stop marks indicating rate of progress of the crack, and (2) a coarse, bright, crystalline *instantaneous fracture* zone. The relative shapes, sizes, and locations of these two zones are determined by the magnitude and direction of the imposed loads as well as by the presence or absence of stress raisers.

Figure 16-1 illustrates the nature of fractured surface resulting from various combinations of bending fatigue loading. The three principal cases illustrated in Figure 16-1 and discussed below are the following:

Case 1. One-way bending load.
Case 2. Two-way bending load.
Case 3. Reversed bending and rotation load.

Case 1 with No Stress Concentration. Maximum stress occurs at the surface or, for a round bar, at the extreme radius. Under this stress a small elliptically shaped fatigue crack starts at the most susceptible nucleus, such as a tool mark or other surface flaw. Because of the decrease in distance from the neutral axis, the stress at the edge of this crack becomes smaller; as the crack progresses inwardly, its radius of curvature increases, as shown by sketches 1a and 1b in Figure 16-1. The relative proportions of the smooth and ragged areas, corresponding to the fatigue and instantaneous zones respectively, depend upon the degree of overstress to which the member is subjected. A relatively large instantaneous zone is indicative of high overstress, sketch 1b; a small instantaneous zone is the result of low overstress and often a great number of cycles prior to failure, sketch 1a. Frequently a second crack starts in the compression area, probably due to tensile stresses caused by elastic forces tending to restore the part to its original shape during the unstressed portion of the fatigue cycle.

177

Case 1 with Mild Stress Concentration. In a member having a notch, the forces around the base of the notch are abnormally high because of stress concentration. This causes the contour of the crack to flatten out, as shown in sketches 1c and 1d, because the crack progresses around the circumference nearly as fast as it progresses inwardly. The size of the instantaneous fracture zone again is determined by the relative amount of overstressing.

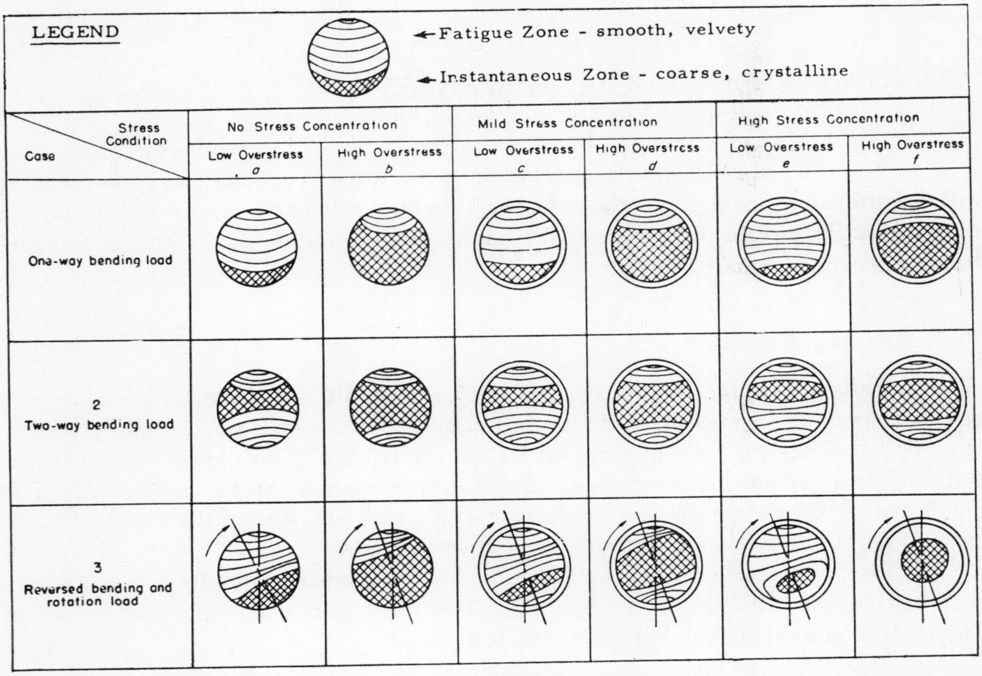

Figure 16–1. Identification of bending fractures.

Case 1 with High Stress Concentration. If the stress concentration is sufficiently large, the curvature of the fracture zone actually changes sign and becomes concave, as shown in Sketches 1e and 1f, because the rate of crack propagation along the periphery is greater than the rate in the radial direction.

Case 2 with No Stress Concentration. For a member highly but uniformly overstressed, the cracks start almost simultaneously at the opposite extreme fibres, proceed toward the center at approximately equal speeds, and produce a symmetrical fracture, as shown in sketch 2b. For a member lightly overstressed, the surface conditions and accidental influences play a much more important part. The fracture starts at a local stress concentration and progresses part way before the crack on the other side starts. This makes the unsymmetrical fracture illustrated in sketch 2a. The amount of overstressing determines the size of the instantaneous fracture zone.

Case 2 with Mild Stress Concentration. The presence of a mild stress concentration has the effect of flattening the curvature of the instantaneous zone due to greater growth of the crack around the periphery than in a radial direction as shown in sketches 2c and 2d.

Case 2 with High Stress Concentration. A high stress concentration causes the crack to propagate around the periphery at such a high rate that the curvature of the fracture zone is inverted from concave to convex, as shown in sketches 2e and 2f. All other factors affecting fracture for the case of one-way bending previously discussed are applicable here.

Whether the fatigue crack terminates with a convex or concave curvature depends not only upon the degree of stress concentration and the degree of over-stress, but also upon the relative toughness or brittleness of the material. For example, sketch 2c is representative of fatigue failure for a mild steel with a moderate stress concentration, such as a circumferential round-bottom notch, but a notch of the same shape in a hardened steel would cause a fracture much more similar in appearance to sketch 2e because of the heightened notch sensitivity of the material. Concavity of the fatigue crack in sketch 2e is caused by accelerated crack growth around the periphery due to stress concentration. In general, concavity of the fatigue crack decreases with increased stress concentration or notch sensitivity.

Case 3 with No Stress Concentration. The maximum stress occurs at the two extreme fibres. If, as usually is the case, the metal is weaker at one side than the other, the fracture starts at one side as a small elliptical crack. Each successive crack boundary advances radially and is of increasing radius, becoming a straight line before the center of the member is reached. Also, it will be noticed that the crack "turns around" against the rotation. This phenomenon is termed crack slip.

Case 3 with Mild Stress Concentration. With high overstress, the notch causes early crack formation and rapid crack progression around most of the periphery. Thus, the instantaneous zone is centrally located on the fracture face, sketch 3d, varying slightly in position with the severity of the notch and ductility of the material. In contrast, slight overstressing tends to start the crack at the weakest point; the instantaneous zone is displaced from the point of crack initiation as shown in sketch 3c. Only an extremely tough material under the latter condition shows no response to the stress concentration caused by a notch and shows an instantaneous area located at the periphery in a manner similar to that indicated in sketch 3a.

Case 3 with High Stress Concentration. A combination of severe stress concentration and high overstress causes fatigue cracks to start simultaneously all around the circumference. Progressing radially, the cracks leave a fairly concentric circular or elliptical instantaneous fracture well inside the fatigue area. Less overstress again displaces the instantaneous zone as shown in sketch 3e.

16.2 Tensile and Compressive Fractures

Because fatigue testing in tension and compression is not very common, little information on fractures from these causes is available. However, a fatigue failure in a rotary bending test is essentially due to tension: hence, the formation of zones is approximately the same.

When a crack starts at the surface, it usually spreads fairly uniformly across the section, keeping approximately the same curvature because the stress is constant.

16.3 Torsional Fractures

Appearances of fatigue fractures caused by alternating torsion are quite different from those resulting from bending and axial loading. Torsional fatigue failures occur in one of two modes: (1) along the planes of maximum shear or, (2) along the plane of maximum tension. The state of stress in a shaft subjected

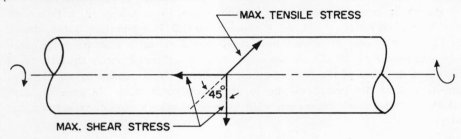

(a)-Shaft without stress concentration

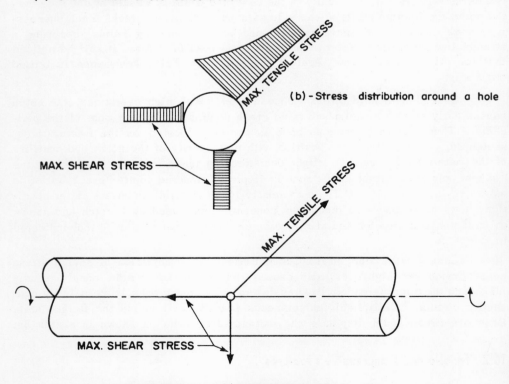

(b)-Stress distribution around a hole

(c)- Shaft with stress concentration

Figure 16-2. Stress distribution in torsionally loaded shaft with and without stress concentration.

to a torsional load is diagrammed in Figure 16-2. Maximum shear stress occurs along the axis of the shaft and at right angles to it, while the maximum tensile stress acts at 45° to the two shear stresses. Therefore, the two basic modes of torsional failure are: (1) longitudinal or transverse, along the planes of maximum shear, (2) helical, at 45° to the shaft axis, along the plane of maximum tension. These basic types of failure are sketched in the first column of Figure 16-3. Fractures which depart in appearance from these basic modes may seem anomalous but can be readily explained when local stress distribution and material properties are taken into account.

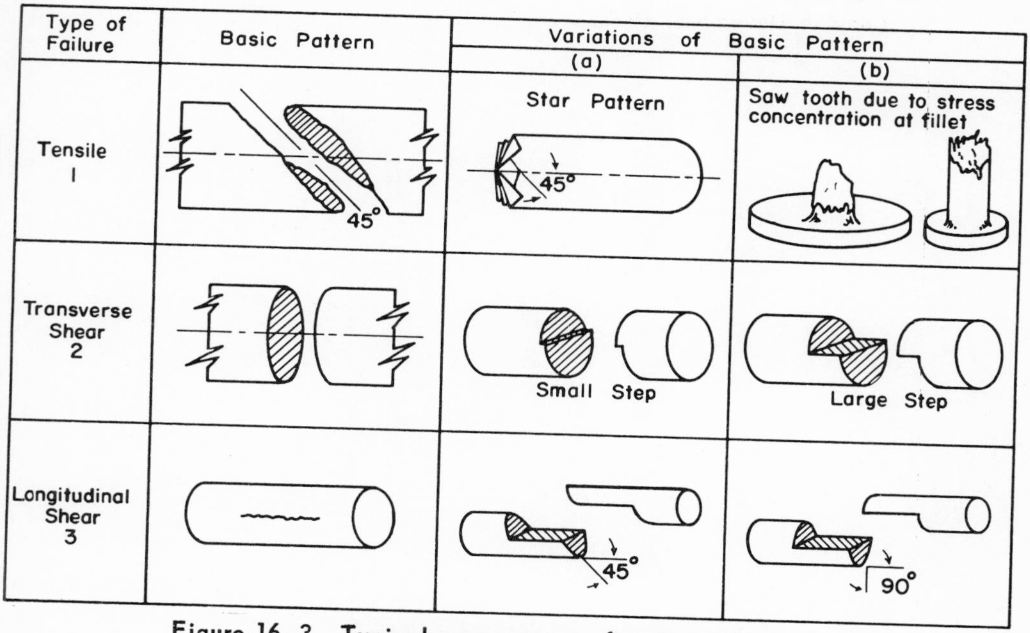

Figure 16-3. Typical appearances of torsional fractures. [1]

It will be noted from Figure 16-2a that in a shaft subjected to a torsional load the maximum shear stress is equal to the maximum tensile stress. However, the corresponding two strengths in steel are not equal, the shear strength being approximately .58 times the tensile strength. Therefore, the shear stress will reach the shear strength long *before* the tensile stress will reach the tensile strength; shear-type failure will result. The reason that transverse cracks are more prevalent than longitudinal cracks is that grinding or machining marks, which accentuate the probability of failure, are oriented in the transverse direction.

When a stress concentration is present, such as a transverse hole in a shaft, it tends to cause a tensile fracture, that is, a crack at 45° to the axis of the shaft. This change in mode of failure is due to the changed stress distribution caused by the stress concentration, which is equivalent to a factor of 4 in the case of a transverse hole. The effect of this stress concentration is to raise the tensile stress to four times its normal value. The shear stress remains substantially the same. This altered relationship is illustrated in Figures 16-2b and 16-2c.

Thus, although the tensile strength is nearly twice the shear strength, the tensile stress is now four times the shear stress. Therefore, the tensile stress will reach the tensile strength long *before* the shear stress will reach the shear strength; a tensile (45°) type of fracture will result.

Geometric stress raisers need not always be present to cause a helical tensile fracture. Internal discontinuities and flaws may act as sufficient stress raisers to magnify the tensile stress to the point where a helical fracture results.

References

1. Lipson, C., "Why Machine Parts Fail," reprinted from *Machine Design,* (May to December, 1950).

PART IV

Elastic Deflection and Elastic Stability

Chapter 17

ELASTIC DEFLECTION

17.1 Deflection of Straight Bars, Axially Loaded

The deflection of axially loaded bars of constant cross-section is given by the equation:

$$\delta = PL/AE \tag{17.1}$$

where
- δ = deflection (in.)
- P = applied load (lb.)
- L = length of bar (in.)
- A = cross-section area (in.^{2})
- E = modulus of elasticity (psi)

The above equation is valid only when the P/A stress is below the elastic limit of the material. In the case of compressive loads, Equation (17.1) is valid only if elastic stability exists (i.e., if the bar does not buckle). Elastic stability is discussed in the following chapter.

17.2 Deflection of Straight Bars in Torsion

The torsional deflection of straight round bars (solid or hollow) is given by the formula:

$$\theta = TL/JG \tag{17.2}$$

where
- θ = angular deflection (radians; 1 radian = 57.3°)
- T = applied torque (lb. in.)
- L = length of bar (in.)
- J = polar moment of inertia of cross-section (in.^{4})
- G = torsional modulus of elasticity (psi)

The torsional deflection of straight bars of any uniform cross-section is given by Equation (17.3):

$$\tag{17.3}$$

185

$$\theta = TL/KG$$

where K is a constant dependent on the size and shape of the cross-section. For circular sections, K is equal to J. For non-circular sections, K is less than J and may be only a small fraction of J. Expressions for K applying to 24 cross-section shapes are given in Reference 1. Constants for 15 shapes are listed in Table 17-1. Values for Cases 1, 2, 3, 5, 6, and 7 were obtained from rigorous mathematical analyses. The other cases involve approximate analyses or are based on the membrane analogy. These cases involve errors which in some instances reach 10 per cent, but are generally much smaller.

17.3 Moments and Deflections of Beams Having Uniform Section

The deflections tabulated in this article are based on two assumptions: (1) there is no deflection of the assumed fixed supports, and (2) deflection due to shear is negligible. Unless an extremely short beam is involved, assumption (2) is completely justified. In the case of rectangular cross-section cantilever beams, for example, the shear deflection is less than 4 per cent of the bending deflection if the beam length is at least 5 times the beam height.

Values of maximum bending moment, deflection at any point, and deflection at critical points are listed for beams with various types of support in Tables 17-2 through 17-5. In all tables, symbols E and I represent modulus of elasticity and rectangular moment of inertia respectively. Moments of inertia for various sections are listed in Table 18-1.

TABLE 17-1

TORTIONAL DEFLECTION CONSTANTS	
No. Section	Constant
1. Solid circle	$K = \dfrac{\pi D^4}{32}$
2. Hollow concentric circle	$K = \dfrac{\pi}{32}(D_o{}^4 - D_i{}^4)$
3. Solid ellipse	$K = \dfrac{\pi a^3 b^3}{a^2 + b^2}$
4. Hollow concentric ellipse	$K = \dfrac{\pi a_o{}^3 b_o{}^3}{a_o{}^2 + b_o{}^2}(1 - q^4);$ where $q = \dfrac{a_o}{a_i} = \dfrac{b_o}{b_i}$
5 Solid square	$K = 0.1406 a^4$
6. Solid equilateral triangle	$K = \dfrac{a^4 \sqrt{3}}{80}$
7. Solid rectangle	$K = a b^3 \left[\dfrac{16}{3} - 3.36 \dfrac{b}{a} \left(1 - \dfrac{b^4}{12 a^4}\right)\right]$
8. Hollow rectangle	$K = \dfrac{2 t t' (\ell - t)^2 (w - t')^2}{\ell t + w t' - t^2 - t'^2}$

TABLE 17-1 (Continued)

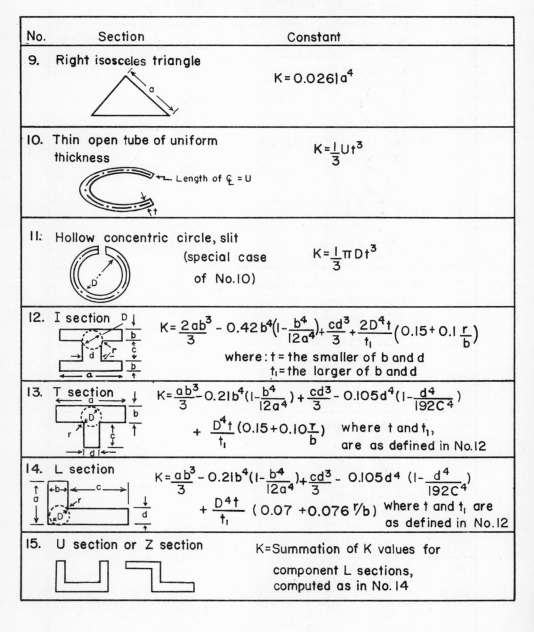

No.	Section	Constant
9.	Right isosceles triangle	$K = 0.0261a^4$
10.	Thin open tube of uniform thickness Length of $\mathcal{C} = U$	$K = \dfrac{1}{3} U t^3$
11.	Hollow concentric circle, slit (special case of No. 10)	$K = \dfrac{1}{3}\pi D t^3$
12.	I section	$K = \dfrac{2 ab^3}{3} - 0.42 b^4\left(1-\dfrac{b^4}{12a^4}\right) + \dfrac{cd^3}{3} + \dfrac{2D^4 t}{t_1}\left(0.15 + 0.1\,\dfrac{r}{b}\right)$ where: t = the smaller of b and d t_1 = the larger of b and d
13.	T section	$K = \dfrac{ab^3}{3} - 0.21 b^4\left(1-\dfrac{b^4}{12a^4}\right) + \dfrac{cd^3}{3} - 0.105 d^4\left(1-\dfrac{d^4}{192 C^4}\right)$ $+ \dfrac{D^4 t}{t_1}\left(0.15 + 0.10\,\dfrac{r}{b}\right)$ where t and t_1, are as defined in No. 12
14.	L section	$K = \dfrac{ab^3}{3} - 0.21 b^4\left(1-\dfrac{b^4}{12a^4}\right) + \dfrac{cd^3}{3} - 0.105 d^4\left(1-\dfrac{d^4}{192 C^4}\right)$ $+ \dfrac{D^4 t}{t_1}\left(0.07 + 0.076\,r/b\right)$ where t and t_1 are as defined in No. 12
15.	U section or Z section	K = Summation of K values for component L sections, computed as in No. 14

TABLE 17-2

Moment and Deflection of Cantilever Beams

No.	Loading	Maximum Moment (Absolute Value)	Deflection at Any Point	Deflection at Critical Points
1.		$M = PL$, at $x = 0$	$\delta = \dfrac{Px^2}{6EI}(3L-x)$	$\delta_{max} = \dfrac{PL^3}{3EI}$, at $x=L$
2.		$M = Pa$, at $x = 0$	$\delta = \dfrac{Px^2}{6EI}(3a-x)$ for $0<x<a$ $\delta = \dfrac{Pa^2}{6EI}(3x-a)$ for $a<x<L$	$\delta_{max} = \dfrac{Pa^2}{6EI}(3L-a)$, at $x=L$
3.		$M = M_0$, at all values of x	$\delta = \dfrac{Mx^2}{2EI}$	$\delta_{max} = \dfrac{ML^2}{2EI}$, at $x=L$
4.		$M = M_0$, at $0 \le x \le a$	$\delta = \dfrac{Mx^2}{2EI}$ for $0<x<a$ $\delta = \dfrac{Ma}{2EI}(2x-a)$ for $a<x<L$	$\delta_{max} = \dfrac{Ma}{2EI}(2L-a)$, at $x=L$
5.	Total load $= W$#	$M = \dfrac{WL}{2}$, at $x = 0$	$\delta = \dfrac{Wx^2}{24EIL}(x^2+6L^2-4Lx)$	$\delta_{max} = \dfrac{WL^3}{8EI}$, at $x=L$
6.	Total load $= W$#	$M = \dfrac{Wa}{2}$, at $x = 0$	$\delta = \dfrac{Wx^2}{24EIa}(x^2+6L^2-4Lx)$, for $0<x<a$ $\delta = \dfrac{Wa^2}{24EI}(4x-a)$, for $a<x<L$	$\delta_{max} = \dfrac{Wa^2}{24EI}(4L-a)$, at $x=L$
7.	Uniformly varying load, Total $= W$#	$M = \dfrac{WL}{3}$, at $x = 0$	$\delta = \dfrac{Wx^2}{60L^2EI}(10L^3-10L^2x+5Lx^2-x^3)$	$\delta_{max} = \dfrac{WL^3}{15EI}$, at $x=L$
8.	Uniformly varying load, Total $= W$#	$M = \dfrac{Wa}{3}$, at $x = 0$	$\delta = \dfrac{Wx^2}{60L^2EI}(10L^3-10L^2x+5Lx^2-x^3)$, for $0<x<a$ $\delta = \dfrac{Wa^2}{60EI}(5x-a)$, for $a<x<L$	$\delta_{max} = \dfrac{Wa^2}{60EI}(5L-a)$, at $x=L$

TABLE 17-3

Moment and Deflection of Simply Supported Beams

No.	Loading	Maximum Moment (Absolute Value)	Deflection at Any Point	Deflection at Critical Points
1.		$M = \dfrac{PL}{4}$, at $x = \dfrac{L}{2}$	$\delta = \dfrac{Px}{12EI}\left(\dfrac{3L^2}{4} - x^2\right)$, for $0 < x < \dfrac{L}{2}$	$\delta_{max} = \dfrac{PL^3}{48EI}$
2.		$M = \dfrac{Pab}{L}$, at $x = a$	$\delta = \dfrac{Pbx}{6LEI}(L^2 - x^2 - b^2)$, for $0 < x < a$; $\delta = \dfrac{Pax_1}{6LEI}(L^2 - x_1^2 - a^2)$, for $0 < x_1 < b$	$\delta = \dfrac{Pa^2b^2}{3EIL}$, at $x = a$; $\delta_{max} = \dfrac{Pbx_0^3}{3LEI}$, at $x = x_0 = \sqrt{\dfrac{L^2 - b^2}{3}}$
3.		$M = Pa$, at $a < x < (L-a)$	$\delta = \dfrac{Px}{6EI}(3aL - 3a^2 - x^2)$, for end segments; $\delta = \dfrac{Pa}{6EI}(3xL - 3x^2 - a^2)$, for center segment	$\delta = \dfrac{Pa^2}{6EI}(3L - 4a)$, at $x = a$; $\delta_{max} = \dfrac{Pa}{24EI}(3L^2 - 4a^2)$, at $x = \dfrac{L}{2}$
4.		$M = M_o$, at $0 < x < L$	$\delta = \dfrac{M_o Lx}{6EI}\left(1 - \dfrac{x^2}{L^2}\right)$	$\delta = \dfrac{M_o L^2}{16EI}$, at $x = \dfrac{L}{2}$; $\delta_{max} = \dfrac{0.0642 M_o L^2}{EI}$, at $x = .577L$
5.	Total load = W#	$M = \dfrac{WL}{8}$, at $x = \dfrac{L}{2}$	$\delta = \dfrac{Wx}{24EIL}(L^3 - 2Lx^2 + x^3)$	$\delta_{max} = \dfrac{5WL^3}{384EI}$, at $x = \dfrac{L}{2}$
6.		$M = \dfrac{WL}{6}$	$\delta = \dfrac{Wx}{6EIL^2}\left(\dfrac{L^2 x^2}{2} - \dfrac{x^4}{5} - \dfrac{5L^4}{16}\right)$, for $0 < x < \dfrac{L}{2}$	$\delta_{max} = \dfrac{WL^3}{60EI}$, at $x = \dfrac{L}{2}$
7.		$M = \dfrac{WL}{12}$	$\delta = \dfrac{W}{12EI}\left(x^3 - \dfrac{x^4}{L} + \dfrac{2x^5}{5L^2} - \dfrac{3L^2 x}{8}\right)$, for $0 < x < \dfrac{L}{2}$	$\delta_{max} = \dfrac{3WL^3}{320EI}$, at $x = \dfrac{L}{2}$
8.		$M = 0.128WL$, at $x = 0.577L$	$\delta = \dfrac{Wx}{180EIL^2}(3x^4 - 10L^2 x^2 + 7L^4)$	$\delta_{max} = \dfrac{0.0130WL^3}{EI}$, at $x = 0.519L$
9.		$M = Pa$	Between load and adjacent support: $\delta = \dfrac{Px_1}{6EI}(3ax_1 - x_1^2 + 2aL)$; between supports: $\delta = \dfrac{Pax_2}{6EIL}(L - x_2)(2L - x_2)$; Between unloaded end and adjacent support: $\delta = \dfrac{PaLx_3}{6EI}$	Deflection at load: $\delta = \dfrac{Pa^2}{3EI}(a + L)$; Max. deflection between supports: $\delta = \dfrac{PaL^2}{15.55EI}$, at $x_2 = 0.423L$; Deflection at unloaded end: $\delta = \dfrac{PabL}{6EI}$

* Uniformly varying load, total = W #

190

TABLE 17-4

Moment and Deflection of Fixed-End Beams

No.	Loading	Moment at Critical Points (Absolute Value)	Deflection at Any Point	Deflection at Critical Points
1.		$M = \dfrac{PL}{8}$, at x=0, $x = \dfrac{L}{2}$, and x = L	$\delta = \dfrac{P}{48EI}(3Lx^2 - 4x^3)$, for $0 < x < \dfrac{L}{2}$	$\delta_{max} = \dfrac{PL^3}{192EI}$, at $x = \dfrac{L}{2}$
2.		At left end (remote from load): $M = \dfrac{Pa^2 b}{L^2}$ At right end (close to load): $M = \dfrac{Pa^2 b}{L^2}$ At load: $M = \dfrac{2Pa^2 b^2}{L^3}$	$\delta = \dfrac{Pb^2 x_1^2}{6EIL^3}(3aL - 3ax_1 - bx_1)$, for $0 < x_1 < a$ $\delta = \dfrac{Pa^2 x_2^2}{6EIL^3}(3bL - 3bx_2 - ax_2)$ for $0 < x_2 < b$	$\delta = \dfrac{Pa^3 b^3}{3EIL^3}$, at $x_1 = a$ $\delta_{max} = \dfrac{2Pa^3 b^2}{3EI(L+2a)^2}$, at $x_1 = \dfrac{2aL}{L+2a}$
3.		At ends, $M = \dfrac{WL}{12}$ At center, $M = \dfrac{WL}{24}$	$\delta = \dfrac{Wx^2}{24EIL}(L-x)^2$	$\delta_{max} = \dfrac{WL^3}{384EI}$, at $x = \dfrac{L}{2}$
4.		At left end: $M = \dfrac{WL}{15}$ At right end: $M = \dfrac{WL}{10}$ In beam: $M_{max} = 0.043 WL$, at x=0.548L	$\delta = \dfrac{W}{60EI}\left(3x^3 - 2Lx^2 - \dfrac{x^5}{L^2}\right)$	$\delta_{max} = 0.00262\dfrac{WL^3}{EI}$, at x=0.525L

TABLE 17-5

Moment and Deflection of Beams; One End Fixed, One End Simply Supported

No.	Loading	Movement at Critical Points (Absolute Value)	Deflection at Any Point	Deflection at Critical Points
1.		At fixed end: $M = \dfrac{3PL}{16}$ In beam: $M_{max} = \dfrac{5WL}{32}$, at $x_1 = \dfrac{L}{2}$	$\delta = \dfrac{Px_1^2}{96EI}(9L - 11x_1)$, for $0 < x_1 < \dfrac{L}{2}$ $\delta = \dfrac{Px_2}{96EI}(3L^2 - 5x_2^2)$, for $0 < x_2 < \dfrac{L}{2}$	$\delta = \dfrac{7PL^3}{768EI}$, at $x = \dfrac{L}{2}$ $\delta_{max} = \dfrac{PL^3}{107.3EI}$, at $x_2 = .447L$
2.		At fixed end: $M = \dfrac{Pab}{2L^2}(L+b)$ In beam: $M_{max} = \dfrac{Pa^2b}{2L^3}(3L-a)$, at $x_1 = a$ $m = (L+a)(L+b) + aL$ $n = aL(L+b)$	$\delta = \dfrac{Pbx_1^2}{12EIL^3}(3n - mx)$, for $0 < x_1 < a$ $\delta = \dfrac{Pa^2x_2}{12EIL^3}(3L^2b - 3Lx_2^2 - ax_2^2)$ for $0 < x_2 < b$	$\delta = \dfrac{Pa^3b^2}{12EIL^3}(3L+b)$, at $x_1 = a$ if $a < 0.586L$, δ_{max} is between load and simple support: $\delta_{max} = \dfrac{Pa^2b}{6EI}\sqrt{\dfrac{b}{2L+b}}$, at $x_2 = L\sqrt{\dfrac{b}{2L+b}}$ If $a = .586L$, δ_{max} is at load: $\delta_{max} = \dfrac{PL^3}{102EI}$ if $a > 0.586L$, δ_{max} is between load and fixed support: $\delta_{max} = \dfrac{Pbn^3}{3EIm^2L^3}$, at $x_1 = \dfrac{2n}{m}$
3.	Total load = W	At fixed end: $M = \dfrac{WL}{8}$ In beam: $M_{max} = \dfrac{9WL}{128}$, at $x = \dfrac{5L}{8}$	$\delta = \dfrac{Wx^2(l-x)}{48EIL}(3L-2x)$	$\delta_{max} = \dfrac{WL^3}{185EI}$, at $x = 0.579L$

References

1. Roark, R. J., *Formulas for Stress and Strain*, McGraw-Hill, 1954.
2. Kent's *Mechanical Engineers' Handbook*, Wiley, 1950.
3. Oberg, E. and Jones, F. D., *Machinery's Handbook*, The Industrial Press, 1953.

Chapter 18

ELASTIC STABILITY

18.1 Slenderness Ratio

Machine parts subjected to compressive loading may be so long in proportion to lateral dimensions that they fail in lateral buckling. Such parts are referred to as columns. At the point of buckling the stress may be considerably below the yield point and yet a small increase in applied load may cause failure of the part. In these cases, slenderness ratio l/r (l = length of column, r = least radius of gyration of the cross-section) is important. The values of r for various cross sections can be computed from the equation: $r = \sqrt{I/A}$, where I and A are given in Table 18-1.

When l/r is less than 20 there is very little danger of buckling and the part should be designed for axial compressive stress [Equation (3.1)].

18.2 Design of Columns

When O < l/r < 150 the design stress, for columns axially loaded, is given by the following equations:

$$\frac{P_{cr}}{A} = S_y - \left(\frac{S_y}{2\pi}\right)^2 \left(\frac{\ell}{r}\right)^2 \left(\frac{1}{nE}\right), \text{ for } 0 < \ell/r < 120 \text{ [J.B. Johnson]}$$

(18.1)

$$\frac{P_{cr}}{A} = \frac{\pi^2 nE}{\left(\frac{\ell}{r}\right)^2}, \text{ for } 120 < \ell/r < 150 \text{ [Euler]}$$

(18.2)

where

$\dfrac{P_{cr}}{A}$ = design stress (psi)

S_y = yield strength of material (psi)

A = cross-sectional area (in.^{2})

n = constant, depending on the end conditions of the column

E = elastic modulus (psi)

TABLE 18-1

Properties of Sections

Section	Area A	Rectangular Moment of Inertia I	Polar Moment of Inertia J	Rectangular Section Modulus Z	Polar Section Modulus Z'
1. Solid Circle	$0.7854\,D^2$	$0.049\,D^4$	$0.098\,D^4$	$0.098\,D^3$	$0.196\,D^3$
2. Hollow Concen. Circle	$0.7854\,(D^2-d^2)$	$0.049(D^4-d^4)$	$0.098\,(D^4-d^4)$	$0.098\dfrac{(D^4-d^4)}{D}$	$0.196\left(\dfrac{D^4-d^4}{D}\right)$
3. Solid Ellipse	$3.1416\,ab$	$0.7854\,a^3b$	—	$0.7854\,a^2b$	—
4. Hollow Concen. Ellipse	$3.1416\,(ab-cd)$	$0.7854\,(a^3b-c^3d)$	—	$0.7854\dfrac{a^3b-c^3d}{a}$	—
5 Solid Square	a^2	$0.0834\,a^4$	$0.1667\,a^4$	$0.1667\,a^3$	$0.208\,a^3$
6. Solid Triangle	$.5\,bd$	$.0278\,bd^3$	—	$.0417\,bd^2$	—
7. Hollow Concen. Squares	a^2-b^2	$.0834(a^4-b^4)$	—	$.1667\dfrac{(a^4-b^4)}{a}$	—
8. Solid Rectangle	bd	$.0834\,bd^3$	$.0834\,bd\,(b^2+d^2)$	$.1667\,bd^2$	$\dfrac{b\,d^2}{3+1.8\,\frac{b}{d}}$
9. Solid Rectangle	bd	$.33\,bd^2$	$.0834\,bd(b^2+d^2)$	$.33\,bd^3$	$\dfrac{b\,d^2}{3+1.8\,\frac{b}{d}}$
10. Hollow Concen. Rectangle	$bd-hk$	$.0834(bd^3-hk^3)$	—	$.1667\dfrac{bd^3-hk^3}{d}$	—

ℓ = length of the column (in.)

r = least radius if gyration of the cross-section (in.)

Equations (18.1) and (18.2) are plotted in Figures 18-1 and 18-2 for various steels having yield strengths ranging from 40,000 psi to 100,000 psi. In Figure 18-1, n = 1/4, which corresponds to a column with one end fixed, the other free. In Figure 18-2, n = 1 which may conservatively be assumed to correspond to all other end conditions.

TABLE 18-1 (Continued)

Section	Area A	Rectangular Moment of Inertia I	Polar Moment of Inertia J	Rectangular Section Modulus Z	Polar Section Modulus Z'
11. Solid I Beam	$dt+2a(s+n)$	$.0834\left[bd^3-\frac{1}{4g}(h^4-\ell^4)\right]$ $g=\frac{h-\ell}{(b-t))}$	———	$\frac{1}{6d}\left[bd^3-\frac{1}{4g}(h^4-\ell^4)\right]$	———
12. Solid Channel	$dt+a(s+n)$	$\frac{1}{12}\left[bd^3-\frac{1}{8g}(h^4-\ell^4)\right]$ $g=\frac{h-\ell}{2(b-t)}$	———	$\frac{1}{6d}\left[bd^3-\frac{1}{8g}(h^4-\ell^4)\right]$	———
13. Solid L-Section	$t(2a-t)$	$.33\left[ty^3+a(a-y)^3-(a-t)(a-y-t)^3\right]$	———	$\frac{I}{y}$	———
14. Solid I-Section	$bd-h(b-t)$	$\frac{bd^3-h^3(b-t)}{12}$	———	$\frac{bd^3-h^3(b-t)}{6d}$	———
15. Solid C-Section	$bd-h(b-t)$	$\frac{bd^3-h^3(b-t)}{12}$	———	$\frac{bd^3-h^3(b-t)}{6d}$	———
16 Solid Unequal Flanged I-Section	$bs+ht+as$	$\frac{1}{3}\left[b(d-y)^3+ay^3-(b-t)(d-y-s)^3-(a-t)(y-s)^3\right]$	———	$\frac{I}{y}$	———
17. Solid T-Section	$bs+ht$	$\frac{1}{3}\left[ty^3+b(d-y)^3-(b-t)(d-y-s)^3\right]$	———	$\frac{I}{y}$	———
18. Solid L-Section	$t(a+b-t)$	$\frac{1}{3}\left[ty^3+a(b-y)^3-(a-t)(b-y-t)^3\right]$	———	$\frac{I}{y}$	———

References

1. Popov, E. P., *Mechanics of Materials*, Prentice-Hall, 1957.
2. Oberg, E. and Jones, F. D., *Machinery's Handbook*, The Industrial Press, 1953.
3. Shigley, J. E., *Machine Design*, McGraw-Hill, 1956.

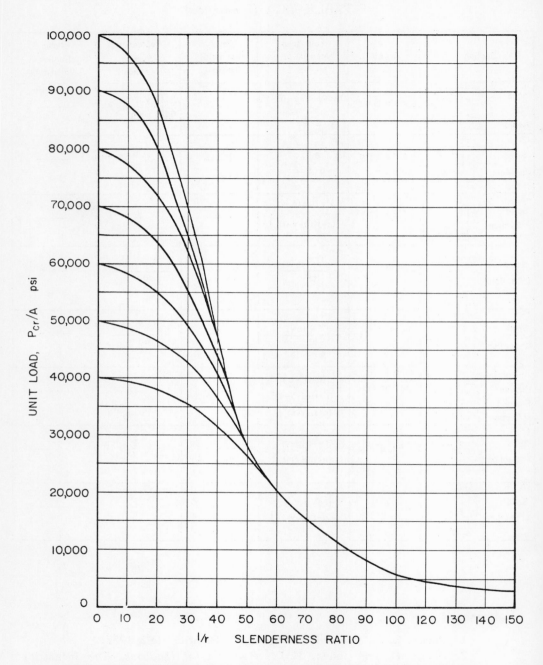

Figure 18–1. Critical loads for various slenderness ratios and yield strengths, n = 1/4, $E = 30 \times 10^6$ psi.

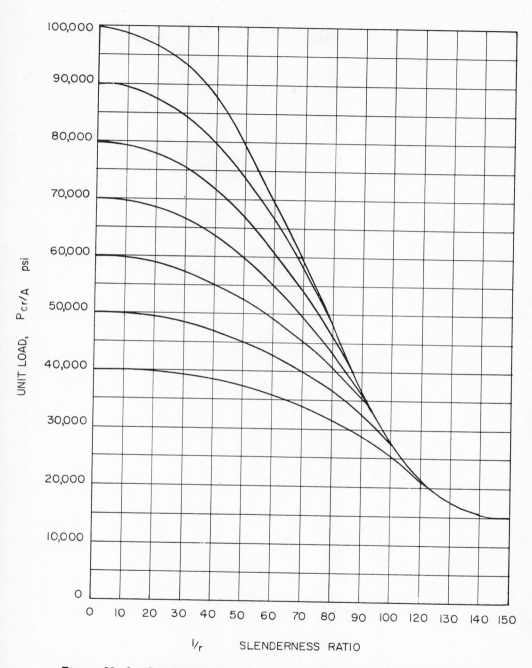

Figure 18–2. Critical loads for various slenderness ratios and yield strengths, n = 1, E = 30 x 10^6 psi.

PART V

Charts

Chapter 19

INSTRUCTIONS FOR USING CHARTS

For details concerning the significance and use of the charts contained in Part V, the reader is referred to the preceding chapters of the book. The purpose of the present chapter is to summarize the methods of using the charts, and to present sample problems illustrating the use of the charts.

The charts contained in Part V comprise four main groups, arranged as follows:

1. Chapter 20, Stress Concentration Factors.
2. Chapter 21, S-N Curves.
3. Chapter 22, Goodman Diagrams.
4. Chapter 23, Tables Giving Material Properties.

19.1 Stress Concentration Factors

With the exception of Figure 20-67, all of the charts in Chapter 20 give theoretical, or geometric stress concentration factors (K_t). These factors are useful primarily for solving problems in fatigue, in which case they must first be converted to "fatigue stress concentration factors," or "fatigue strength reduction factors" (K_f). Except for parts made of hardened steel with highly polished surfaces, K_f is smaller than K_t. The preferred method of computing K_f from K_t involves use of Equation (11.4). This equation makes corrections for both notch sensitivity and surface finish. The customary method of computing K_f employs Equation (11.3), which corrects for notch sensitivity only.

Values of K_f thus obtained represent the fatigue strength reduction for fully reversed loading (bending, torsional, or axial, depending upon whether the original value of K_t pertained to bending, torsional, or axial loading), and for infinite life in the case of steel. Steel parts are assumed to be unaffected by stress raisers for fewer than 1000 stress cycles. Hence, in drawing an S-N curve for a notched part, the endurance strength is divided by K_f, the 1000 cycle strength is not changed, and a straight line is used to connect the infinite life (10^6 cycle) and 1000 cycle points on log-log coordinates.

Values of K_f for non-ferrous parts apply specifically to the 10^8 to 5×10^8 cycle range. The influence of the stress raiser does not diminish with reduced life as rapidly as with steel. Figure 11-17 shows an example illustrating nearly the full stress concentration effect with as few as 1000 cycles. In the absence of further data, this curve may be used as a guide in estimating values of K_f for non-ferrous parts designed for fewer than 10^8 cycles.

Whenever available, direct test values of K_f are to be preferred to values computed from a knowledge of the geometry, surface finish, and material notch sensitivity. Due to the infinite number of combinations of shapes, surfaces, and materials, test data for K_f are understandably limited. Figure 20-67 contains direct test values of K_f for commercially finished threads and keyways cut in soft and in hard steel.

19.2 S-N Curves

Chapter 21 contains S-N curves for various grades of steel, cast iron, and aluminum. These curves are determined in accordance with the procedures described in Chapter 11, and pertain to standard 0.3 inch diameter test specimens subjected to completely reversed bending stresses. For notched parts, the infinite life end of the line should be divided by K_f, as discussed in article 19.1. For parts of a size other than 0.3 inch diameter, the infinite life end of the S-N curve should be multiplied by a size correction factor in accordance with article 11.4.

19.3 Goodman Diagrams

Chapter 22 contains Goodman diagrams for various grades of steel, cast iron, and aluminum. These curves are obtained on the basis of the procedures given in article 11.9. They apply directly to cases involving infinite life, 0.3 inch diameter parts, and freedom from notches. For all other cases, Goodman diagrams can be obtained by first constructing an S-N curve in accordance with the procedures given in article 19.2. From this curve, the points on the "Y axis" of the Goodman diagram are obtained. The point on the 45° line of the Goodman diagram is not affected by life, size, or the presence of a notch. Hence, this point may be taken from the Goodman diagrams in Chapter 22. In all cases, straight lines are drawn between the "Y axis" points and the 45° line point.

19.4 Sample Problems

Problem 1

The straight round link shown below (Figure 19-1) is subjected to a torsional load varying from zero to T inch pounds, and must withstand 10^7 stress

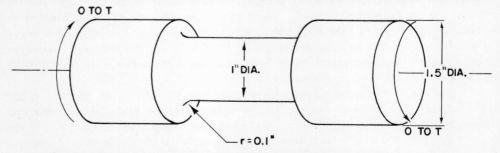

Figure 19–1. Link subjected to a torsional load, problems 1 and 2.

cycles without failure. The shaft has a machined surface and is made of a steel having a hardness of 190 BHN. What value of T corresponds to the use of a factor of safety of 1.75?

1. The basic Goodman diagram appropriate to this part is the "machined" line of Figure 22-38. This diagram must be modified because (a) the diameter is not 0.3 inch, and (b) a notch is present. These corrections are determined as follows:

   (a) C_{size} = .85 (conservative value from article 11.4)

   (b) K_t = 1.40 (Figure 20-3, where r/d = 0.1, h/r = 2.5)

   K_f = $1 + (K_t-1)q\ C_{surf.}$ [Equation (11.4)]

   q   = .96 (Figure 11-16)

   C_{surf} = .77 (Figure 11-13)

   K_f = 1 + (1.40-1)(.95)(.77) = 1.29

2. The desired Goodman diagram is constructed in Figure 19-2, where the zero mean stress points are ±20 ksi (from Figure 22-38) multiplied by C_{size} and divided by K_f, or ±20 ksi (.85)/(1.29) = ±13.2 ksi. The 45° static load point is unchanged from Figure 22-38.

3. The nature of the fluctuating load is as shown in Figure 19-3, i.e., maximum stress (τ_{max}) equals twice mean stress (τ_m). A line representing $\tau_{max} = 2\tau_m$ is drawn on Figure 19-2. (It should be noted here that since the effect of stress concentration was taken into account in plotting the Goodman line, stress concentration should *not* be involved in the stress computations.)

4. Figure 19-2 shows the "design overload point" at τ_m = 11.5 ksi, τ_{max} = 23 ksi. These are the values of mean and maximum TR/J stress at an overloading just sufficient to cause eventual fatigue fracture. Since a factor of safety of 1.75 is to be employed, the shear stress corresponding to the usable value of T is 23/1.75 = 13.1 ksi.

5.

$$\tau = TR/J = T/Z' \qquad [\text{Equation (4.3)}]$$

$$Z' = \pi D^3/16 \qquad (\text{Table 18-1})$$

$$= \pi/16 = .196 \text{ in.}^3$$

$$13,100 \text{ psi} = T/.196 \text{ in.}^3$$

$$T = 2,580 \text{ in.lb.}$$

6. The answer should imply no more than two place accuracy; hence, the answer is given as:

$$T = 2600 \text{ in. lb.}$$

Problem 2
Same as Problem 1 except only 50,000 cycles of life are required:

1. The basic S-N curve appropriate to this part is the "machined" line of the lower

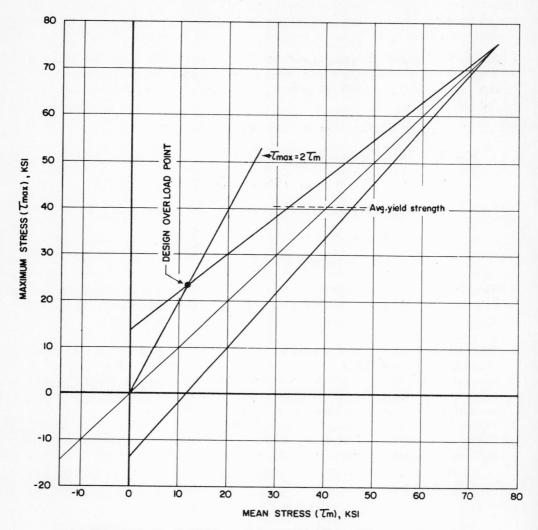

Figure 19–2. Goodman diagram for problem 1, Figure 19–1.

Figure 21-2, applying to torsional loading. In Problem 1 it was determined that the 20 ksi endurance limit (10^6 cycle point) should be reduced to 13.2 ksi to account for size and notch effects. These two effects do not influence the 10^3 cycle point of the S-N curve. Hence, an S-N curve appropriate to this part is as shown in Figure 19-4.

2. From Figure 19-4, the endurance strength of the part for 50,000 cycles of life is determined as 28 ksi. Hence, the Goodman diagram appropriate to the present problem is identical with Figure 19-2 except that the ± 13.2 ksi zero mean stress points are increased to ± 28 ksi.

3. The new Goodman diagram is shown in Figure 19-5. The design overload point corresponds to $\tau_{max} = 41$ ksi. Note that this is approximately equal to the

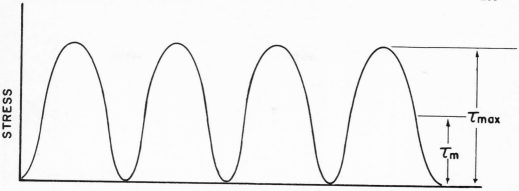

TIME

Figure 19–3. Fluctuating load for problems 1 and 2.

average torsional yield strength of the material. At this point, the actual torsional yield strength of the specific steel involved should be determined as closely as possible. Suppose this is found to be 38 ksi. Good judgment would then indicate that τ_{max} should be limited to 38 ksi (see Chapter 11).

4. From this point on, the solution is exactly as in Problem 1:

$$\tau = T/Z'$$

$$\frac{38,000 \text{ psi}}{1.75} = \frac{T}{.196 \text{ in.}^3}$$

$$T = 4250 \text{ in.lb.}$$

Answer:
$$T = 4200 \text{ in.lb.}$$

Problem 3

A cylinder head bolt is made of SAE 6 bolt steel (S_u = 140 ksi) and has rolled threads. The initial tensile force due to tightening is 5000 lb. When the machine is in operation, the bolt is subjected to an additional tensile force which fluctuates between zero and 1500 lb. Select an appropriate size of bolt.

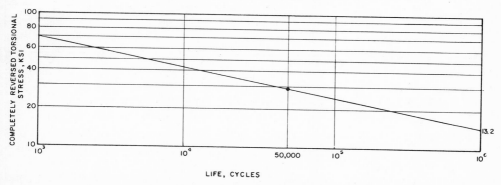

LIFE, CYCLES

Figure 19–4. S-N curve for problem 2.

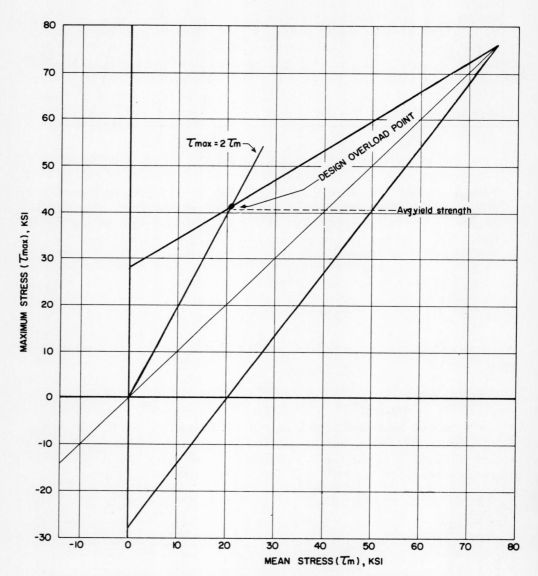

Figure 19–5. Goodman diagram for problem 2, Figure 19–1.

1. Assume that the safety factor should be such that increasing both the tightening force and the fluctuating force by a factor of 1.3 will put the bolt on the verge of eventual fatigue failure. Thus, the "design overload" forces will be comprised of a static force of 6500 lb. plus a zero to 2000 lb. fluctuating force. This is shown diagramatically in Figure 19-6.

2. Nominal P/A stresses are $\sigma_m = 7500/A_s$, $\sigma_{max} = 8500/A_s$ where A_s = bolt stress area. Regardless of the bolt size, $\sigma_{max}/\sigma_m = 1.13$.

3. The basic Goodman diagram for the bolt material is given in Figure 22-26. (The bolt steel, with S_u = 140 ksi, has a hardness of approximately 280 BHN.) The zero mean stress points must be modified to account for the fatigue strength reduction factor of the threads. Figure 20-67 gives K_f = 3.0 for rolled threads and hardened steel. (Steels having a hardness of over 200 BHN generally fall into the hardened range.)

The factor of 3.0 represents the total difference in endurance limit between a polished and unnotched test sample, and a threaded sample. Hence, the zero mean stress points of ±57 ksi shown in Figure 22-26 are divided by 3.0 giving ±19 ksi. The threads do not affect the 135 ksi static strength point (on the 45° line). Hence, the Goodman diagram for the threaded bolt is as shown in Figure 19-7.

4. Intersection with the line $\sigma_{max}/\sigma_m = 1.13$ gives σ_{max} = 83 ksi. Hence, $\sigma_{max} = 8500/A_s = 83,000$ psi, and $A_s = .102$ in.^{2} Thus, the smallest standard bolt size having a stress area $\geq .102$ in.^{2} is required.

Answer: 7/16" – 14, or 7/16" – 20

Since this problem involved axial loading for which $C_{size} = 1$, no problem involving size factor is encountered. For torsional and bending loading, size factor varies with diameter of part. Hence, if the part being designed is subjected to a bending or torsional load, a size factor must be estimated in advance, in order to draw the Goodman diagram. A "trial-and-error" modification of the original solution is then necessary if the part size as finally determined is not compatible with the originally assumed size factor.

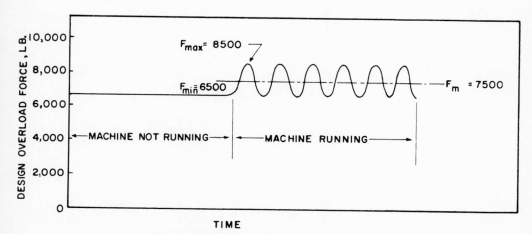

Figure 19–6. Fluctuating load for problem 3.

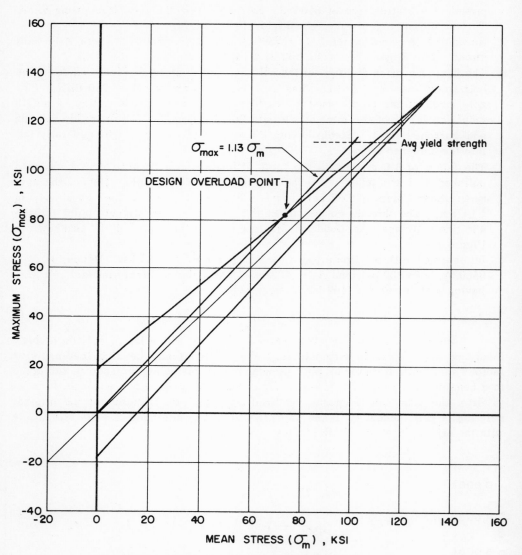

Figure 19–7. Goodman diagram for problem 3.

References

The following references pertain to the entire Part V (Chapters 19 through 23).

1. Heywood, R. B., *Designing by Photoelasticity*, Chapman and Hall, 1952.
2. Briggs, Chas. W., *Steel Castings Handbook*, Electric Printing Co., 1960.
3. Lipson, C. and Thiel, D. H., *Applications of Stress Analysis*, University of Michigan Press, 1959.
4. Hu, L. W. and Marin, Joseph, *Mechanical Properties of Metals*, Pennsylvania State University, 1958.
5. Faires, Virgil M., *Design of Machine Elements*, Macmillan, 1959.
6. Grover, H. J., Gordon, S. A., and Jackson, L. P., *Fatigue of Metals and Structures*, Rev. Ed., Batelle Institute, 1960.
7. Lessells, J. M., *Strength and Resistance of Metals*, Wiley, 1954.
8. Borik, F., Chapman, R. D., and Jominy, W. E., *The Effect of Per Cent Tempered Martensite on Endurance Limit*, ASME Paper from 39th Convention in Chicago (November 4-8, 1957).
9. ASME Handbook, *Metals Engineering Design*, McGraw-Hill, 1953.
10. Lee, L. H. N. and Ades, C. S., *Stress Concentration Factors for Circular Fillets in Stepped Wall Cylinders Subject to Axial Tension*, Paper from Society for Experimental Stress Analysis, Meeting in Chicago (November, 1955).
11. Peterson, R. E., *Stress Concentration Design Factors*, Wiley, 1953.
12. Durelli, A. J., Lake, R. L., and Phillips, E. A., "Design Factors for Stress Concentration," *Machine Design* (December, 1951).
13. Lipson, Noll, and Clock, *Stress and Strength of Manufactured Parts*, McGraw-Hill, 1950.
14. *The Aluminum Data Book*, Reynolds Metals Company, 1959.
15. *Sheet and Plate Product Information*, Kaiser Aluminum Company, 1958.
16. Jennings, C. H., *Welding Design*, ASME Trans., Vol. 58.
17. Frocht, M. M. "Factors of Stress Concentration Photoelastically Determined," *Trans. ASME*, Ap. M., Vol. 57, p. A-67, 1935.
18. Timoshenko, S. and Dietz, W., "Stress Concentration Produced by Holes and Fillets," *Trans. ASME*, Vol. 47, p. 199, 1925.
19. Sonntag, R., *Math. Mech.*, Vol. 9, p.1, 1929.
20. Berkey, D. C., "Reducing Stress Concentration with Elliptical Fillets," *Proc. SESA*, Vol. 1, No. 2, 1943.
21. Neuber, H. P., "*Kerbspannungslehre*," Verlag Julius Springer, Berlin, 1937.
22. Seely, F. B. and Dolan, T. J., *Stress Concentration at Fillets, Holes and Keyways* as Found by the Plaster Model Method, Univ. Ill. Eng. Expt. Sta. Bull. 276, 1935.
23. Peterson, R. E. and Wahl, A. M., "Two and Three Dimensional Cases of Stress Concentration and Comparison with Fatigue Tests," *Trans. ASME*, Ap.M., Vol. 58, p. A-15, 1936.
24. Griffith, A. A. and Taylor, G. I., "The Use of Soap Films in Solving Torsion Problems," *Proc, Inst. Mech. Engrs.*, London p. 755, 1917.
25. Hetenyi, M., "Some Applications of Photoelasticity in Turbine-Generator Design," *Trans. ASME*, Ap.M., pp. A-155, A-15 (December, 1939).

26. Neugebauer, G. H., "Stress Concentration Factors and Their Effect on Design," *Product Engineering*, p. 82 (February, 1943).
27. Wahl, A. M. and Beeuwkes, R., Jr., "Stress Concentration Produced by Holes and Notches," *Trans. ASME*, Ap. M., Vol. 56, p. 527, 1934.
28. Lee, G. H., "Influence of Hyperbolic Notches on the Transverse Flexure of Elastic Plates," *Trans. ASME*, Ap. M., Vol. 62, p. A-53, 1940.
29. Föppl, A., *Vorlesungen Über Technische Mechanik*, Vol. 5, p. 352; also *Drang Und Zwang*, Vol. 1, p. 314, Oldenboure, Munich, 1924.
30. Howland, R. C. J., "On The Stress in the Neighborhood of a Circular Hole in a Strip Under Tension," *Trans. Roy. Soc.*, London, A, Vol. 229, 1929.
31. Jeffery, J. B., "Plane Stress and Plane Strain in Bipolar Coordinates," *Trans. Roy. Soc.*, London, Vol . 221, p. 265, 1921.
32. Inglis, C. E., "Stresses in a Plate Due to the Presence of Cracks and Sharp Corners," *Trans. Inst. Naval Arch.*, British, Vol. LV, Part 1, p. 219, 1913.
33. Coker, E. G. and Filon, L. N. G., *A Treatise on Photo-Elasticity*, p. 532, Cambridge Press, England, 1931.
34. Maleev, V. L., *Machine Design*, International Textbook Company, p. 39, 1939.
35. M. M. Leven and Hartman, J. B., "Factors of Stress Concentration for Flat Bars and Shafts with Centrally Enlarged Section," *Proc. SESA*, Vol. IX, No. 1, 1951.

Chapter 20

CHARTS, STRESS CONCENTRATION FACTORS

Index

GEOMETRY		FIGURE NUMBER		
		Tension	Bending	Torsion
Solid Circular Shaft Circular Fillet		20-1	20-2	20-3
Solid Circular Shaft, Elliptical Fillet			20-4	
Solid Circular Shaft Circular Groove		20-5	20-6	20-7
Solid Circular Shaft, Hyperbolic Groove		20-8	20-9	
Solid Circular Shaft Transverse Hole		20-10	20-11	20-12
Solid Circular Shaft Plain Press Fit			20-13	
Solid Circular Shaft Curved			20-14	
Solid Circular Shaft Keyway				20-38
Hollow Circular Shaft, External Circular Groove		20-15	20-16	20-17
Hollow Circular Shaft, Internal Circular Groove		20-18	20-19	20-20

Index (continued)

GEOMETRY		FIGURE NUMBER		
		Tension	Bending	Torsion
Hollow Circular Shaft Keyway				20-21
Hollow Circular Shaft Longitudinal Circular Groove				20-22
Hollow Circular Shaft Curved			20-23	
Stepped Wall Cylinder Circular Fillet		20-24		
Flat Plate Circular Fillet		20-25	20-26	
Flat Plate Circular Fillet: Uniformly Distributed Reaction		20-27		
on Flanges and Concentrated Reaction on Flanges		20-28		
Flat Plate Circular Fillet Concentrated Load			20-29	
Flat Plate, T-Heads, Variable Concentrated Flange Reactions		20-30		
Flat Plate Circular Groove		20-31	20-32	

GEOMETRY		FIGURE NUMBER		
		Tension	Bending	Torsion
Flat Plate Circular Groove Transverse Bending			20-33	
Flat Plate Hyperbolic Groove		20-34	20-35	
Flat Plate Hyperbolic Groove Transverse Bending			20-36	
Flat Plate Hyperbolic Groove On One Edge		20-37		
Flat Plate Semi-Circular Notches		20-39 20-40 20-41		
Flat Plate Two Semi-Circular Notches		20-42		
Flat Plate Transverse Hole at Center		20-43	20-44	
Flat Plate Transverse Hole Near Edge		20-45	20-46	
Flat Plate Pin in Transverse Hole at Center		20-47		
Flat Plate Hyperbolic Groove On One Edge			20-48	

Index (continued)

GEOMETRY		FIGURE NUMBER		
		Tension	Bending	Torsion
Flat Plate Circular Transverse Hole at Center Biaxial Tension		20-49		
Flat Plate Elliptical Transverse Hole at Center Biaxial Tension		20-50		
Flat Plate Spaced Holes		20-51		
Flat Plate Elliptical Hole at Center Transverse Bending			20-52	
Flat Plate Filled Hole at Center		20-53		
I-Beam Curved			20-54	
L-Section			20-55	
L-Section Concentrated Load			20-56	
L-Section		20-57		
Flat Plate Single Protrusion		20-58		

GEOMETRY		FIGURE NUMBER		
		Tension	Bending	Torsion
Flat Plate Double Protrusion			20-59 20-60 20-61	
Flat Plate Curved			20-62	
Flat Plate Slotted		20-63	20-64	
Pin Joint		20-65		
Box-Section				20-66
Fatigue Stress Concentration Factors:Threads, Keyways			20-67	20-67

Curves for K_t

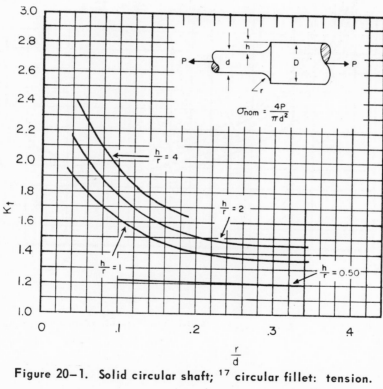

Figure 20–1. Solid circular shaft; [17] circular fillet: tension.

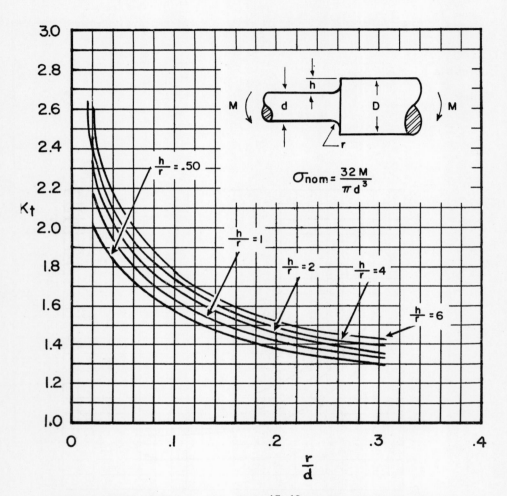

Figure 20–2. Solid circular shaft; [17], [18] circular fillet: bending.

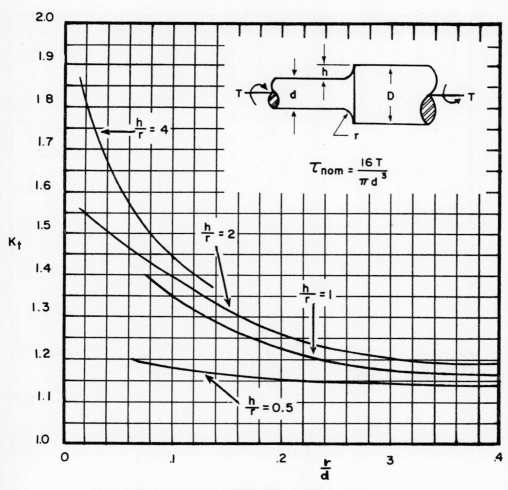

Figure 20–3. Solid circular shaft; circular fillet: torsion.

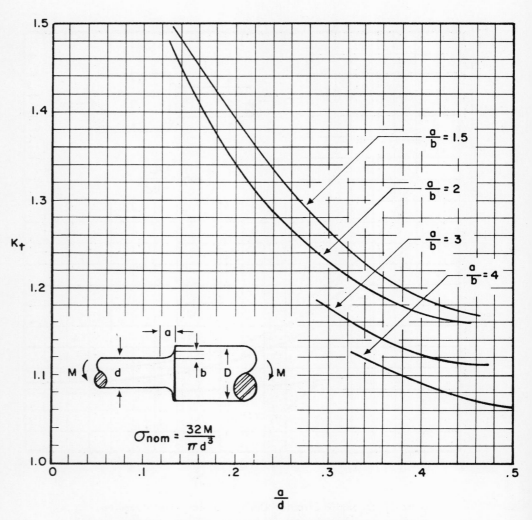

Figure 20–4. Solid circular shaft; [20] elliptical fillet: bending.

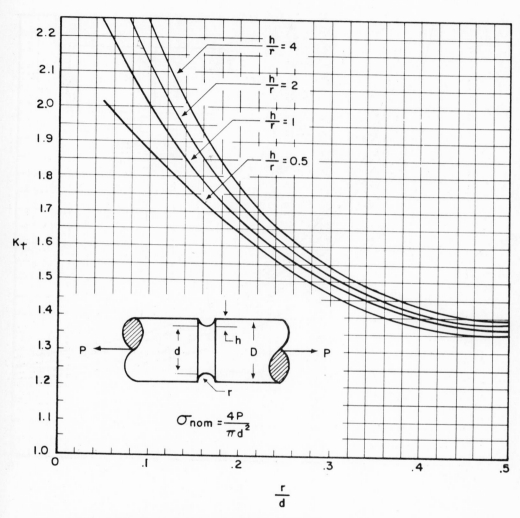

Figure 20–5. Solid circular shaft; [17] circular groove: tension.

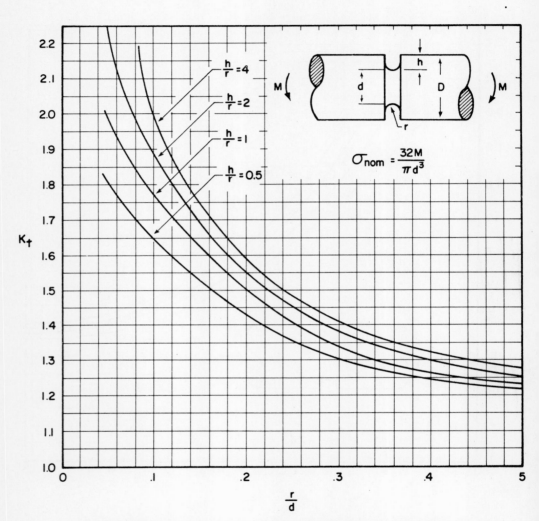

Figure 20–6. Solid circular shaft; [17] circular groove: bending.

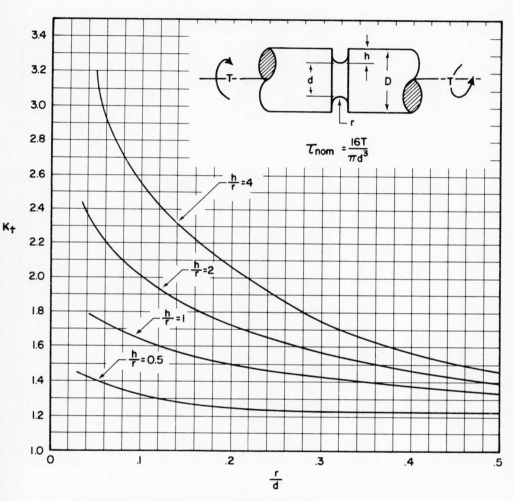

Figure 20–7. Solid circular shaft, [19] circular groove: torsion.

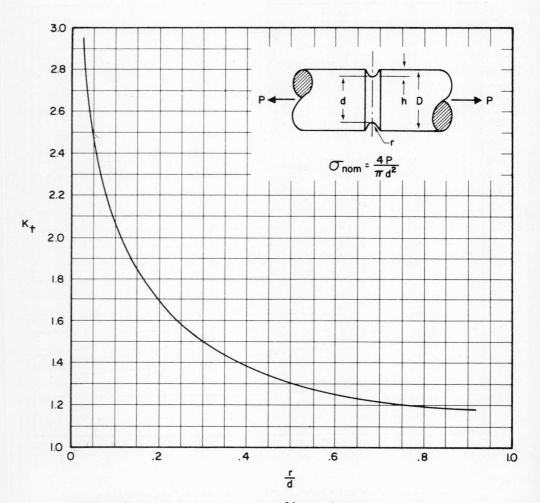

Figure 20–8. Solid circular shaft; [21] hyperbolic groove: tension.

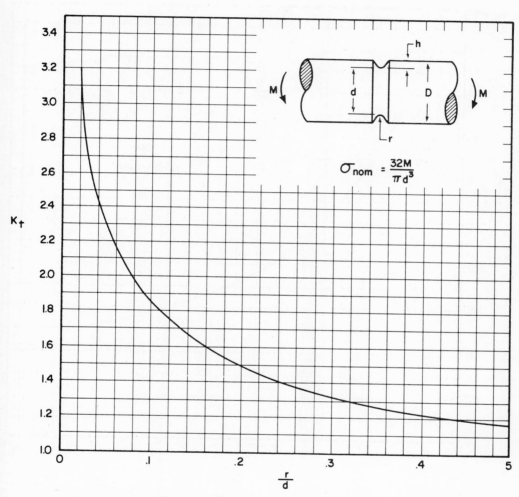

Figure 20–9. Solid circular shaft; [21] hyperbolic groove: bending.

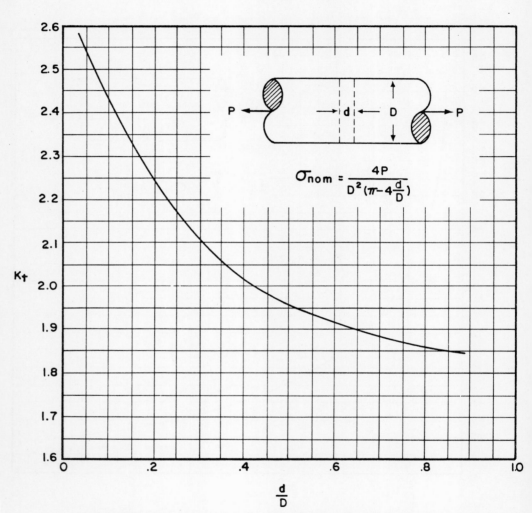

Figure 20–10. Solid circular shaft; [17] transverse hole: tension.

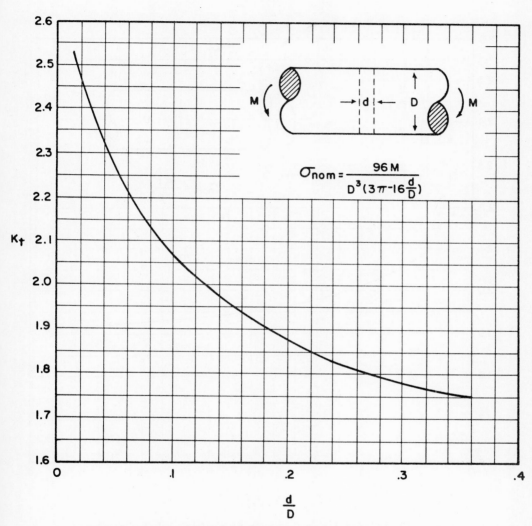

Figure 20–11. Solid circular shaft; [17] transverse hole: bending.

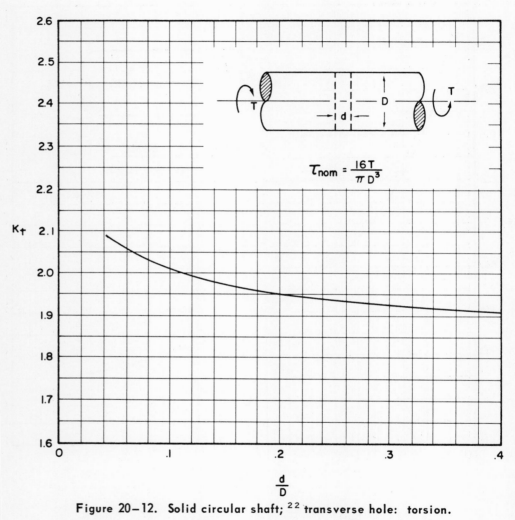

Figure 20–12. Solid circular shaft;[22] transverse hole: torsion.

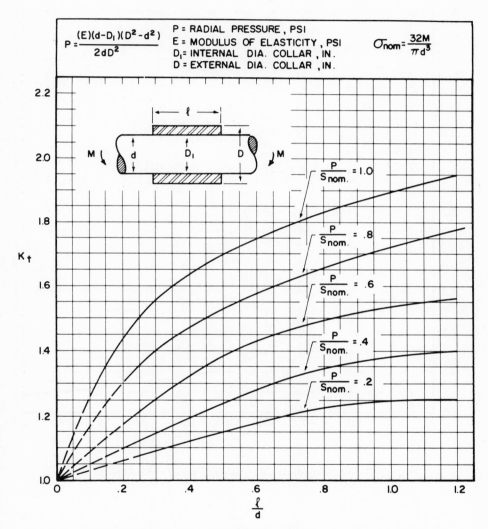

Figure 20–13. Solid circular shaft; [23] plain press fit: bending.

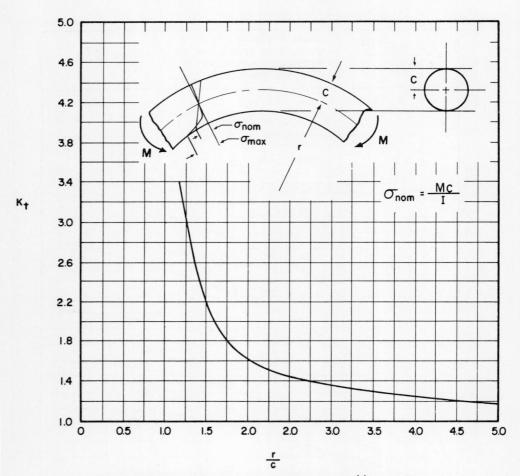

$$\sigma_{nom} = \frac{Mc}{I}$$

K_t

$\dfrac{r}{c}$

Figure 20–14. Solid circular shaft, curved: [11] bending.

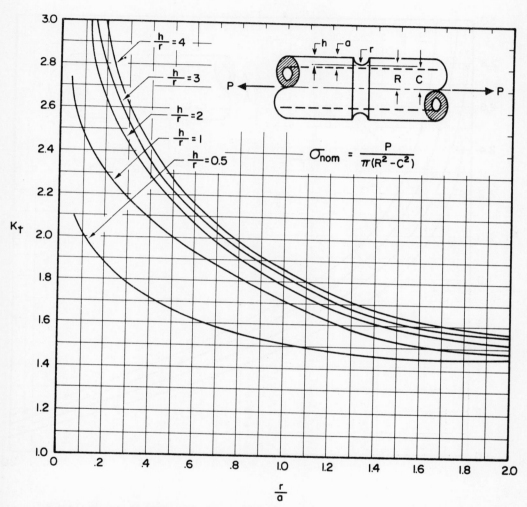

Figure 20–15. Hollow circular shaft; [21] external circular groove: tension.

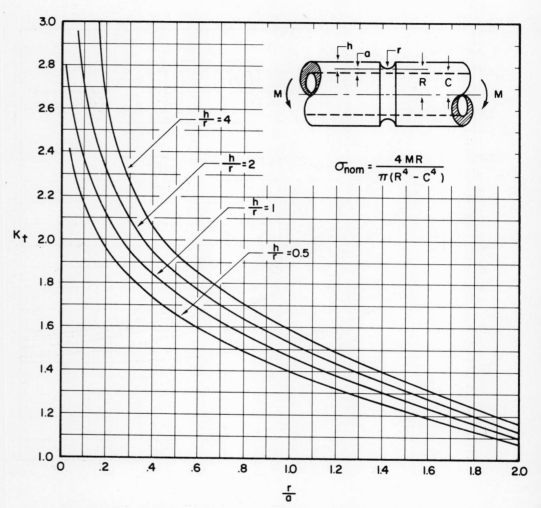

Figure 20–16. Hollow circular shaft; [21] external circular groove: bending.

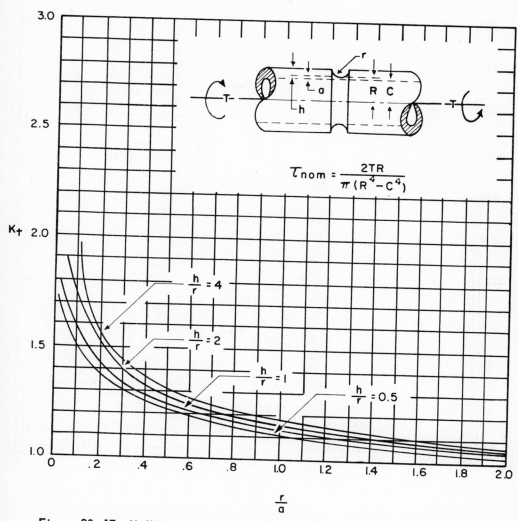

Figure 20–17. Hollow circular shaft; [21] external circular groove: torsion.

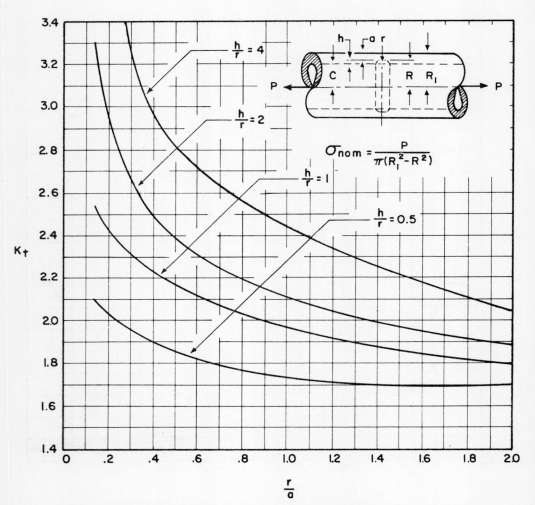

Figure 20–18. Hollow circular shaft; [21] internal circular groove: tension.

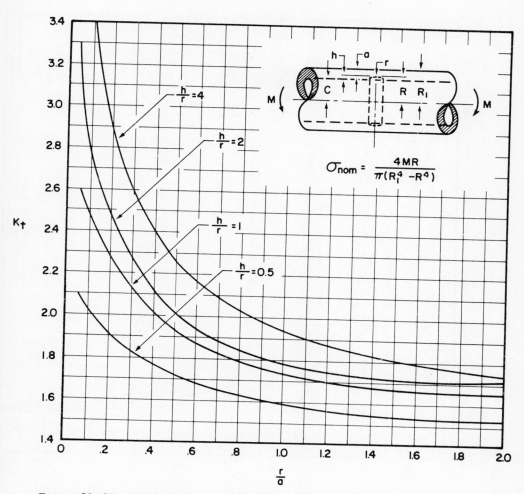

Figure 20–19. Hollow circular shaft; [21] internal circular groove: bending.

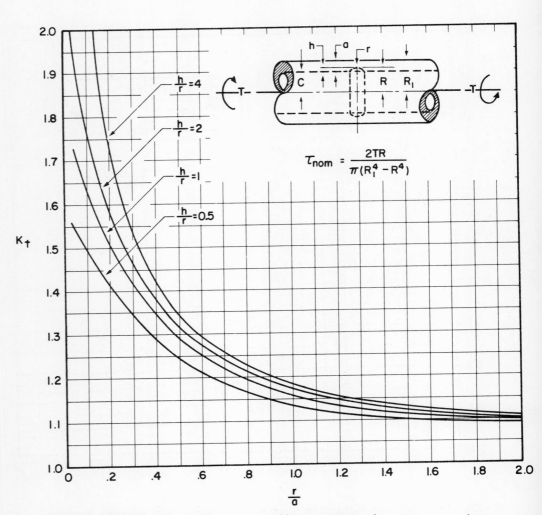

Figure 20–20. Hollow circular shaft; [21] internal circular groove: torsion.

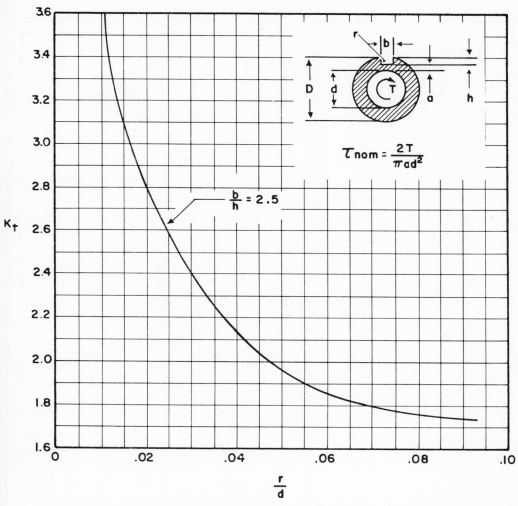

Figure 20–21. Hollow circular shaft;[24] keyway: torsion.

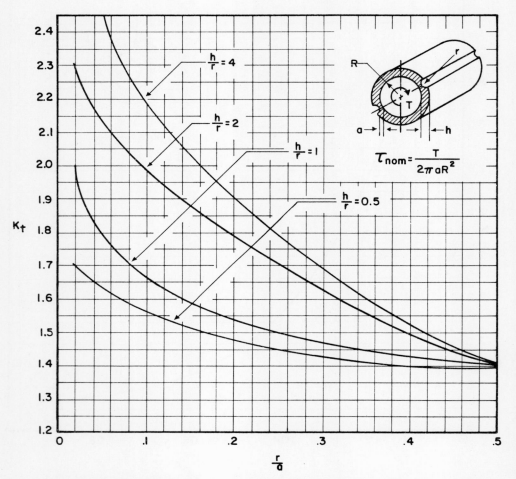

Figure 20–22. Hollow circular shaft;[21] longitudinal circular groove: torsion.

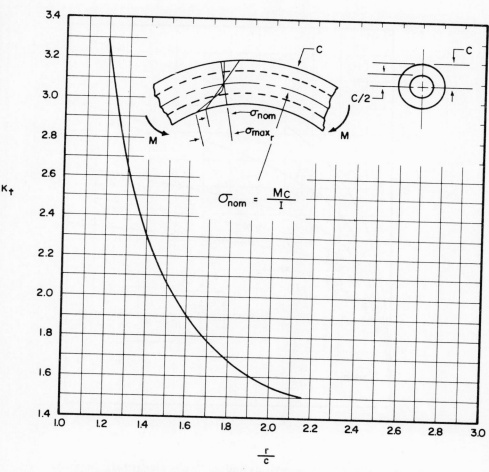

Figure 20–23. Hollow circular shaft, curved:[11] bending.

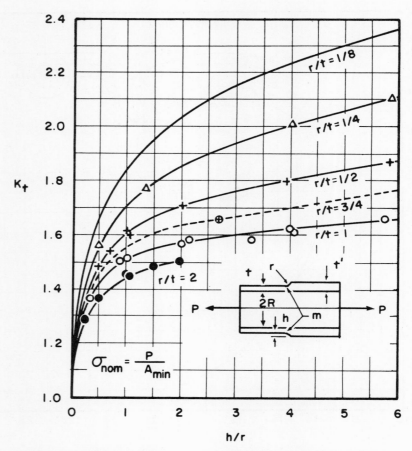

Figure 20–24. Stepped wall cylinder; [10] circular fillet: tension.

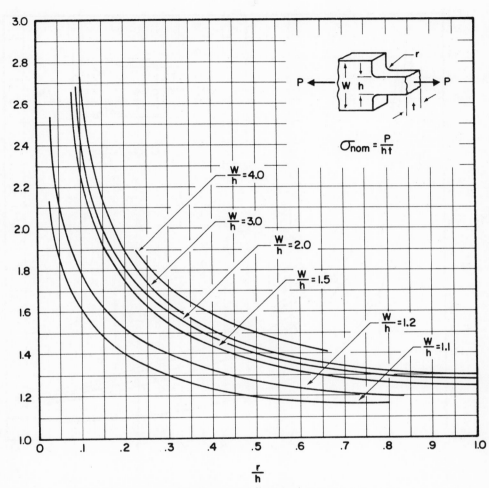

Figure 20—25. Flat plate; [17] circular fillet: tension.

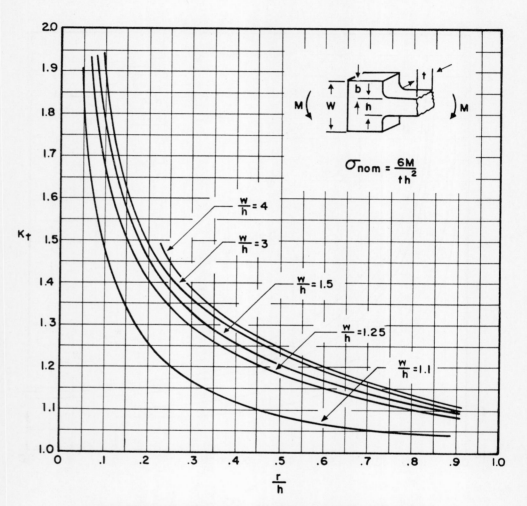

Figure 20–26. Flat plate, [17, 18] circular fillet: bending.

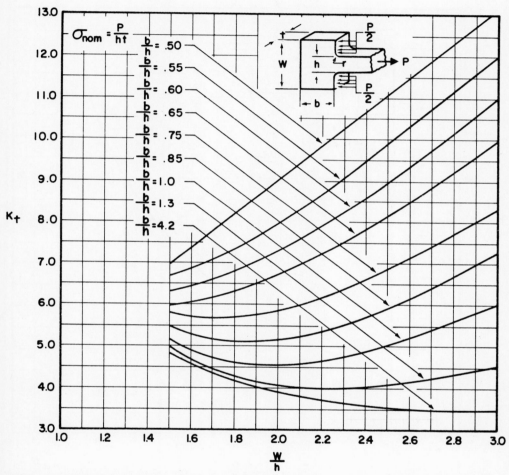

Figure 20–27. Flat plate, [25] circular fillet: tension with uniformly distributed reaction on flanges.

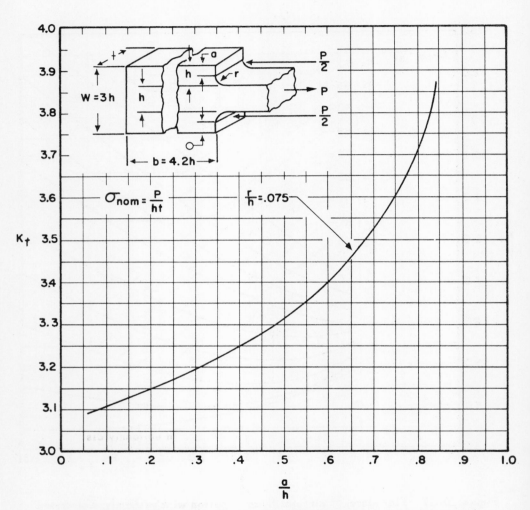

Figure 20–28. Flat plate; [25] circular fillet: tension with concentrated
reaction on flanges.

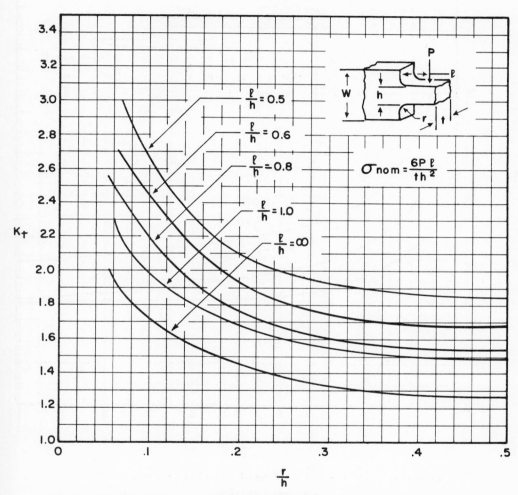

Figure 20–29. Flat plate;[26] circular fillet, concentrated load: bending.

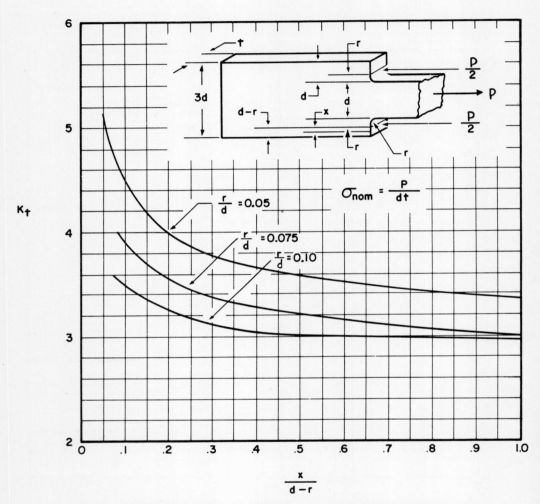

Figure 20–30. Flat plate; [11] T-head, variable concentrated flange
reactions: tension.

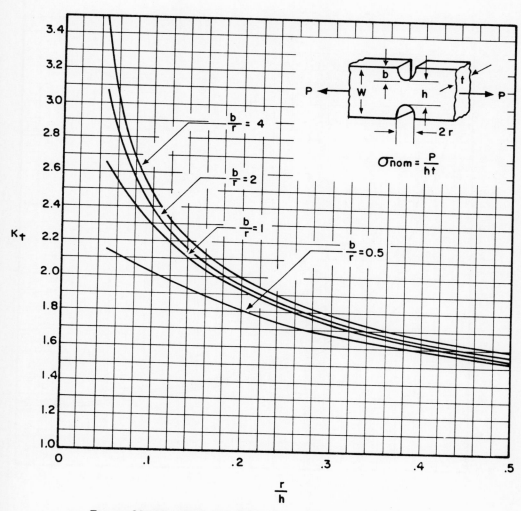

Figure 20–31. Flat plate;[17, 27] circular groove: tension.

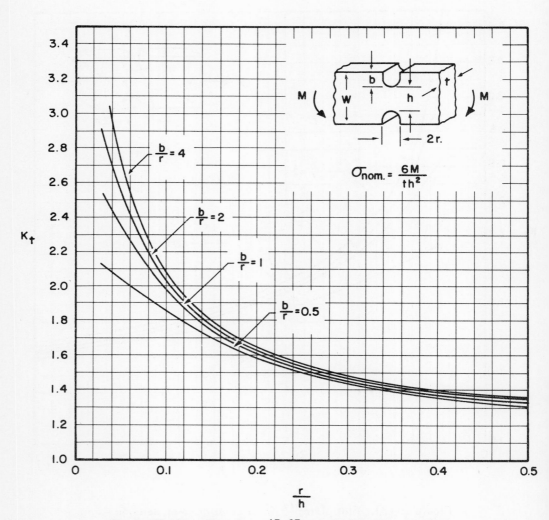

Figure 20–32. Flat plate, [17, 27] circular groove: bending.

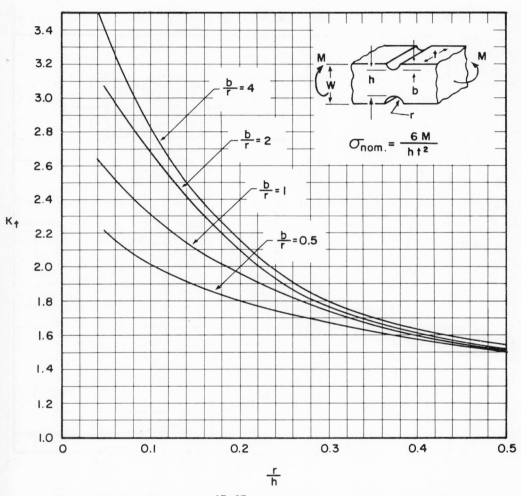

Figure 20–33. Flat plate; [17, 27] circular groove: transverse bending.

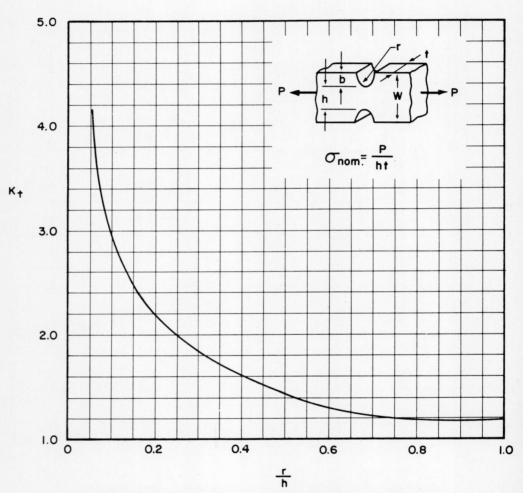

Figure 20–34.   Flat plate; [21], [26], [28] hyperbolic groove: tension.

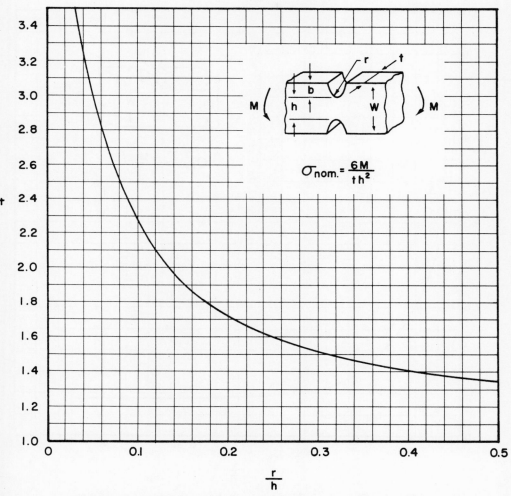

Figure 20–35. Flat plate; [21, 26, 28] hyperbolic groove: bending.

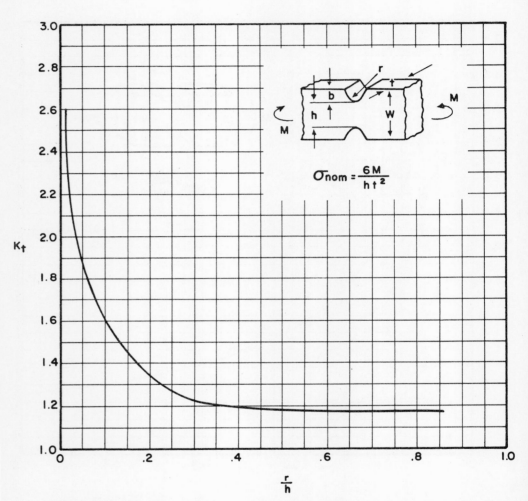

$$\sigma_{nom} = \frac{6M}{ht^2}$$

$$\frac{r}{h}$$

Figure 20–36. Flat plate;[21, 28] hyperbolic groove: transverse bending.

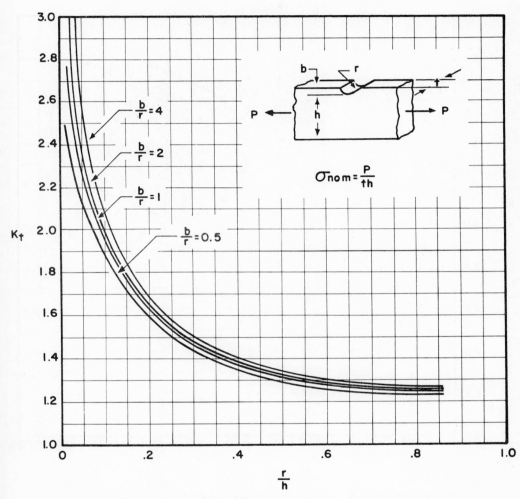

Figure 20–37. Flat plate; [21] hyperbolic groove on one edge: tension.

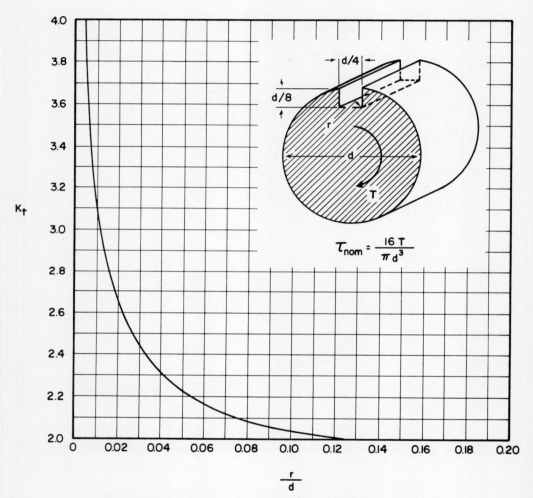

$$\tau_{nom} = \frac{16\,T}{\pi\,d^3}$$

Figure 20–38. Solid circular shaft; [11] keyway: torsion.

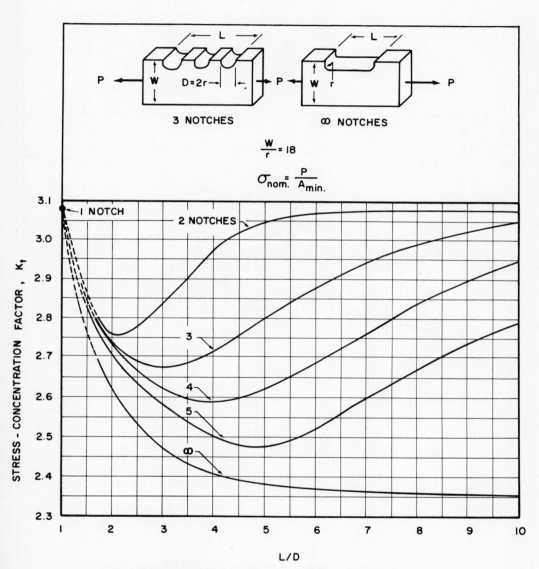

Figure 20–39. Flat plate;[12] semi-circular notches: tension.

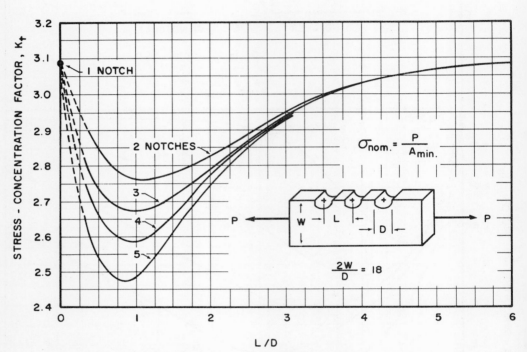

Figure 20–40. Flat plate; [12] semi-circular notches: tension.

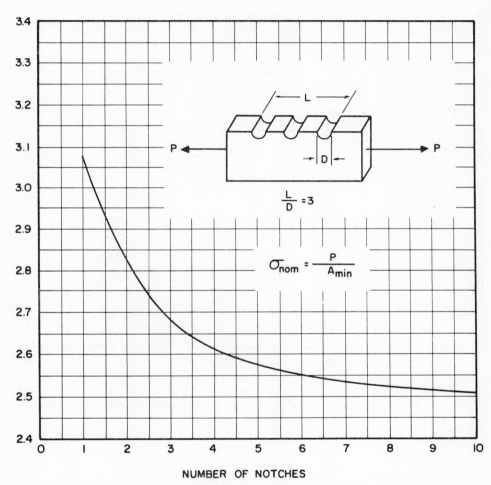

Figure 20–41. Flat plate; [12] semi-circular notches: tension.

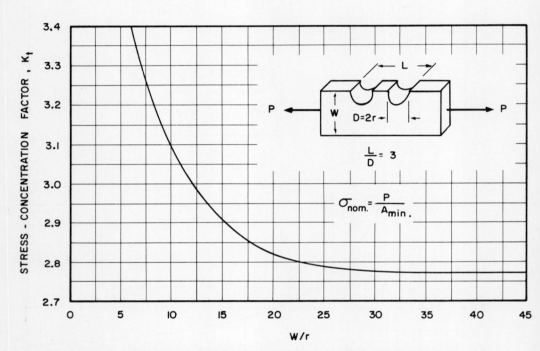

Figure 20—42. Flat plate;[12] two semi-circular notches: tension.

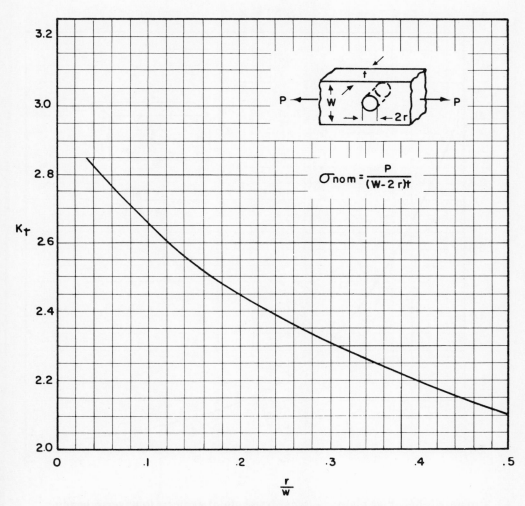

Figure 20—43. Flat plate,[29, 30] transverse hole at center: tension.

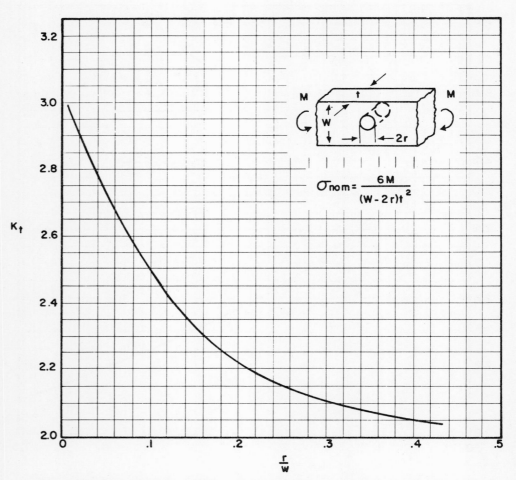

$$\sigma_{nom} = \frac{6M}{(W-2r)t^2}$$

Figure 20–44. Flat plate;[27] transverse hole at center: transverse bending.

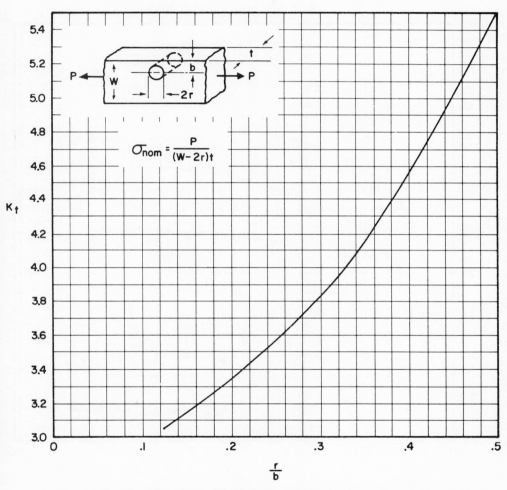

Figure 20–45. Flat plate; [26, 31] transverse hole near edge: tension.

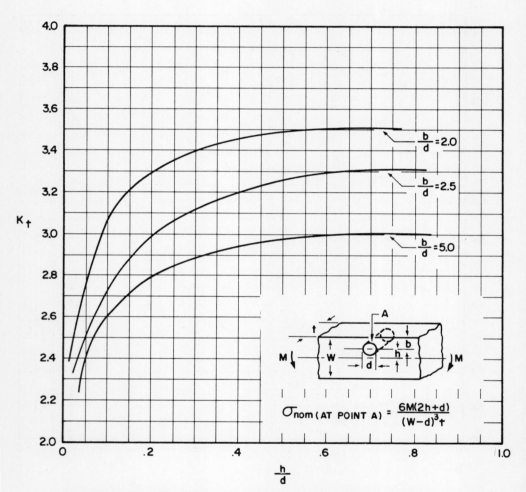

Figure 20–46. Flat plate;[26] transverse hole near edge: bending.

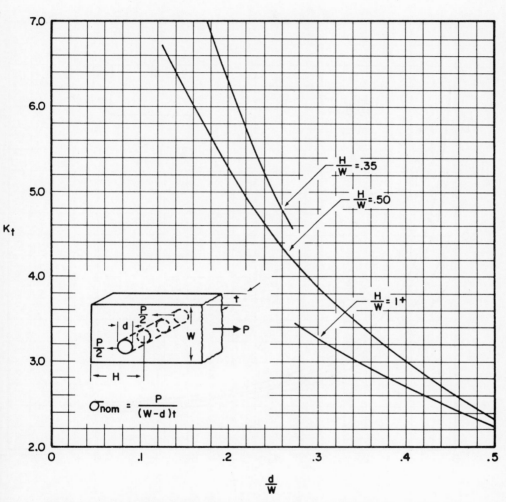

Figure 20–47. Flat plate;[32] pin in transverse hole at center: tension.

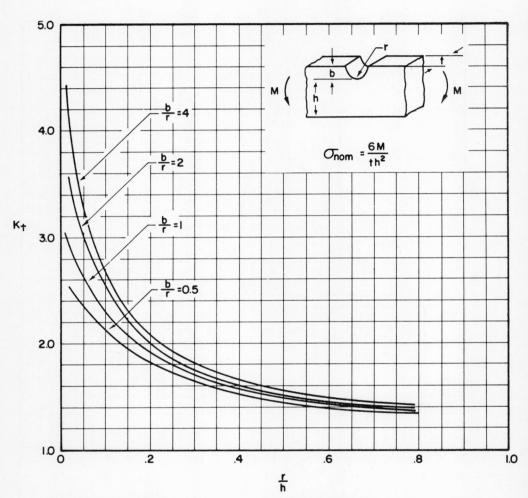

Figure 20–48. Flat plate; [21] hyperbolic groove on one edge: bending.

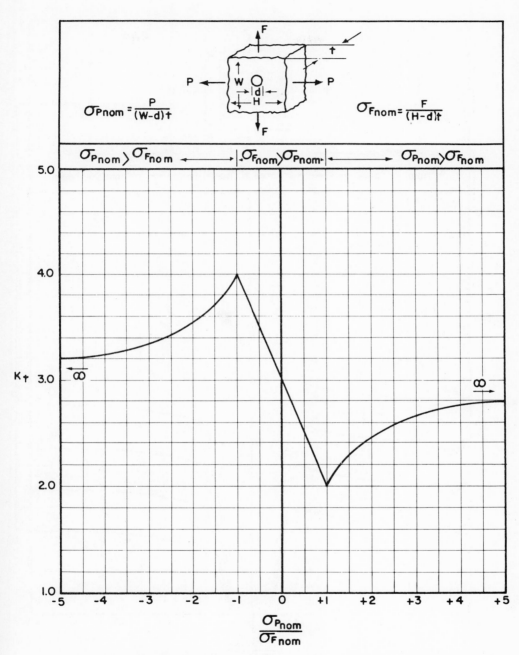

Figure 20–49. Flat plate; [17, 32] circular transverse hole at center:
biaxial tension.

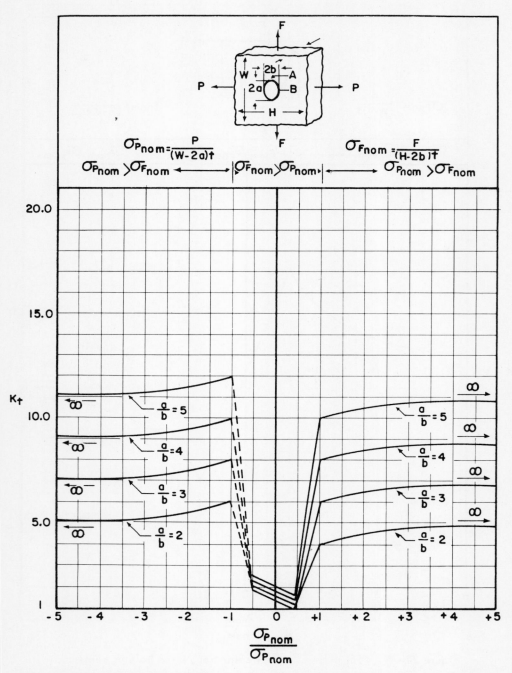

Figure 20–50. Flat plate;[33] elliptical transverse hole at center: biaxial tension.

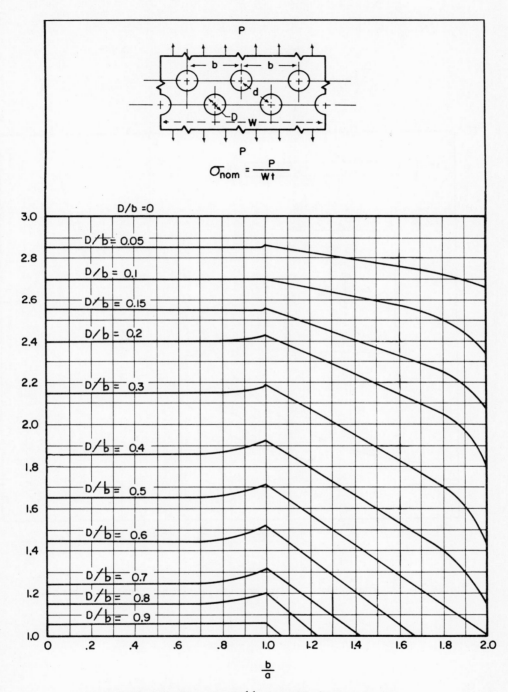

Figure 20–51. Flat plate; [11] spaced holes: tension.

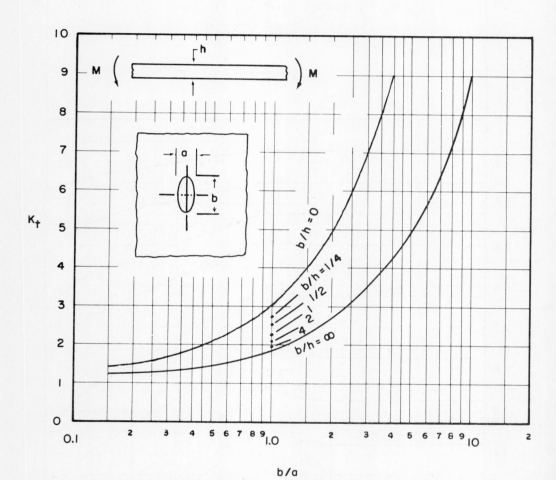

Figure 20–52. Flat plate;[11] elliptical hole at center: transverse bending.

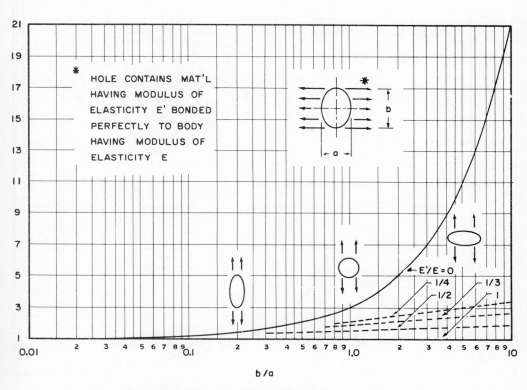

Figure 20–53. Flat plate; [11] filled hole at center: tension.

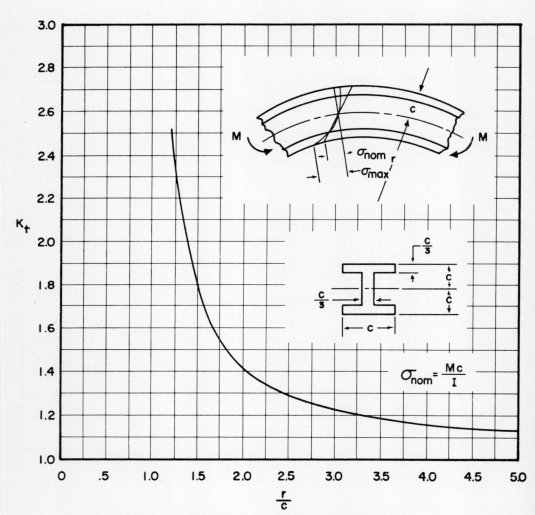

Figure 20—54. I-beam, curved:[11] bending.

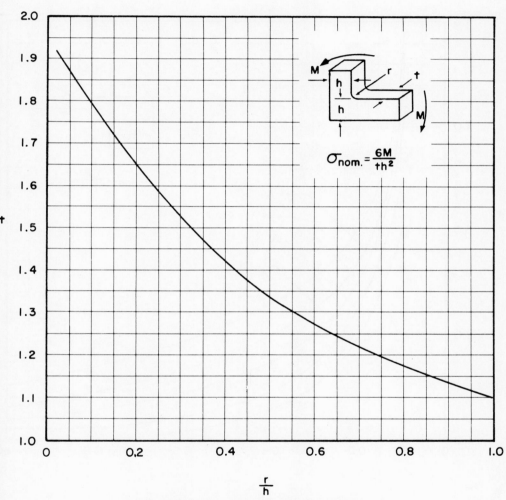

Figure 20–55. L-section:[29, 30] bending.

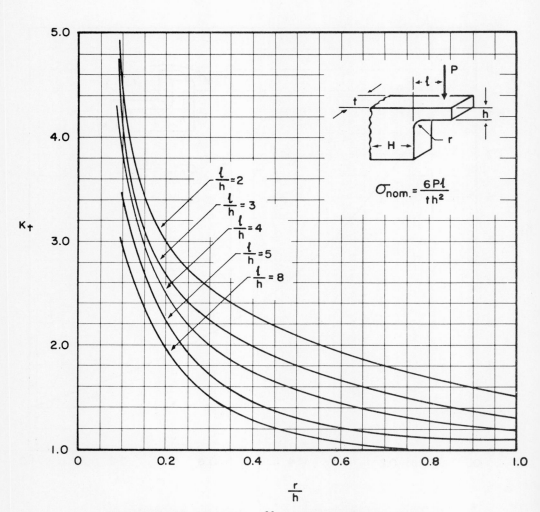

$$\sigma_{nom.} = \frac{6P\ell}{th^2}$$

Figure 20–56. L-section; [29] concentrated load: bending.

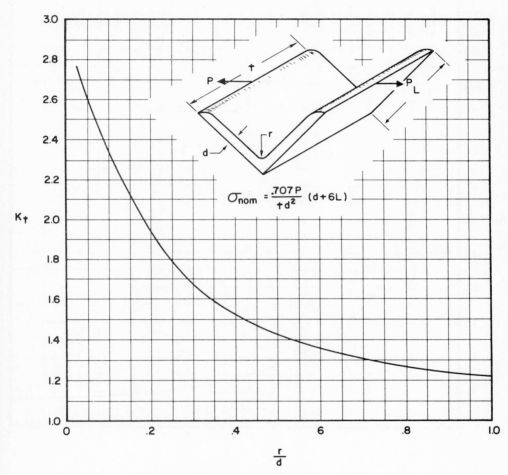

$$\sigma_{nom} = \frac{.707P}{t\,d^2}(d+6L)$$

Figure 20–57. L-section:[34] tension.

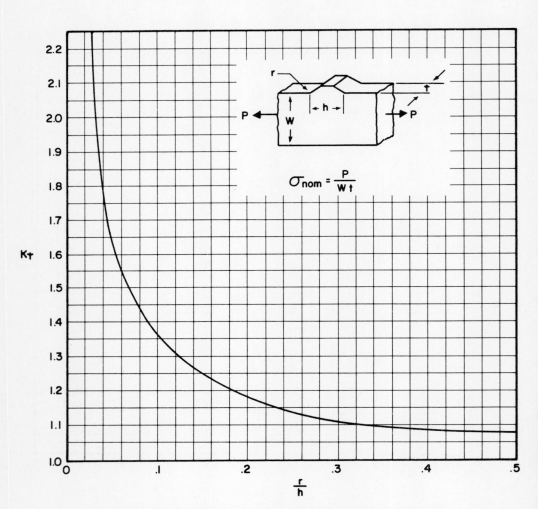

Figure 20–58. Flat plate;[21] single protrusion: tension.

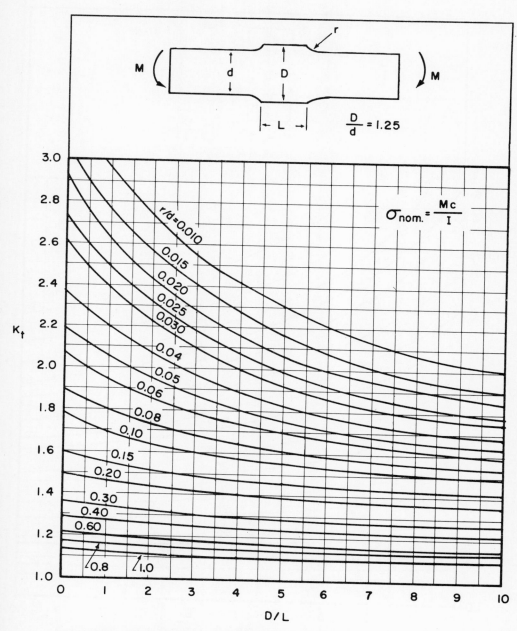

Figure 20–59. Flat plate,[35] double protrusion (D/d = 1.25): bending.

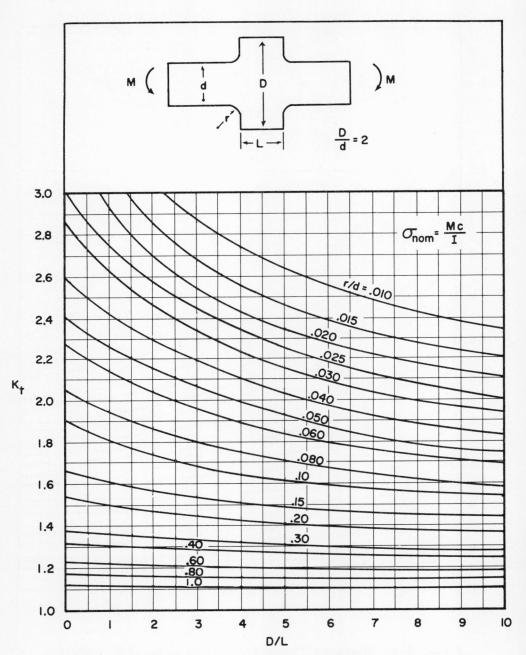

Figure 20–60. Flat plate, [35] double protrusion (D/d = 2): bending.

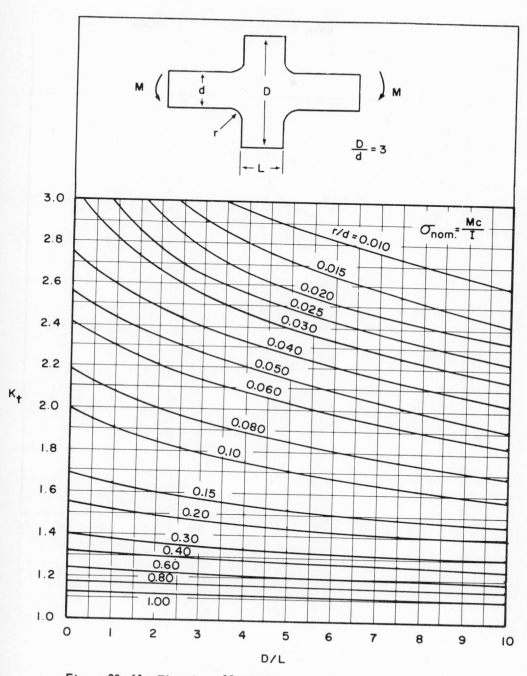

Figure 20-61. Flat plate,[35] double protrusion (D/d = 3): bending.

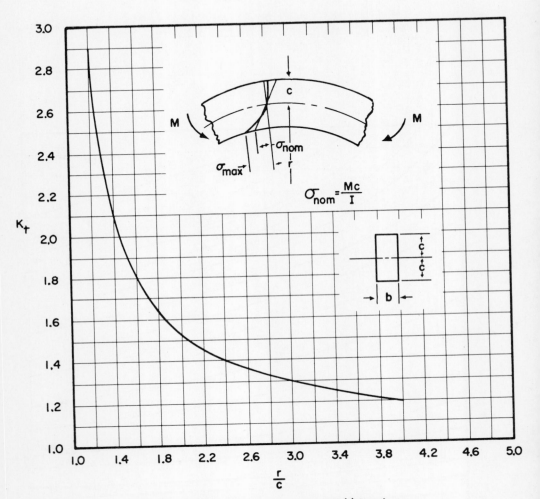

Figure 20–62. Flat plate, curved:[11] bending.

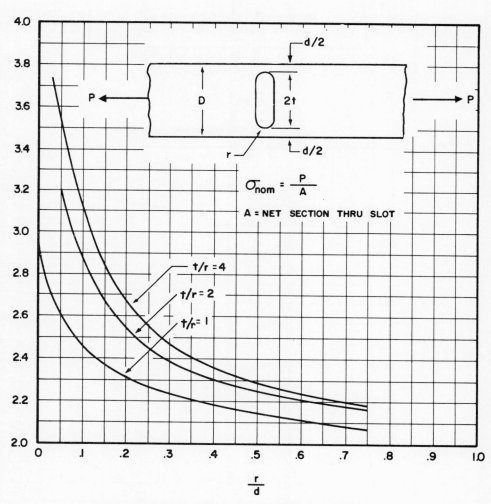

Figure 20–63. Flat plate,[11] slotted: tension.

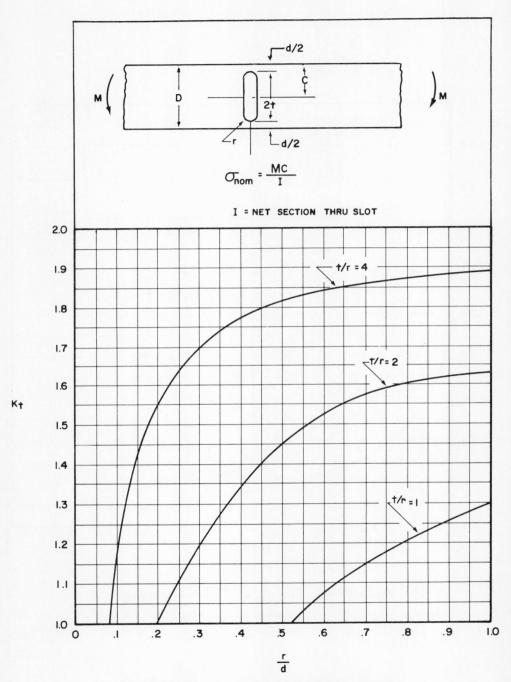

Figure 20—64. Flat plate, [11] slotted: bending.

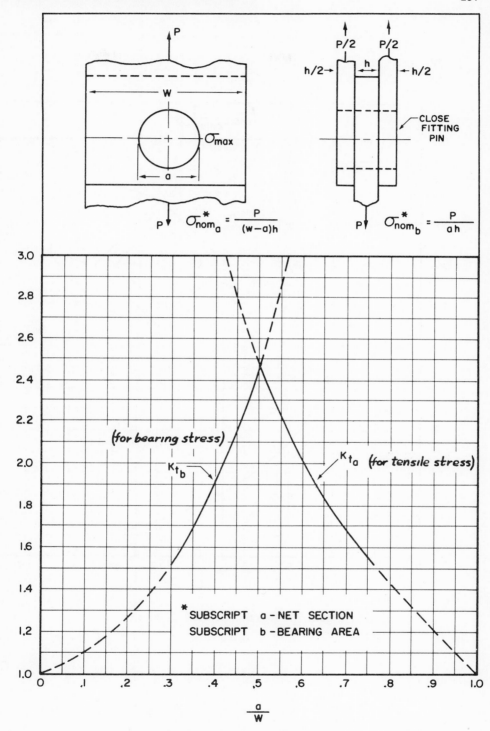

Figure 20–65. Pin joint:[11] tension.

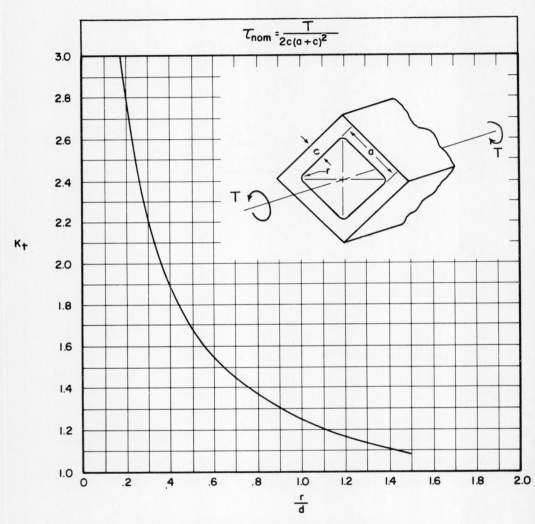

$$\tau_{nom} = \frac{T}{2c(a+c)^2}$$

Figure 20–66. Box section: [11] torsion.

Charts for K_f of Threads and Keyways

UNIFIED AND AMERICAN THREAD DESIGN

		BENDING OR TENSION	
		ROLLED	CUT
K_f	ANNEALED	2.2	2.3
	QUENCHED & DRAWN	3.0	3.8

KEYWAYS

PROFILE   SLED – RUNNER

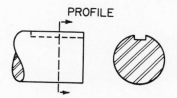 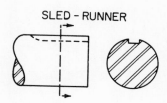

		PROFILE		SLED – RUNNER	
		BENDING	TORSION	BENDING	TORSION
K_f	ANNEALED	1.6	1.3	1.3	1.3
	QUENCHED & DRAWN	2.0	1.6	1.6	1.6

Figure 20–67. Fatigue stress concentration factors: threads and keyways.

Chapter 21

CHARTS, S-N CURVES

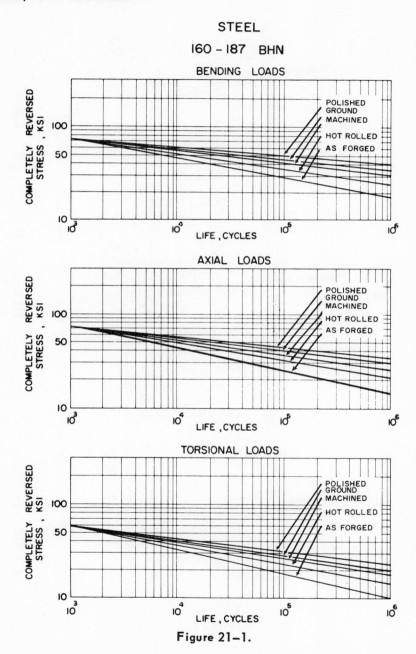

STEEL

160 – 187 BHN

BENDING LOADS

AXIAL LOADS

TORSIONAL LOADS

Figure 21–1.

STEEL

187-207 BHN

BENDING LOADS

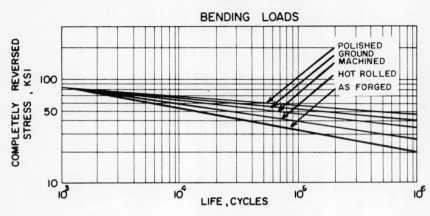

AXIAL LOADS

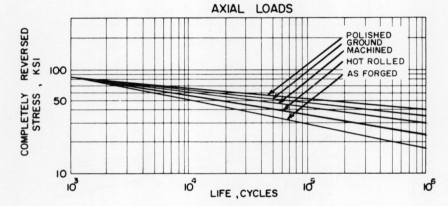

TORSIONAL LOADS

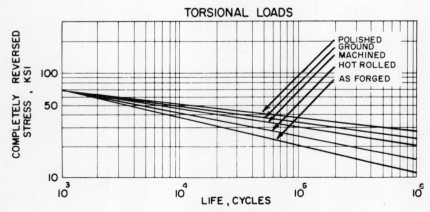

Figure 21-2.

STEEL
207-217 BHN

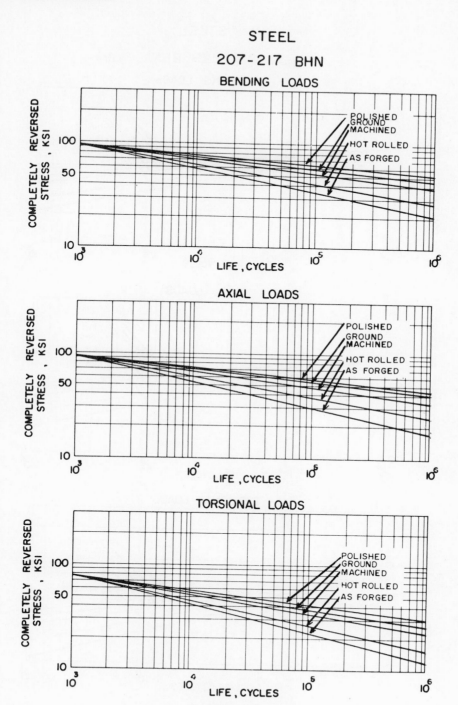

Figure 21-3.

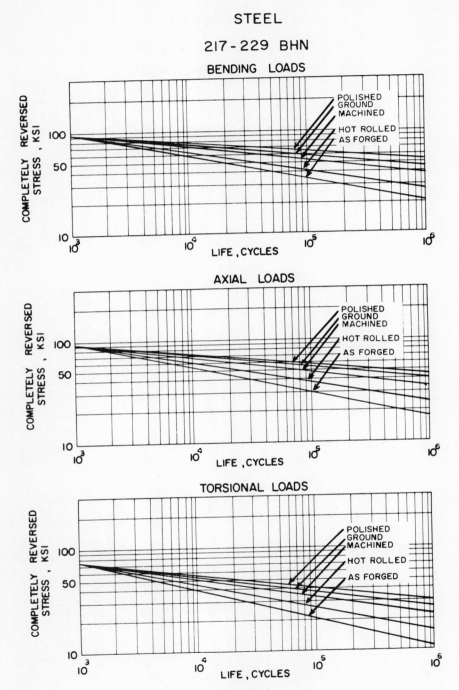

Figure 21–4.

STEEL

229 - 241 BHN

BENDING LOADS

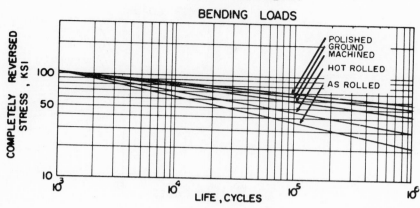

AXIAL LOADS

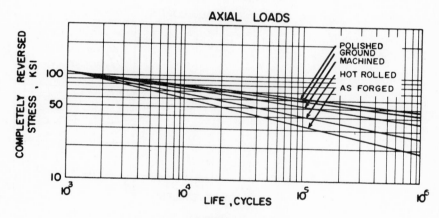

TORSIONAL LOADS

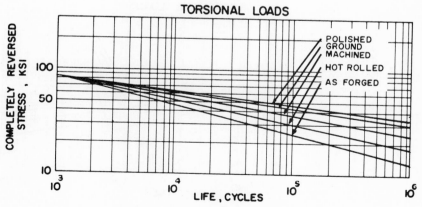

Figure 21–5.

STEEL

241 - 255 BHN

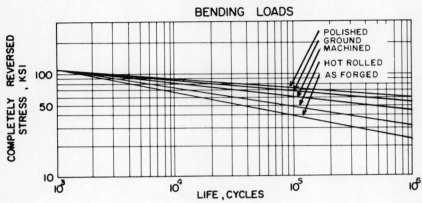

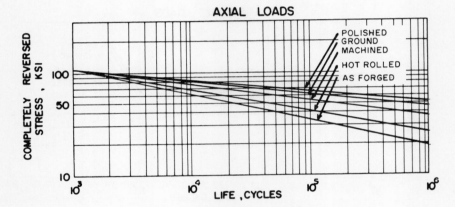

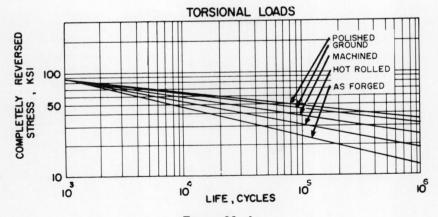

Figure 21-6.

STEEL

255 – 269 BHN

BENDING LOADS

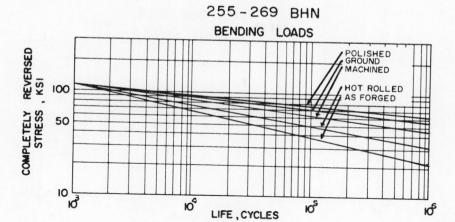

AXIAL LOADS

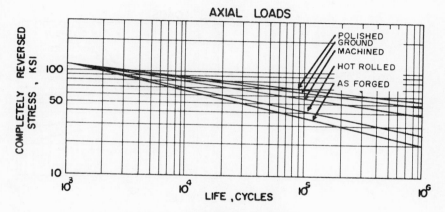

TORSIONAL LOADS

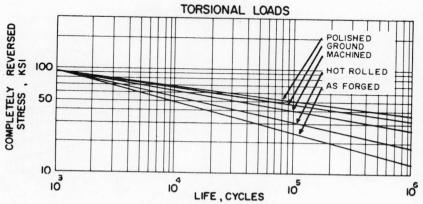

Figure 21–7.

STEEL

269-285 BHN

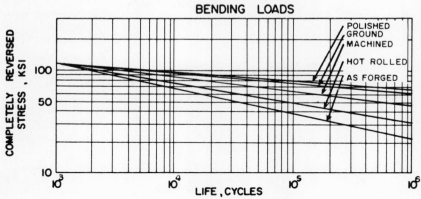

BENDING LOADS

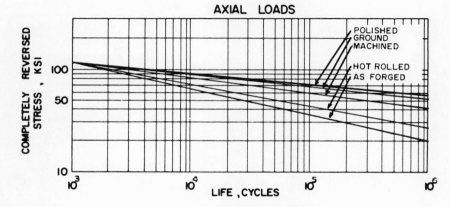

AXIAL LOADS

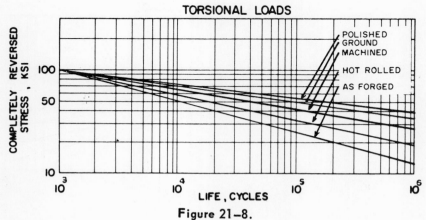

TORSIONAL LOADS

Figure 21-8.

STEEL
285-302 BHN

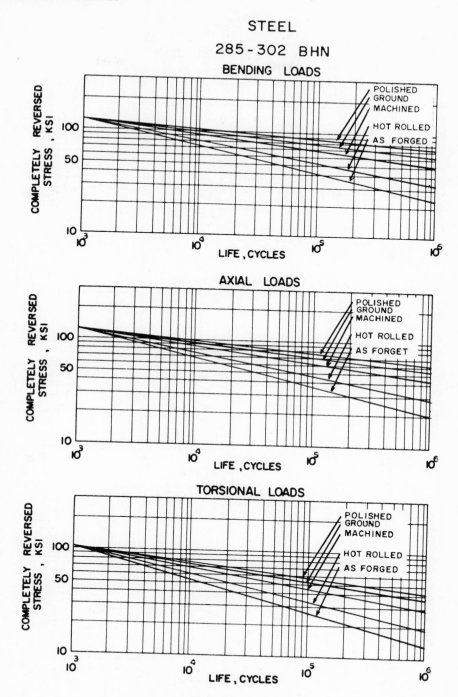

Figure 21-9.

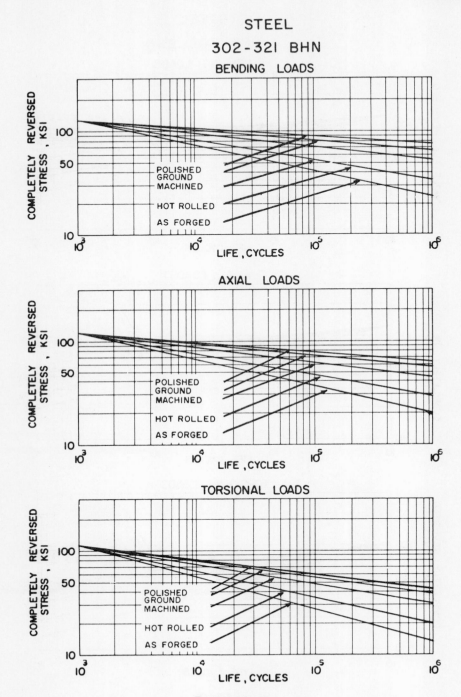

Figure 21-10.

STEEL

321-352 BHN

BENDING LOADS

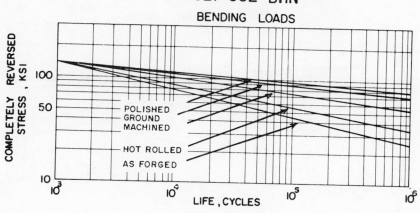

AXIAL LOADS

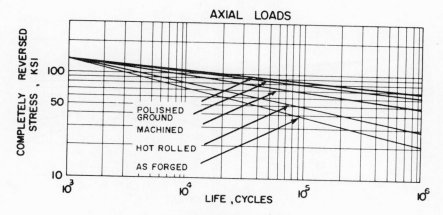

TORSIONAL LOADS

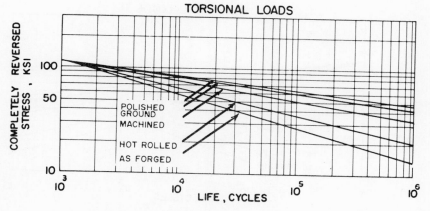

Figure 21—11.

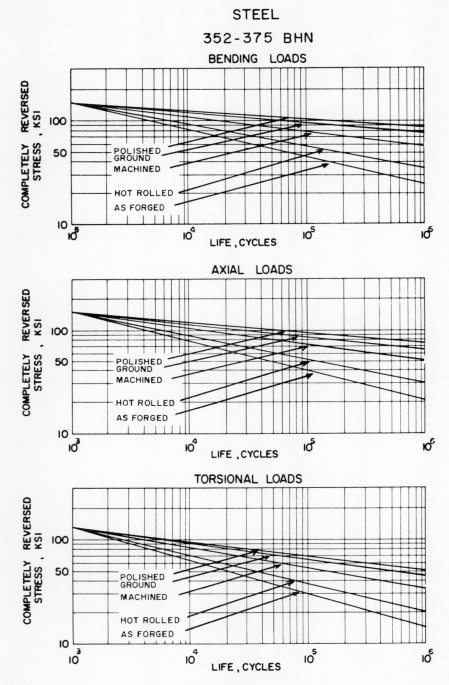

Figure 21–12.

STEEL

375 - 401 BHN

BENDING LOADS

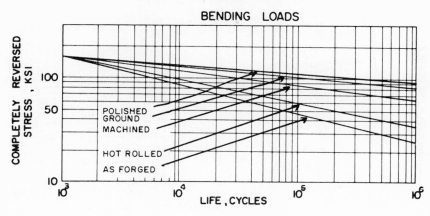

AXIAL LOADS

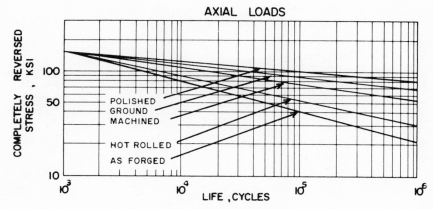

TORSIONAL LOADS

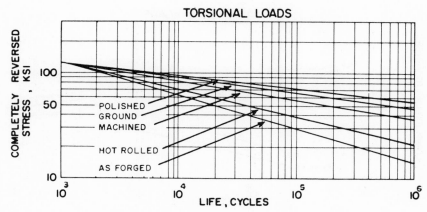

Figure 21–13.

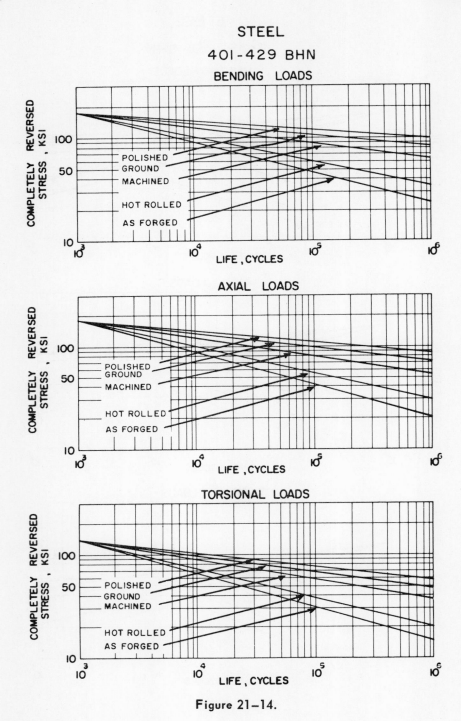

Figure 21-14.

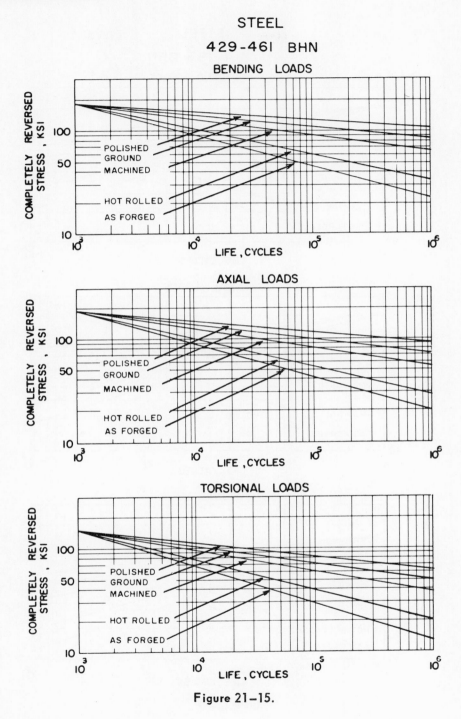

Figure 21-15.

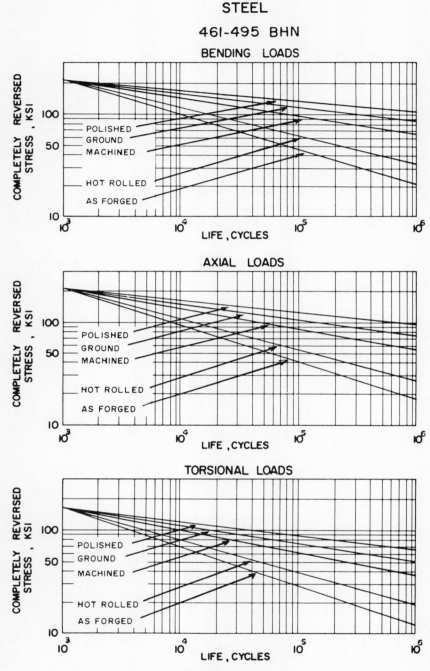

Figure 21—16.

STEEL

495 - 514 BHN

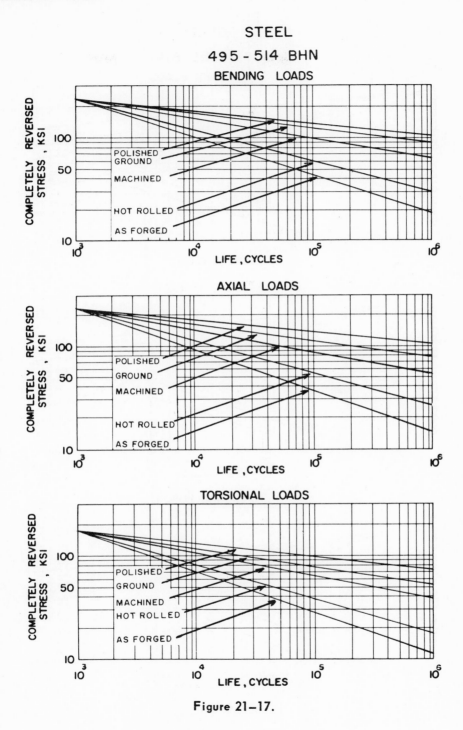

Figure 21-17.

STEEL
514-555 BHN

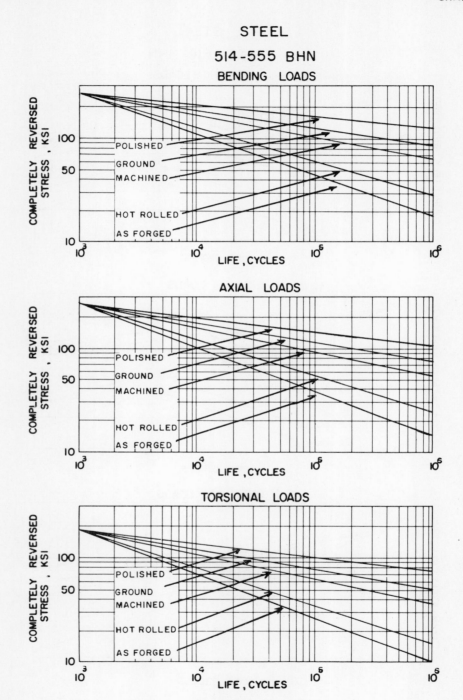

Figure 21-18.

CAST IRON

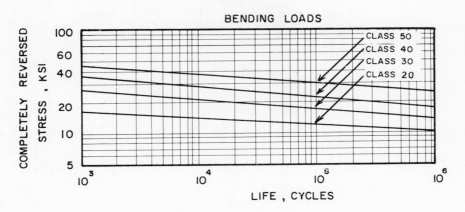

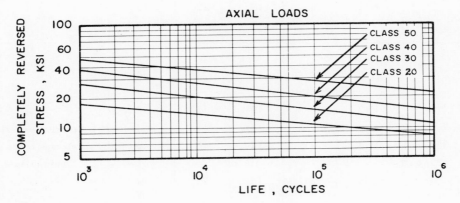

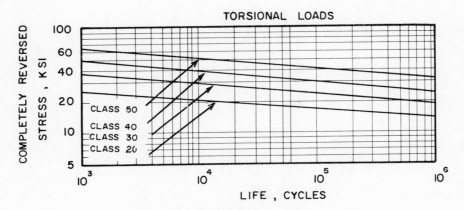

Figure 21–19.

Wrought Aluminum

Material	Treatment	Strength, ksi			% Elong*	Typical Uses
		Ultimate		Yield		
		Tension	Shear	Tension		
1100 (2S)	0	13.	9	5	45	Cold headed parts and light duty forgings
	H12	15.5	10	14	25	
	H14	17.5	11	16	20	
	H16	20	12	17	17	
	H18	24	13	22	15	
3003 (3S)	0	16	11	6	40	Pressure vessels, storage tanks and piping
	H12	19	12	17	20	
	H14	21.5	14	19	16	
	H16	25	15	22	14	
	H18	29	16	27	10	
2014 (14S)	T4	62	38	42	20	Heavy duty structure and truck frames
	T6	70	42	60	13	
2017 (17S)	T4	62	38	40	22	Screw machine products

* % Elongation for a 1/2" specimen, 2 inches long.

Figure 21–20a.

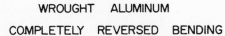

WROUGHT ALUMINUM
COMPLETELY REVERSED BENDING

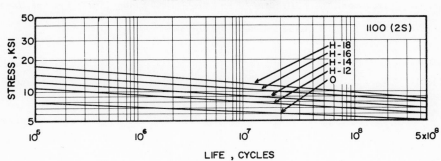

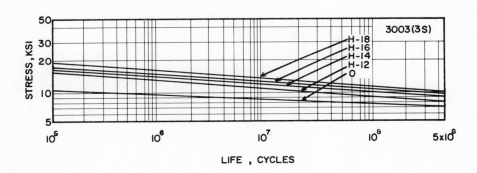

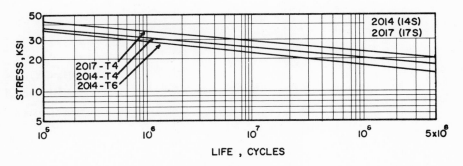

Figure 21—20b.

Wrought Aluminum

Material	Treatment	Strength, ksi			% Elong*	Typical Uses
		Ultimate		Yield		
		Tension	Shear	Tension		
2018 (18S)	T61	61	39	46	12	Pistons and cylinder heads
2024 Alclad Sheet	T3	65	40	45	18	Aircraft structures and truck bodies
	T81	65	40	60	6	
	T86	70	42	66	6	
2024 (24S)	0	27	18	11	22	Cold heading, aircraft structures, truck wheels
	T3	71	41	50	18	0, T4 in bar and rod form
	T36	73	42	57	13	
	T4	68	41	46	19	T3, T36 in sheets
4032 (32S)	T6	55	38	46	9	Pistons, low coefficient of thermal expansion
6151 (61S)	T6	47	32	43	17	Forgings

* % Elongation for a 1/2" specimen, 2 inches long.

Figure 21–21a.

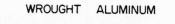

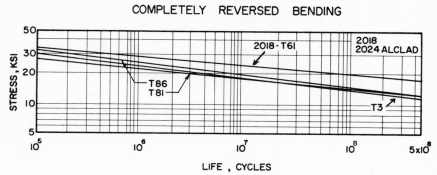

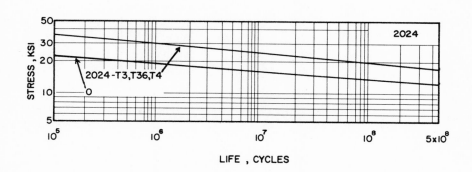

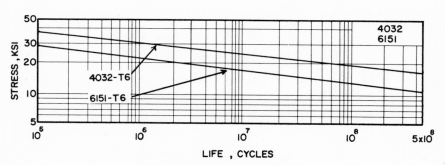

Figure 21–21b.

Wrought Aluminum

Material	Treatment	Strength, ksi			% Elong*	Typical Uses
		Ultimate		Yield		
		Tension	Shear	Tension		
5052 (52S)	0	29	18	12	30	Truck, marine and chemical applications requiring corrosion resistance
	H32	34	20	28	18	
	H34	37	21	30	14	
	H38	41	24	36	8	
6061 (61S)	0	18	12	8	30	Heavy duty corrosion resistant structure
	T4	35	24	21	25	
	T6	45	30	40	17	
7075 (75S)	T6	82	48	73	11	Airframe
7075 Alclad sheet	T6	76	46	66	11	Construction

* % Elongation for a 1/2" specimen, 2 inches long.

Figure 21–22a.

WROUGHT ALUMINUM
COMPLETELY REVERSED BENDING

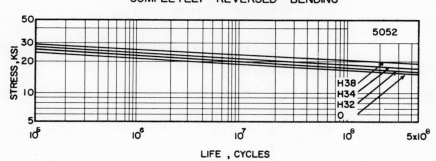

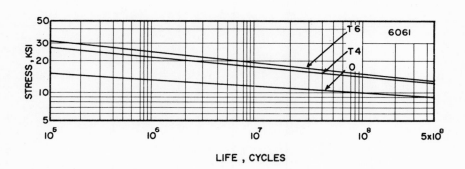

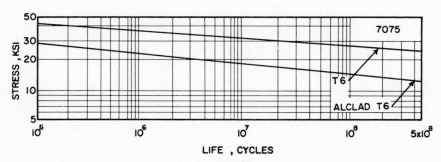

Figure 21-22b.

Cast Aluminum

| Material | Treatment | Strength, ksi | | | % Elong* | Typical Uses |
| | | Ultimate | | Yield | | |
		Tension	Shear	Tension		
13		39	25	21	2.0	Die Large, intricate die casting
43		30	19	16	9.0	Die General purpose
43	F	23	16	9	10	Perm General purpose
43	F	19	14	8	8.0	Sand General
108	F	21	17	14	2.5	Sand Manifolds
C113	F	30	24	24	1.5	Perm Cylinder heads, gears
	T551	37	30	35	—	Perm
122	T61	41	32	40	—	Sand Bushing and bearings
	T2	27	21	20	1.0	Sand Caps
A132	T551	36	28	28	0.5	Perm Diesel piston
D132	T5	36	28	28	1.0	Perm Automotive pistons

* % in 2 inches.

Figure 21–23a.

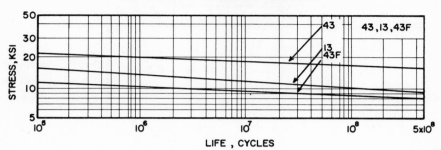

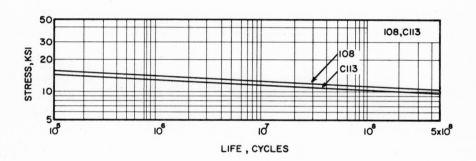

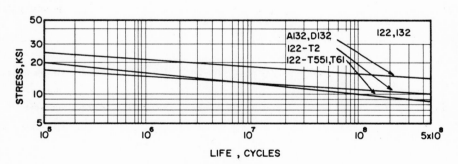

Figure 21–23b.

Cast Aluminum

Material	Treatment	Ultimate Tension	Shear	Yield Tension	% Elong*	Typical Uses	
142	T21	27	21	18	1.0		
	T571	40	26–30	30–34	0.5–1.0	Sand & Perm	Heavy duty pistons and air cooled heads
	T61	47	35	42	0.5		
	T77	30	24	23	2.0		
195	T4	32	26	16	8.5	Sand	Machinery, structural members
	T4	32	30	24	5.0		
	T62	40	33	32	2.0		
B195	T4	37	30	19	9.0	Perm	Aircraft fittings, gear housings
	T6	40	32	26	5.0		
	T7	39	30	20	4.5		
220	T4	46	34	26	16.0	Sand	Schock resistant structure
319	F	27	22	18	2.0	Sand	Cylinder heads, general purpose
	T6	36	29	24	2.0		
355	T51	28	22–24	23–24	1.5–2.0	Sand & Perm	Crank cases and aircraft fittings
	T6	35	28–34	25–27	3.0–4.0		
	T71	35	26–27	29–31	1.5–3.0		
	T6	33–38	26–30	25–27	3.5–5.0	Sand & Perm	Truck axle housing, wheels cylinder blocks
	T51	25	20	20	20		

* When two values appear, the higher value is for permanent mold material.

Figure 21–24a.

CAST ALUMINUM
COMPLETELY REVERSED BENDING

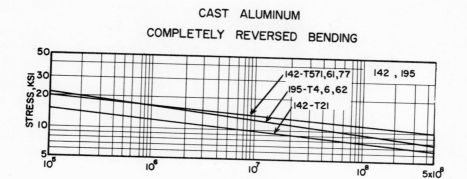

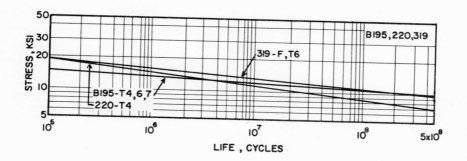

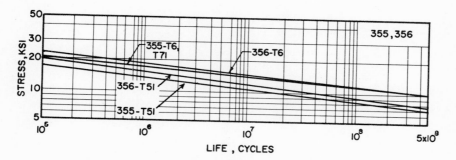

Figure 21-24b.

Chapter 22

CHARTS, GOODMAN DIAGRAMS

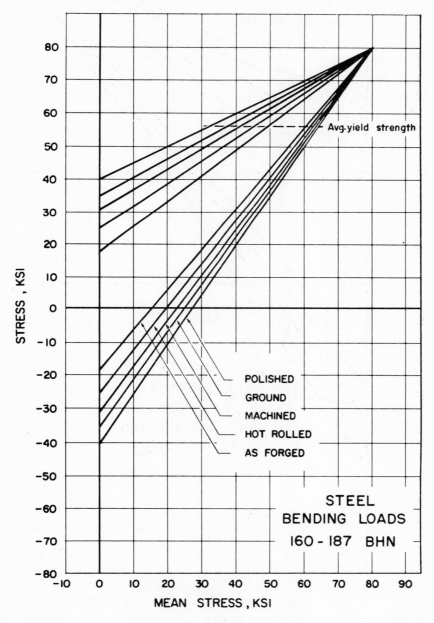

Figure 22-1.

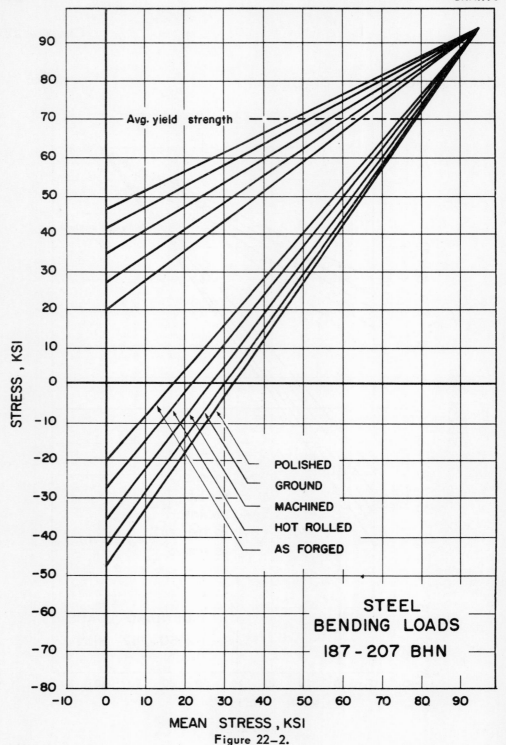

STEEL
BENDING LOADS
187 - 207 BHN

MEAN STRESS, KSI
Figure 22-2.

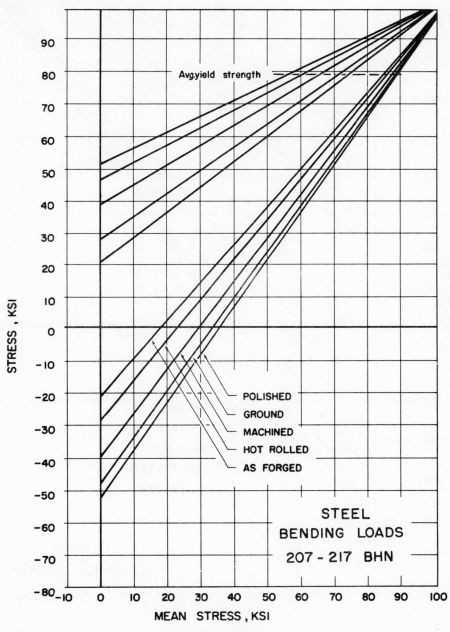

Figure 22–3.

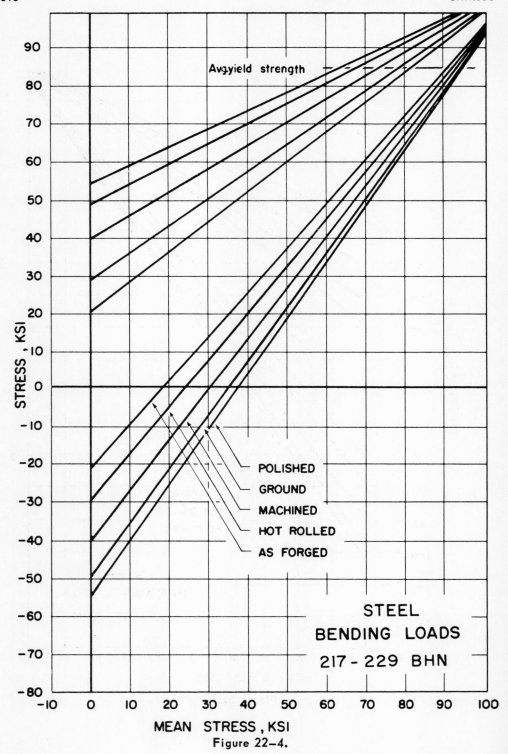

Figure 22-4.

STEEL
BENDING LOADS
217 - 229 BHN

STRESS , KSI

MEAN STRESS , KSI

Avg.yield strength

POLISHED
GROUND
MACHINED
HOT ROLLED
AS FORGED

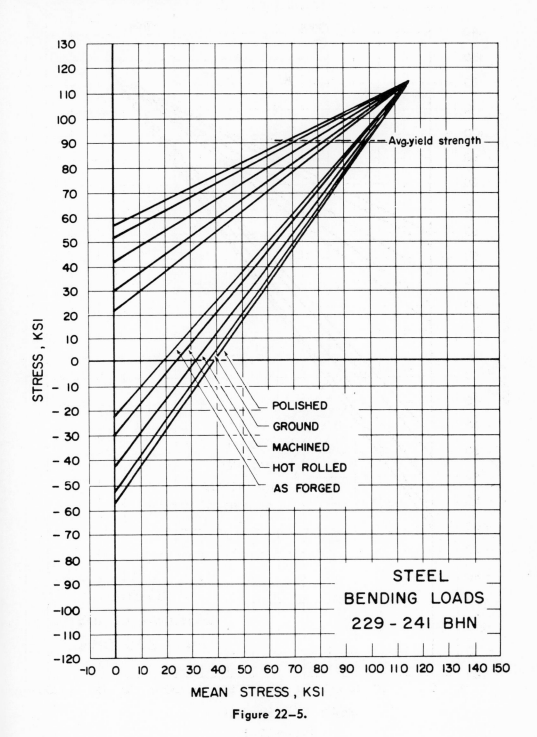

STEEL
BENDING LOADS
229 - 241 BHN

MEAN STRESS, KSI

Figure 22-5.

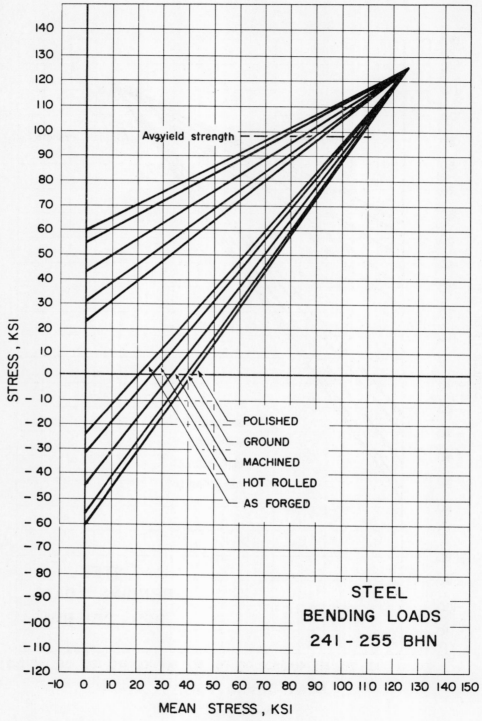

Figure 22-6.

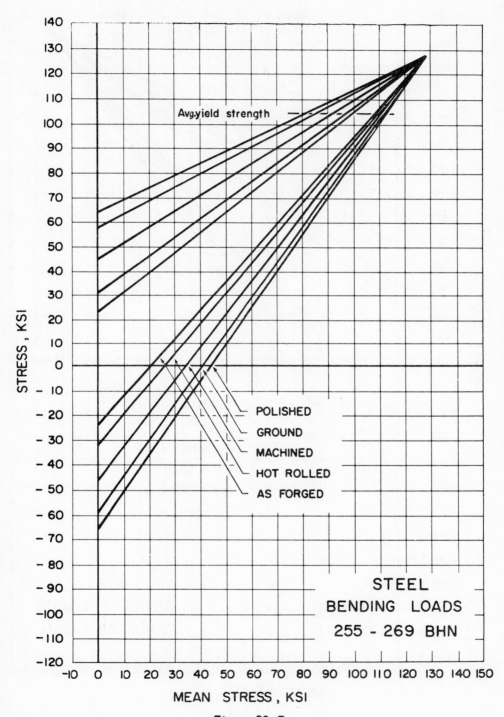

MEAN STRESS, KSI

Figure 22–7.

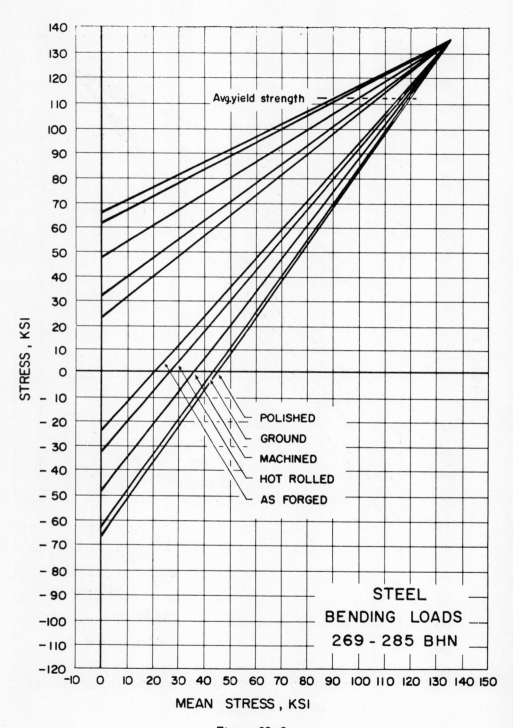

Figure 22—8.

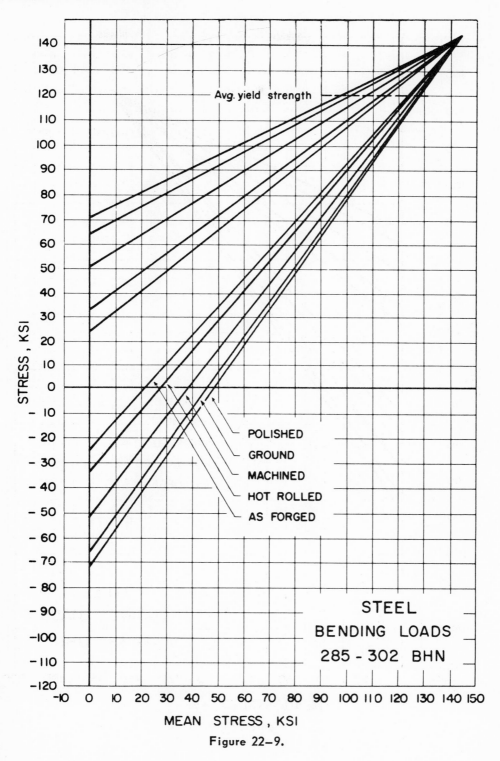

Figure 22-9.

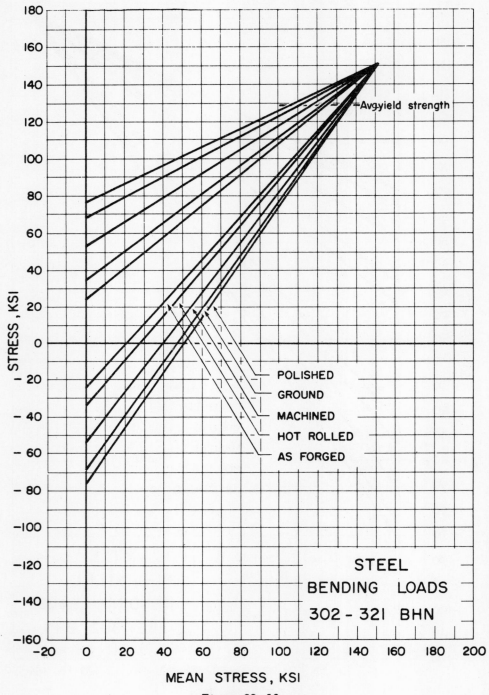

Figure 22–10.

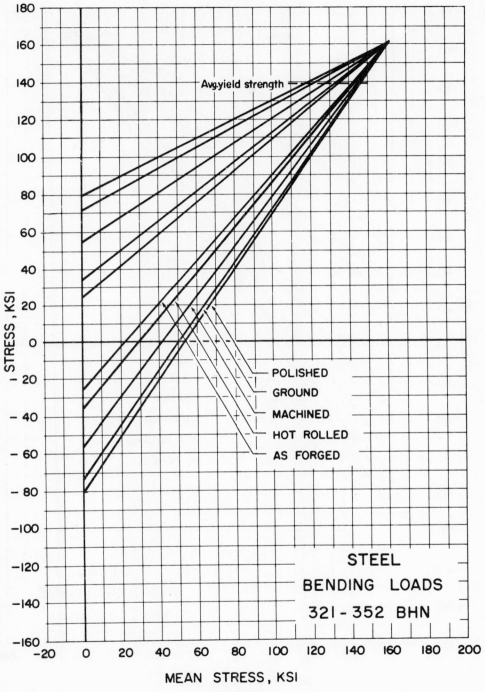

Figure 22–11.

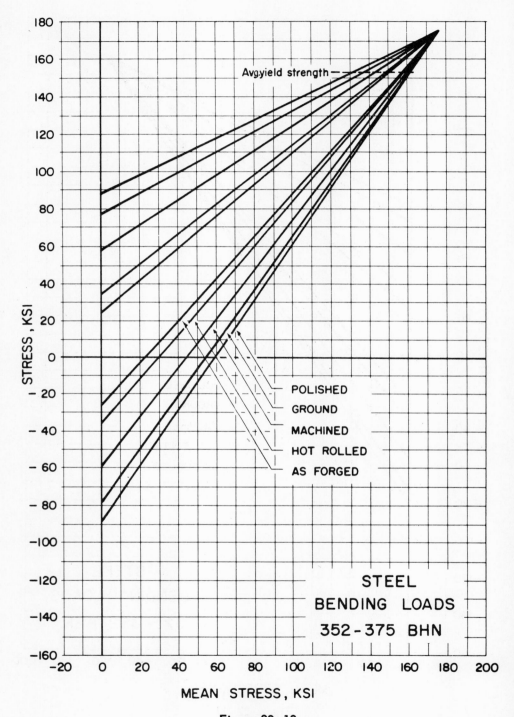

Figure 22-12.

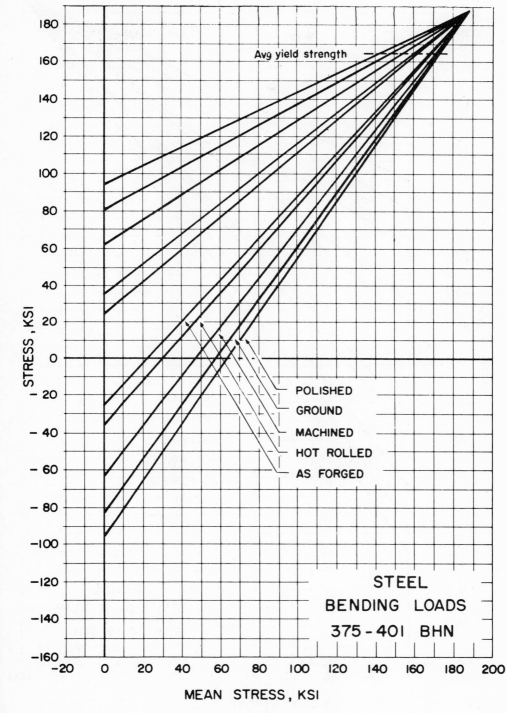

Figure 22-13.

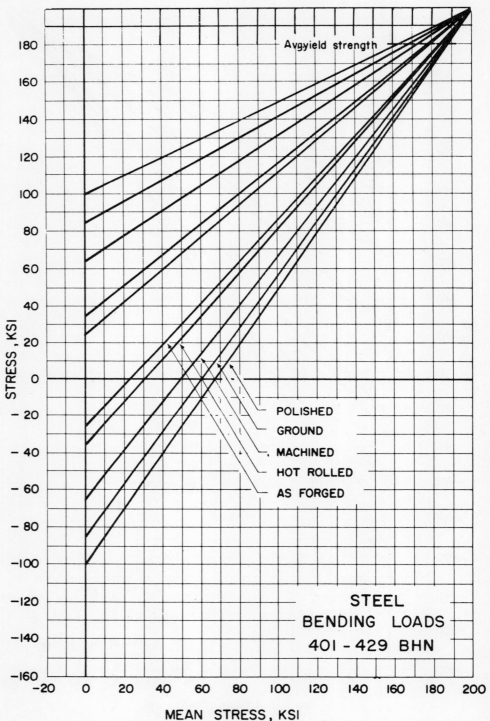

Figure 22-14.

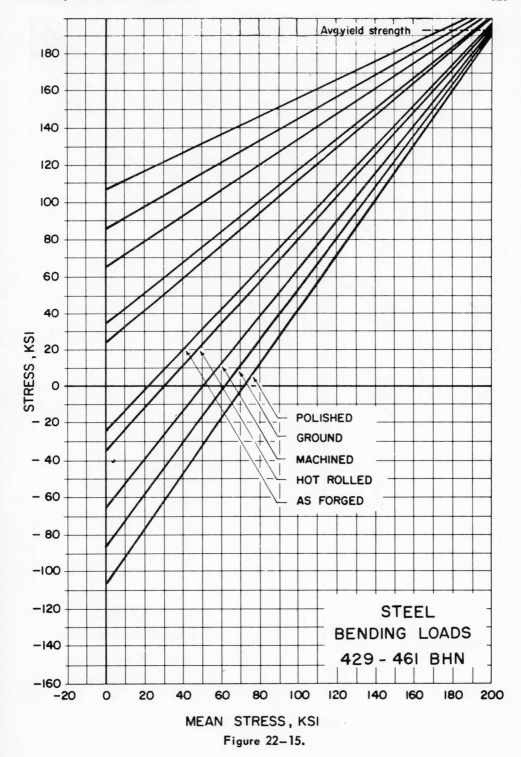

Figure 22-15.

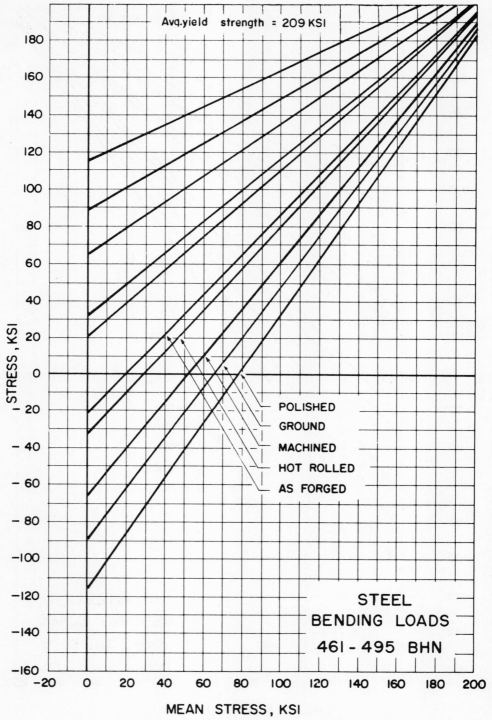

Avg. yield   strength = 209 KSI

STRESS , KSI

POLISHED
GROUND
MACHINED
HOT ROLLED
AS FORGED

STEEL
BENDING LOADS
461 - 495 BHN

MEAN STRESS, KSI

Figure 22—16.

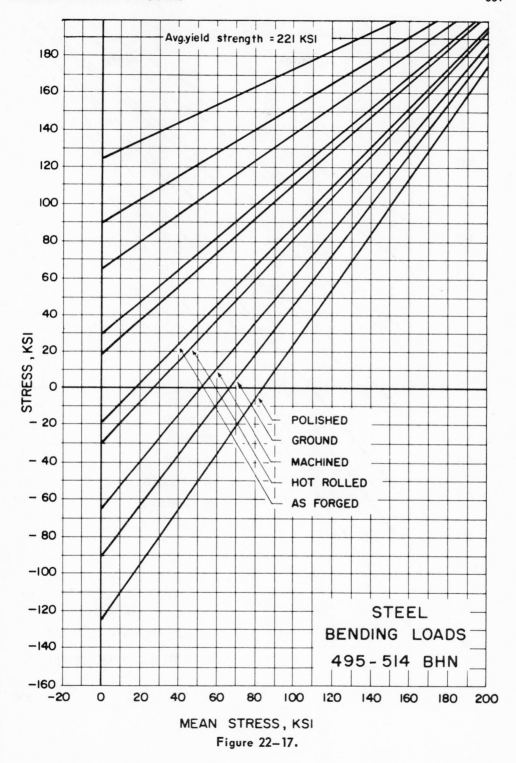

MEAN STRESS, KSI

Figure 22-17.

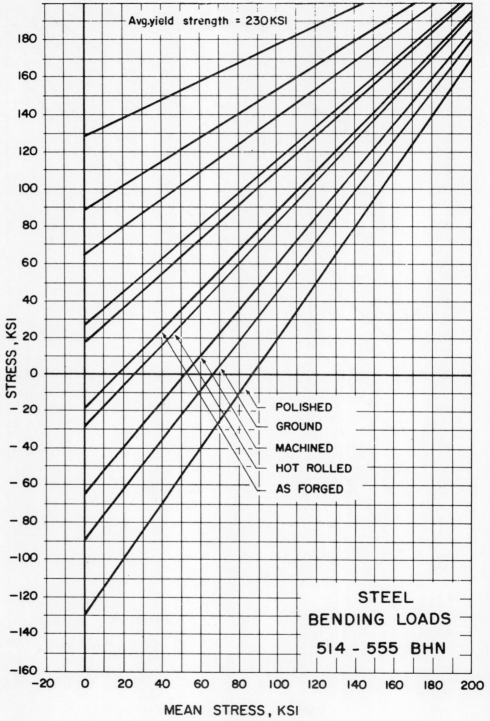

MEAN STRESS, KSI

Figure 22–18.

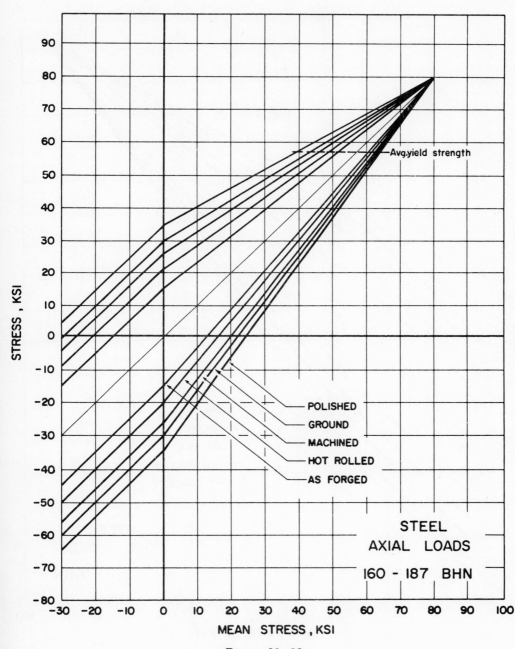

Figure 22–19.

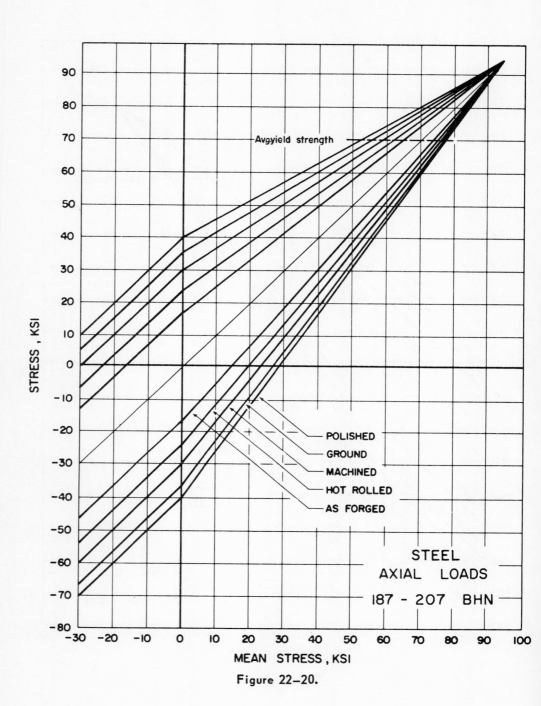

Figure 22–20.

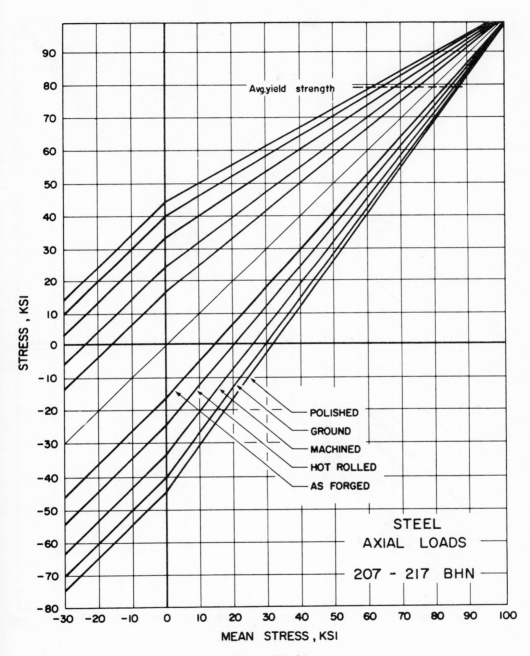

STRESS , KSI

MEAN STRESS , KSI

Avg.yield strength

POLISHED
GROUND
MACHINED
HOT ROLLED
AS FORGED

STEEL
AXIAL LOADS
207 - 217 BHN

Figure 22-21.

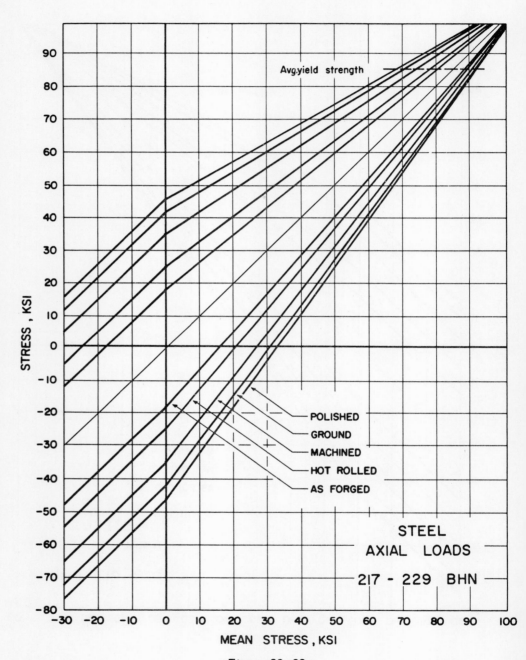

Figure 22-22.

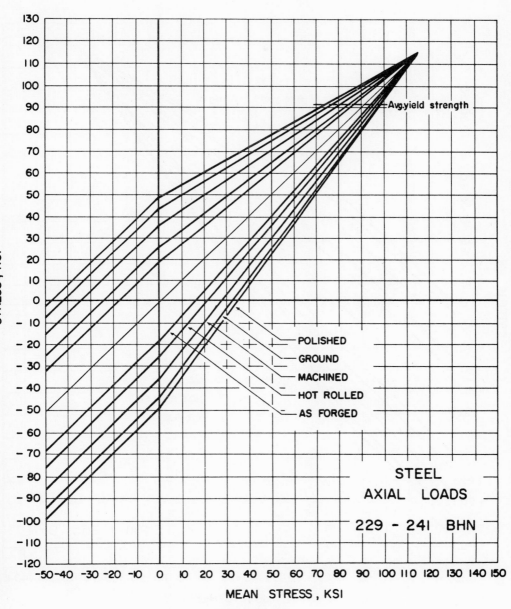

Figure 22–23.

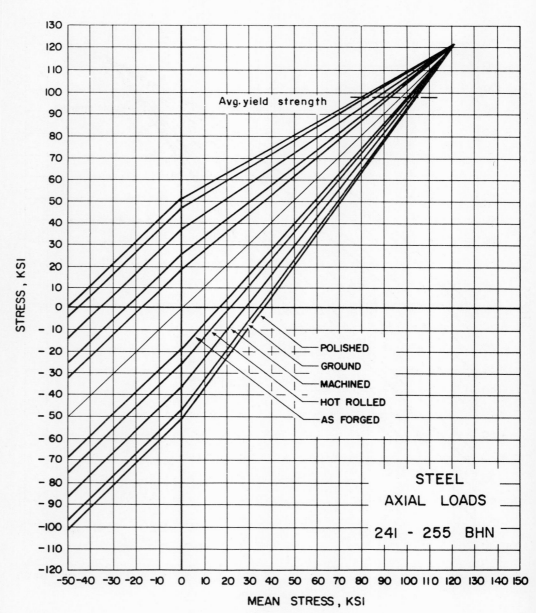

Figure 22—24.

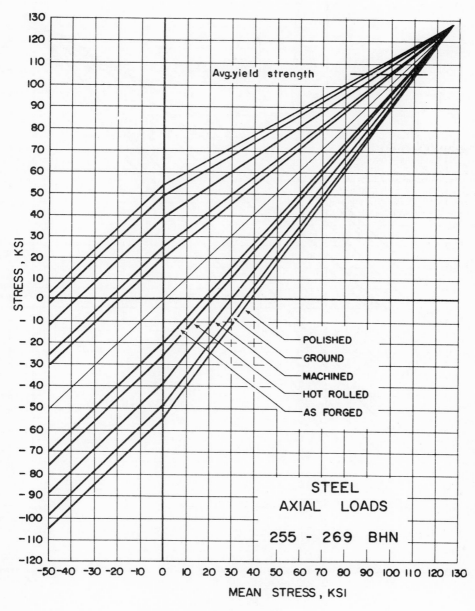

Figure 22–25.

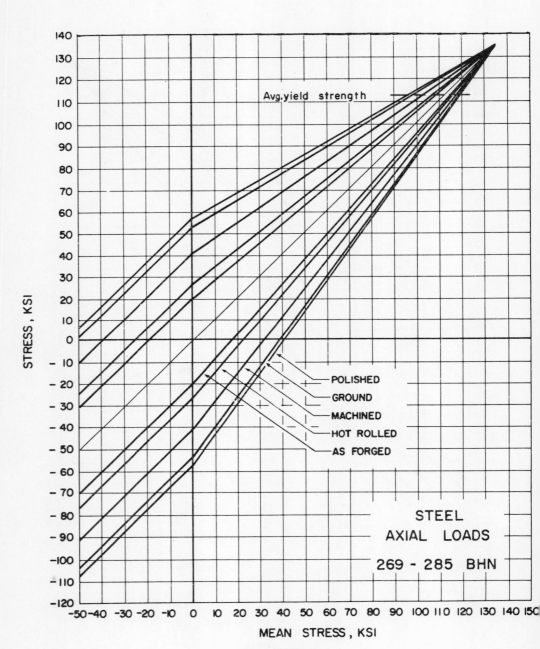

Figure 22-26.

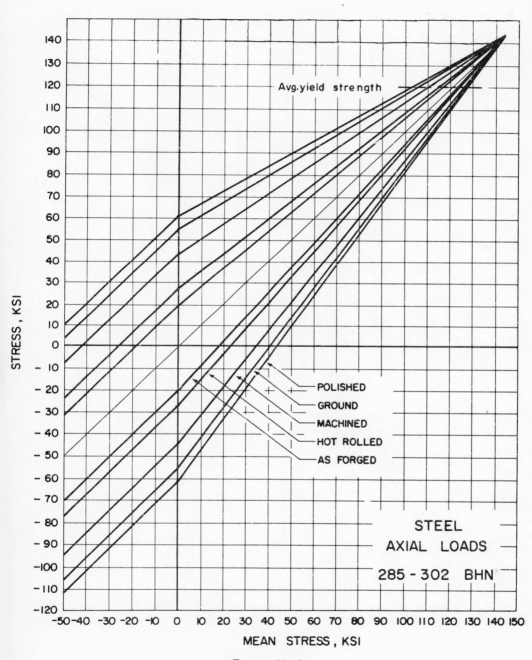

Figure 22-27.

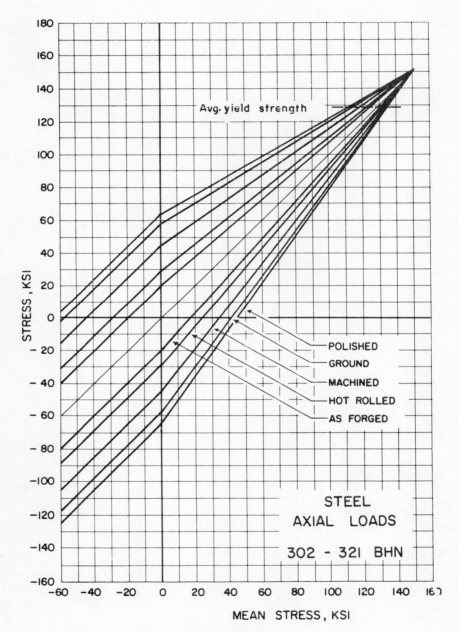

Figure 22–28.

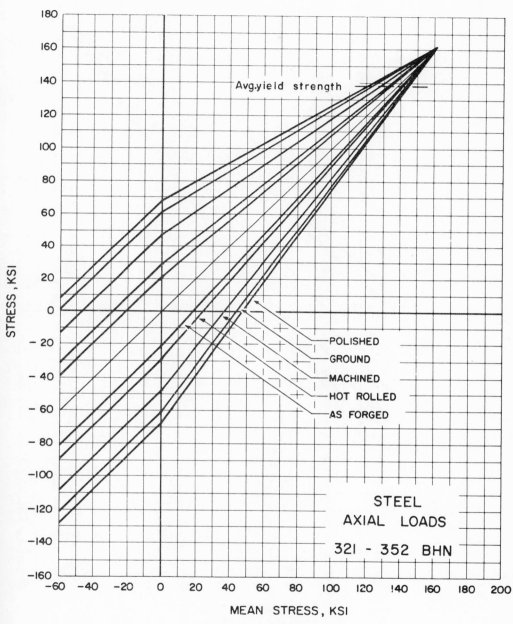

STRESS , KSI

Avg. yield strength

POLISHED
GROUND
MACHINED
HOT ROLLED
AS FORGED

STEEL
AXIAL LOADS
321 - 352 BHN

MEAN STRESS, KSI

Figure 22–29.

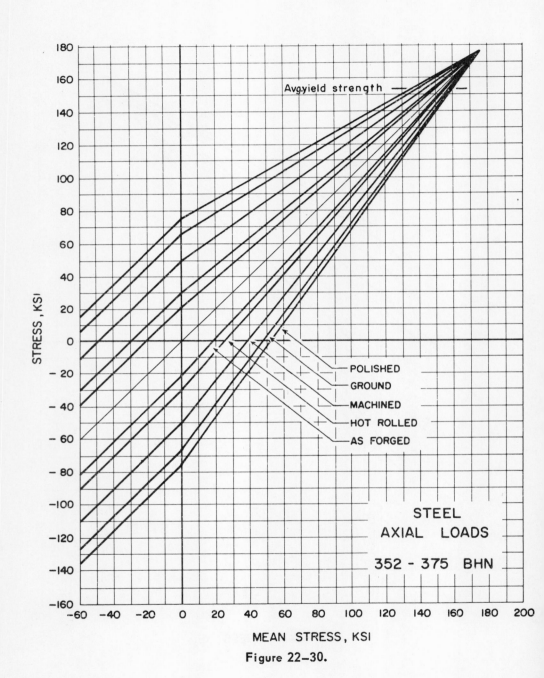

Figure 22-30.

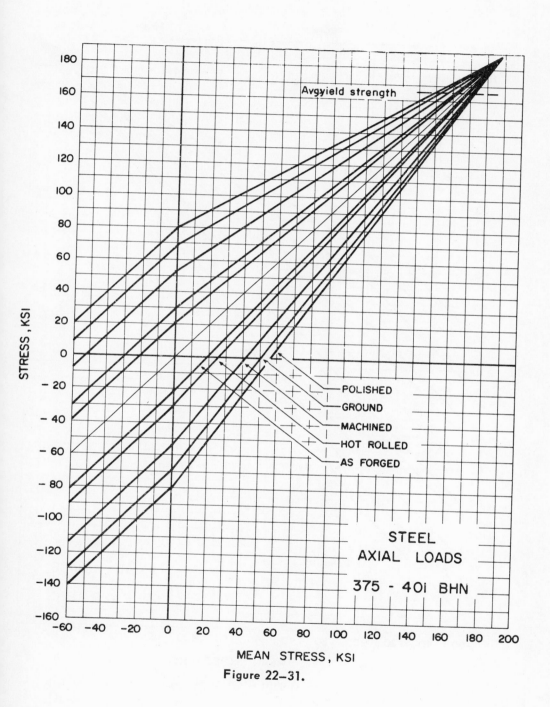

STRESS, KSI

Avgyield strength

POLISHED
GROUND
MACHINED
HOT ROLLED
AS FORGED

STEEL
AXIAL LOADS
375 - 40i BHN

MEAN STRESS, KSI

Figure 22–31.

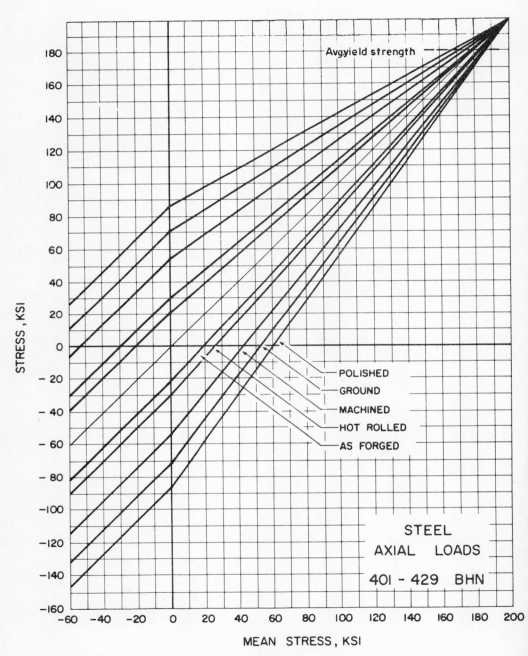

Figure 22-32.

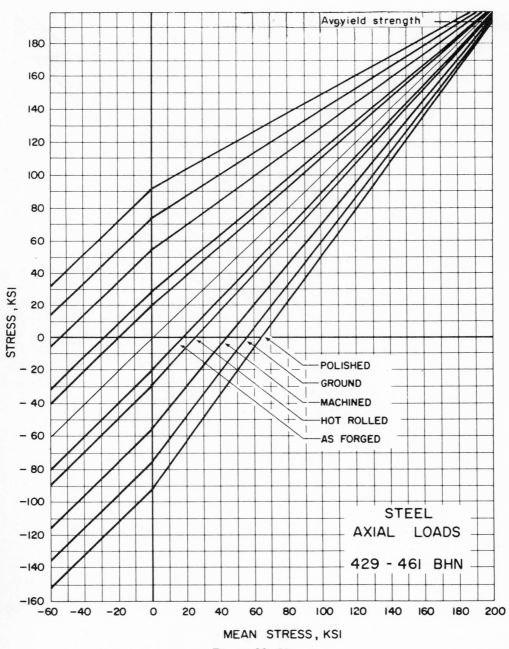

Figure 22–33.

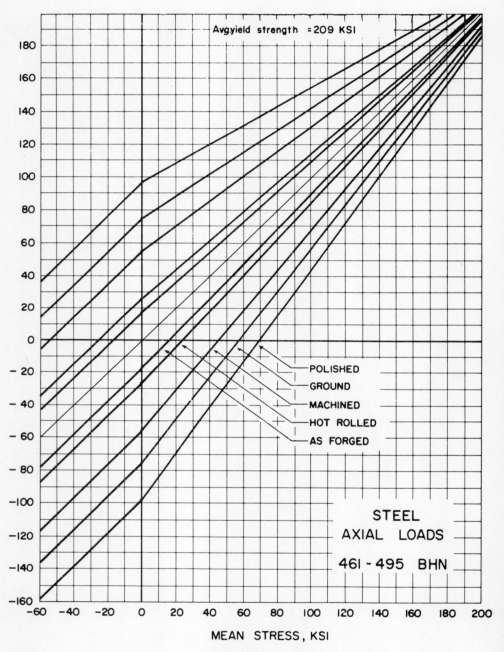

MEAN STRESS, KSI

Figure 22–34.

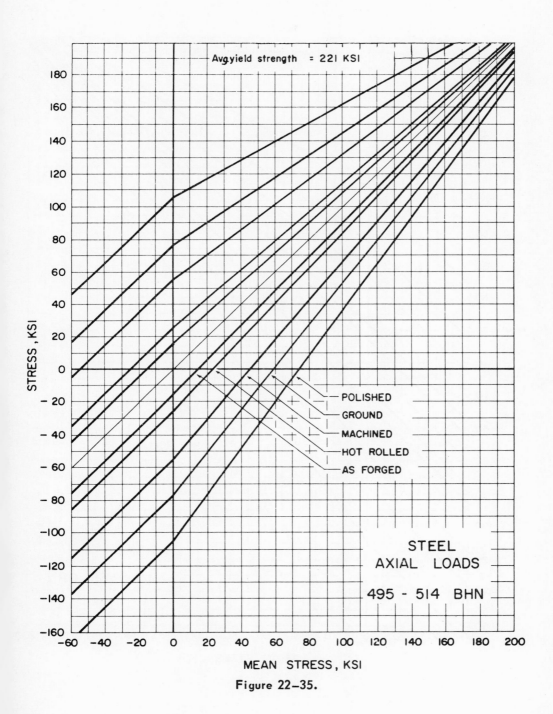

Figure 22-35.

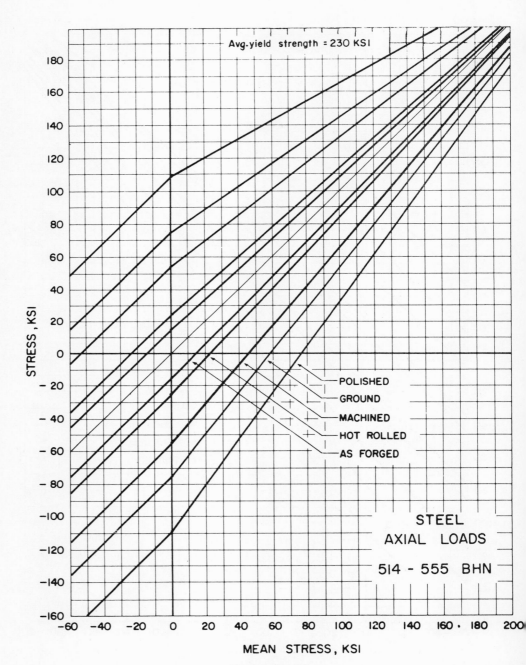

Figure 22–36.

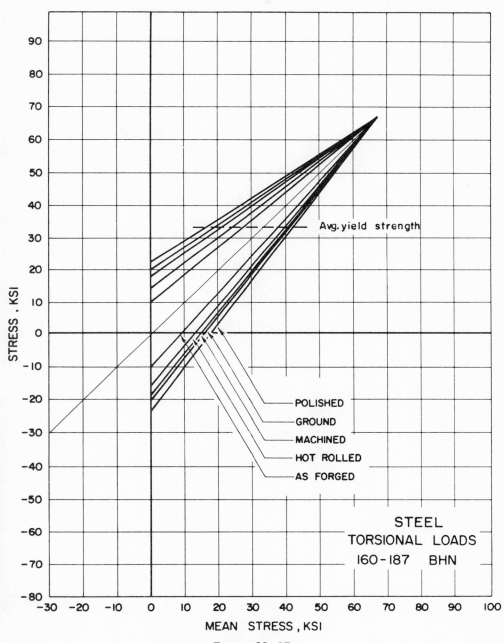

Figure 22–37.

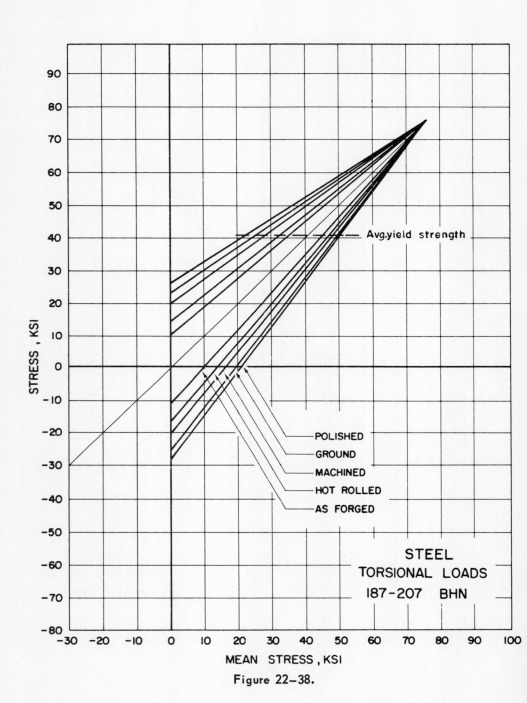

Figure 22-38.

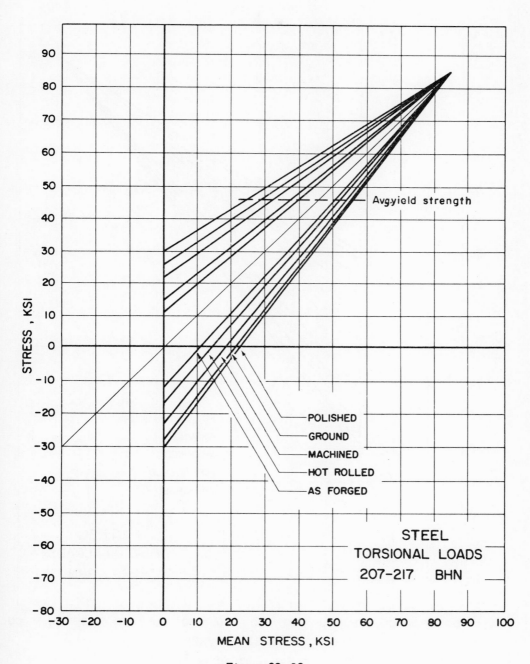

Figure 22-39.

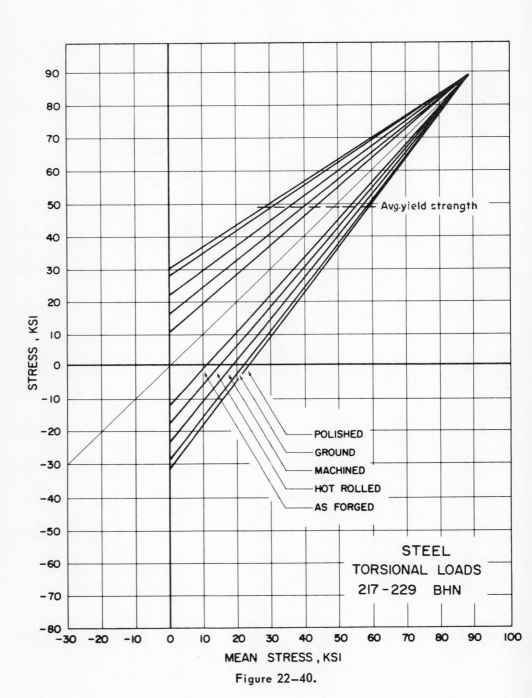

Figure 22—40.

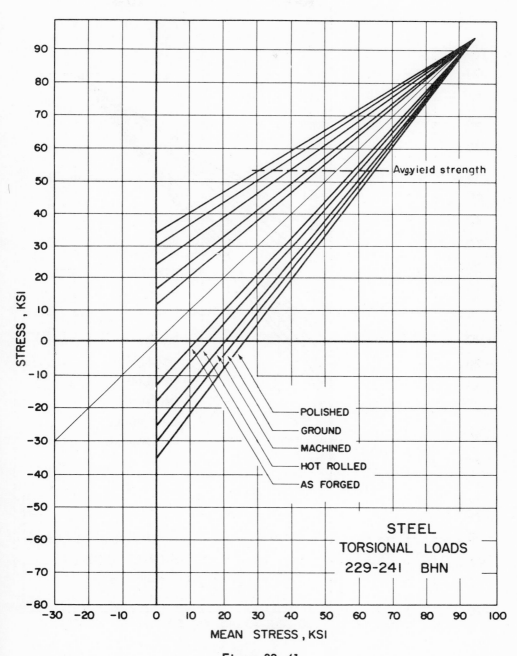

Figure 22-41.

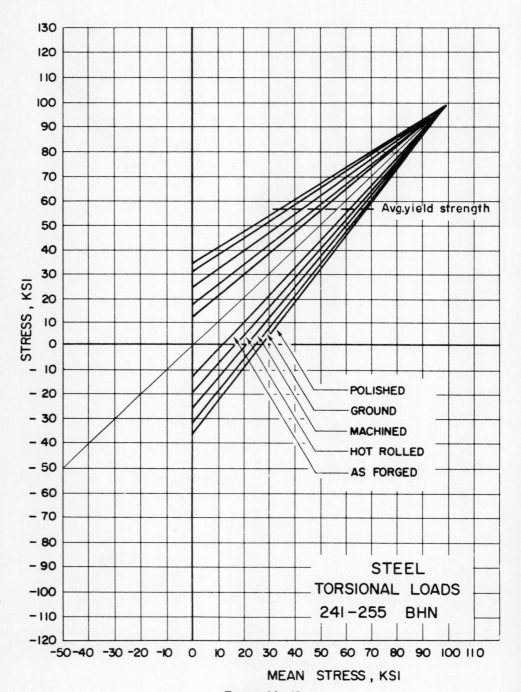

Figure 22-42.

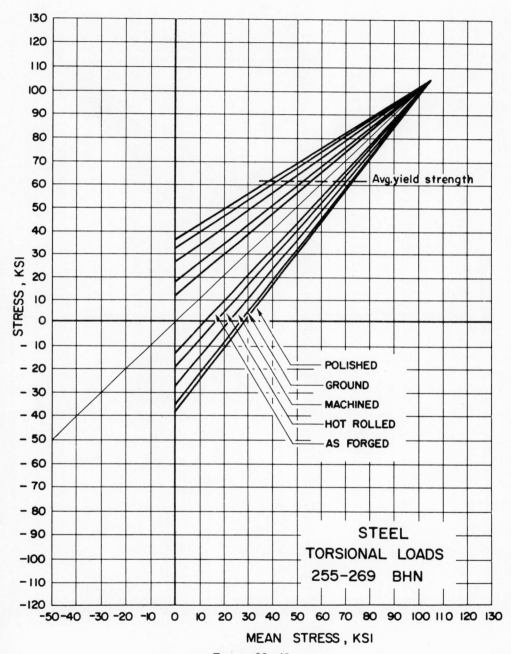

Figure 22–43.

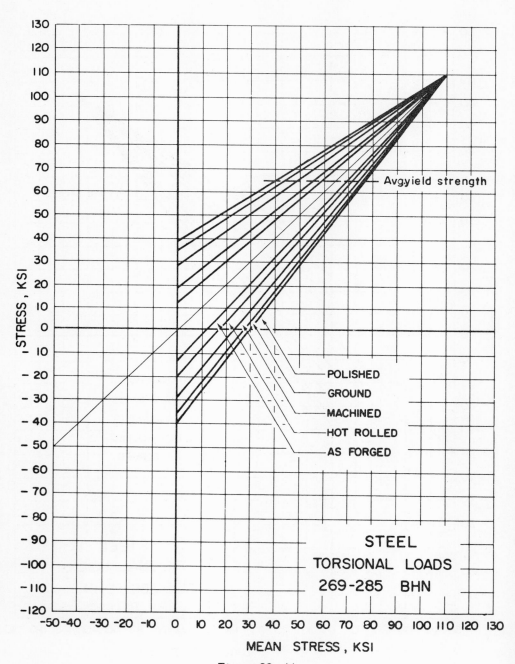

Figure 22—44.

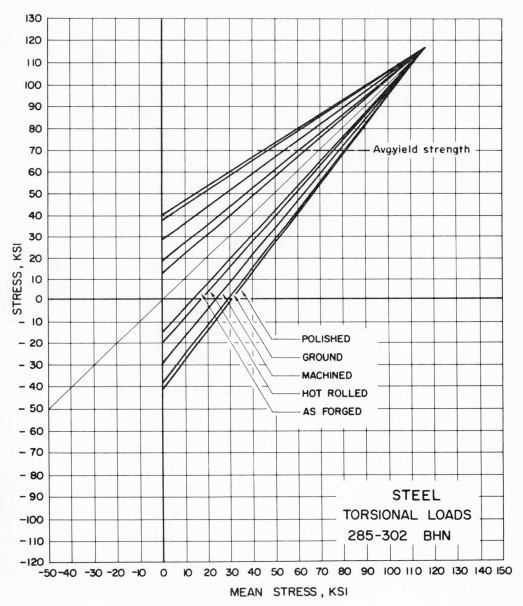

Figure 22—45.

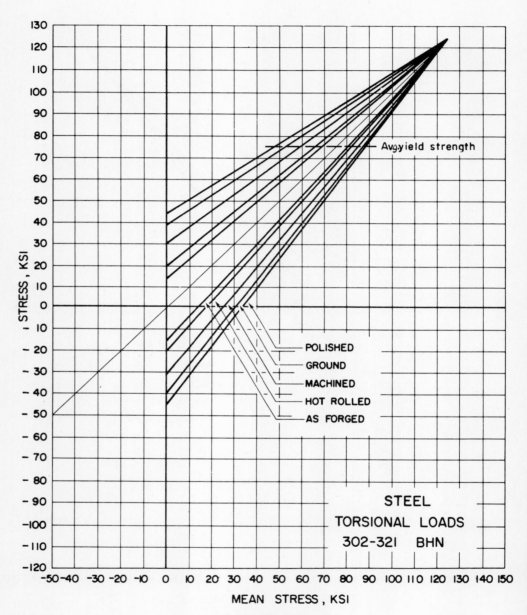

Figure 22–46.

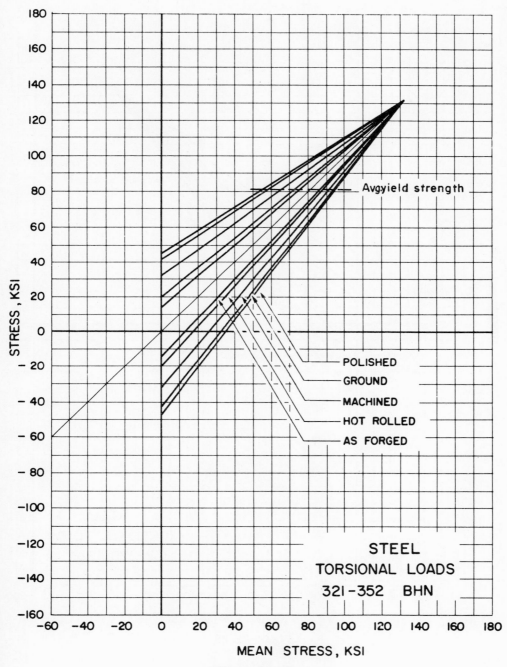

Figure 22–47.

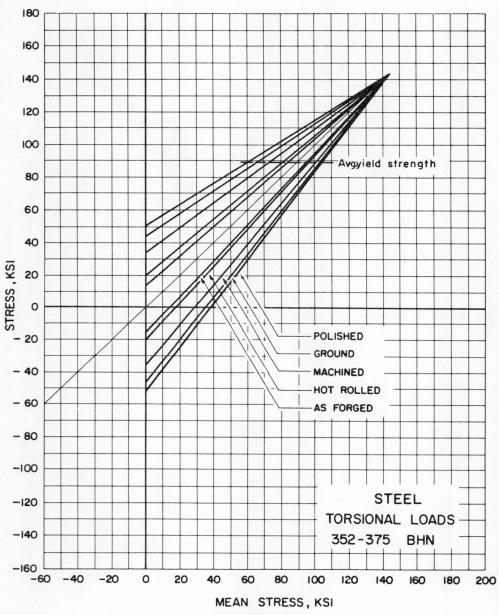

Figure 22-48.

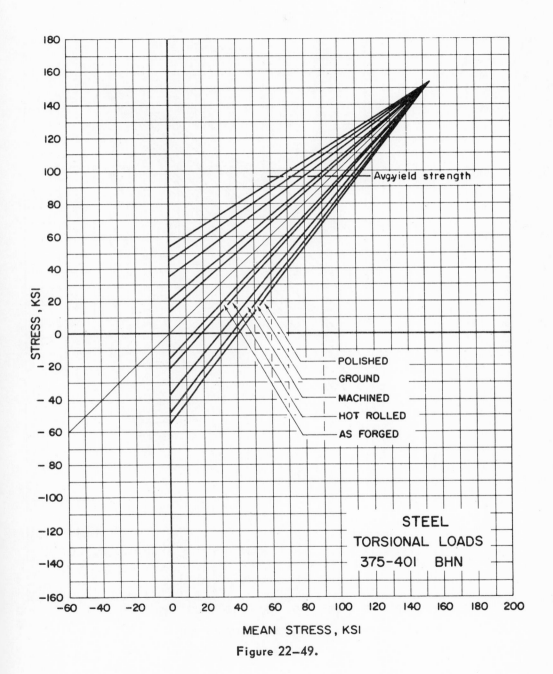

MEAN STRESS, KSI

Figure 22-49.

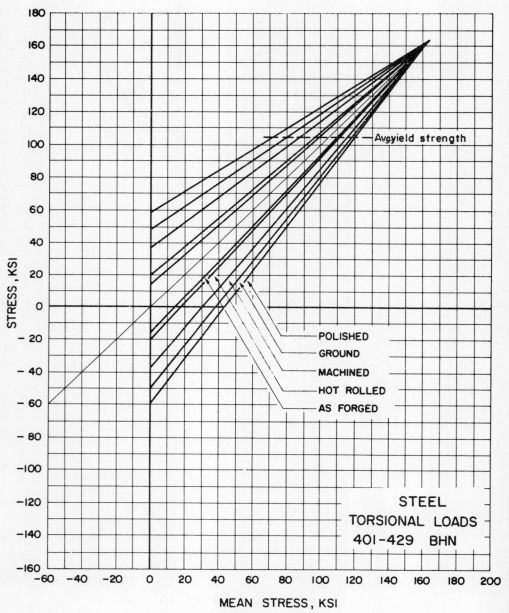

MEAN STRESS, KSI

Figure 22–50.

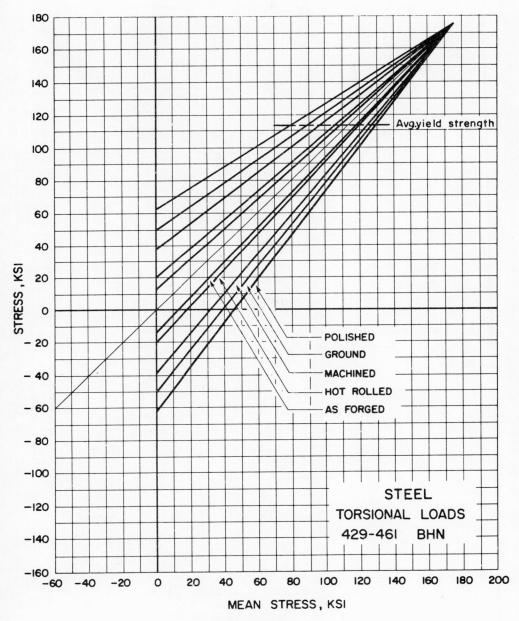

Figure 22—51.

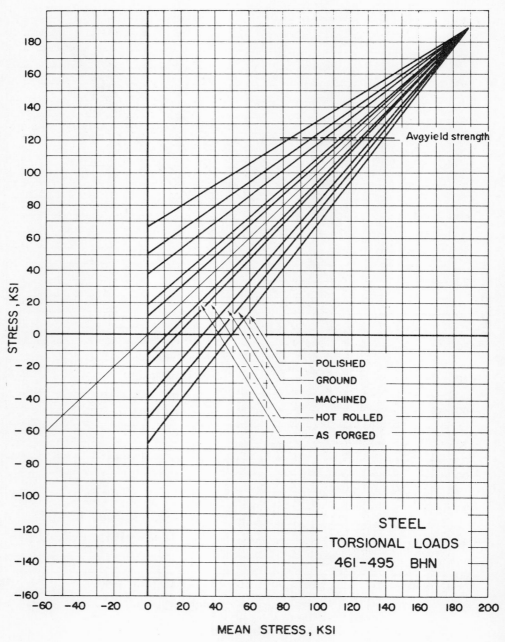

Figure 22-52.

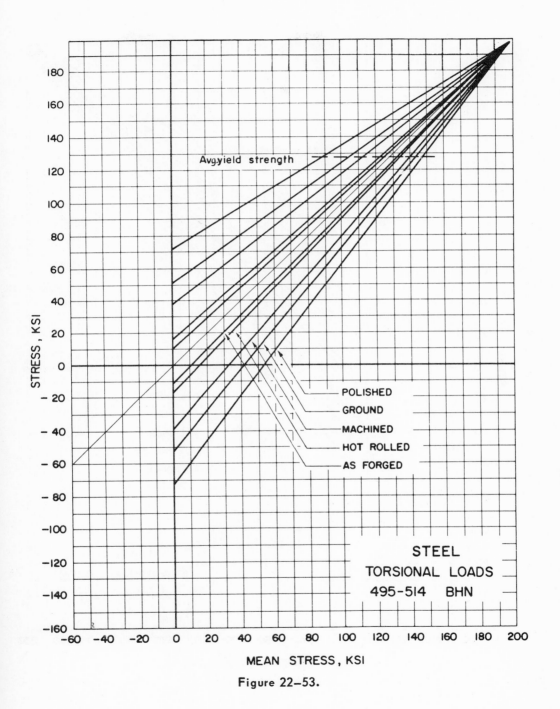

Figure 22-53.

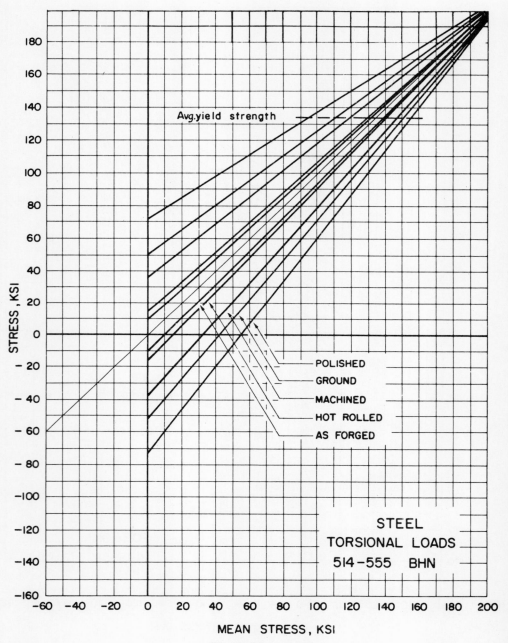

Figure 22-54.

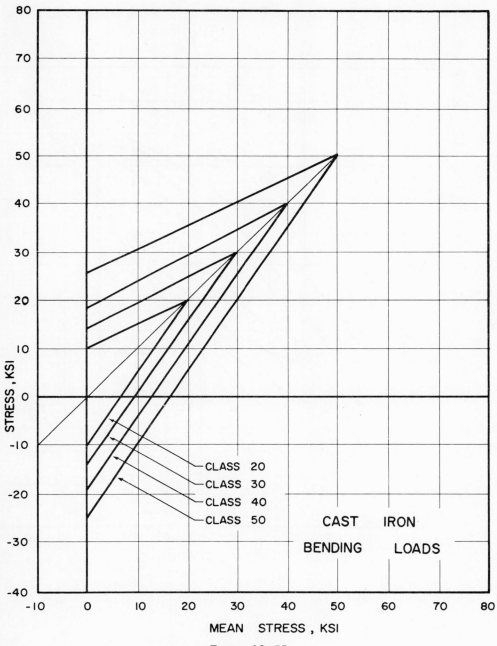

Figure 22–55.

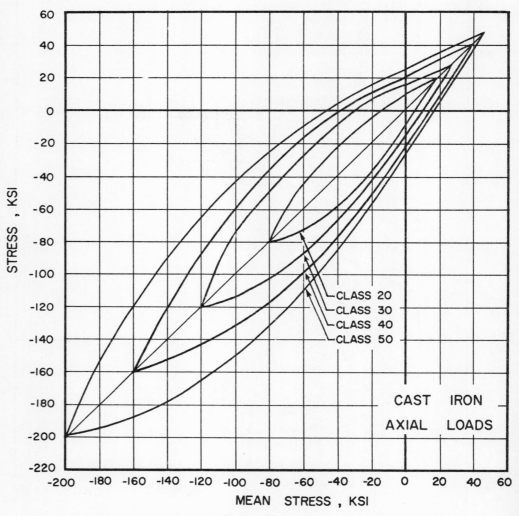

Figure 22–56.

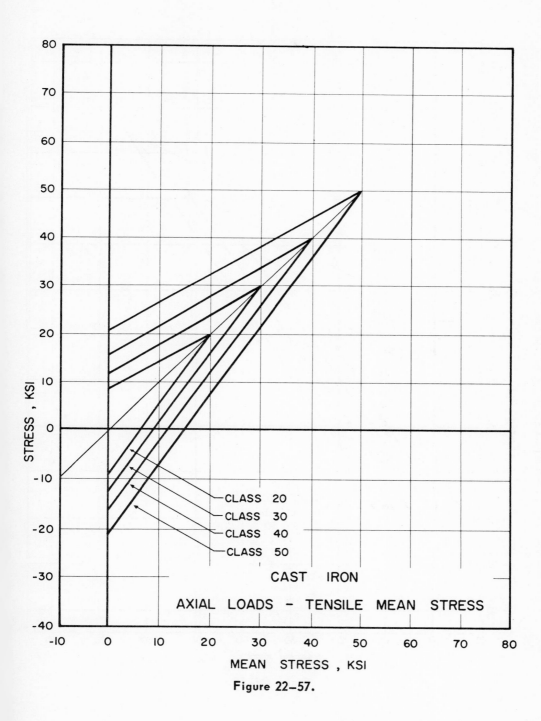

Figure 22–57.

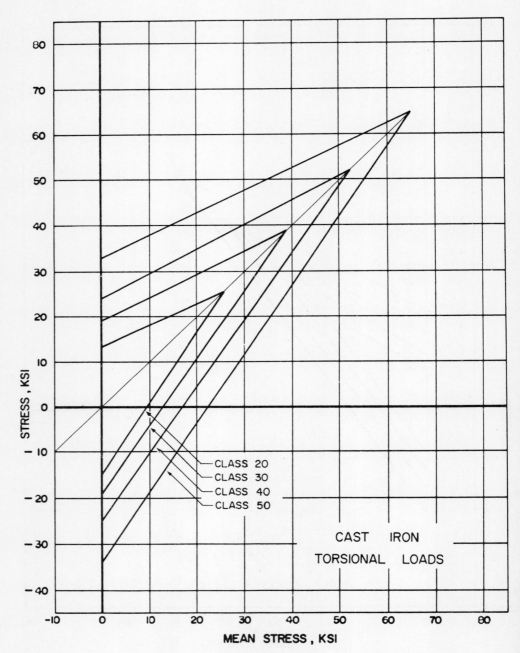

Figure 22–58.

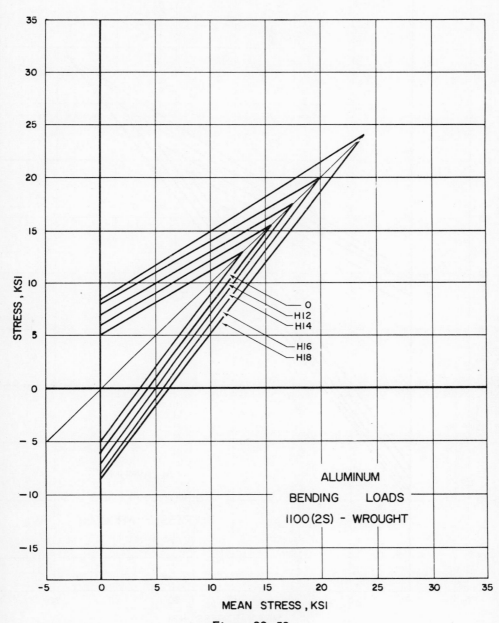

Figure 22–59.

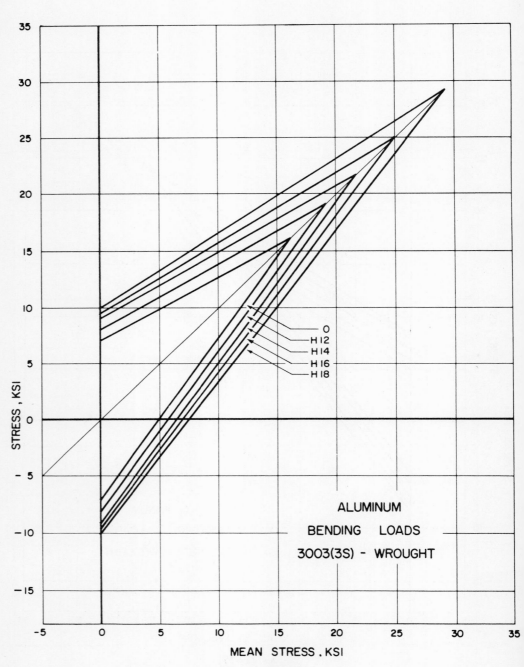

ALUMINUM

BENDING   LOADS

3003(3S) - WROUGHT

MEAN STRESS , KSI

Figure 22–60.

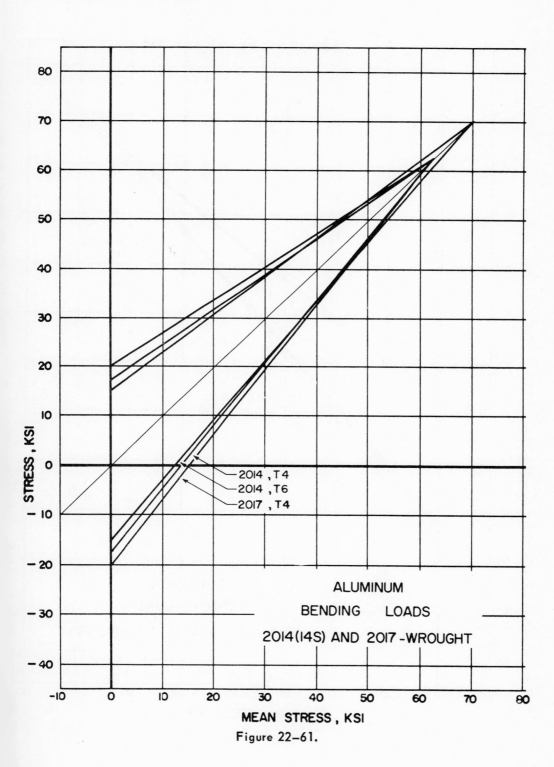

ALUMINUM

BENDING   LOADS

2014(14S) AND 2017-WROUGHT

Figure 22-61.

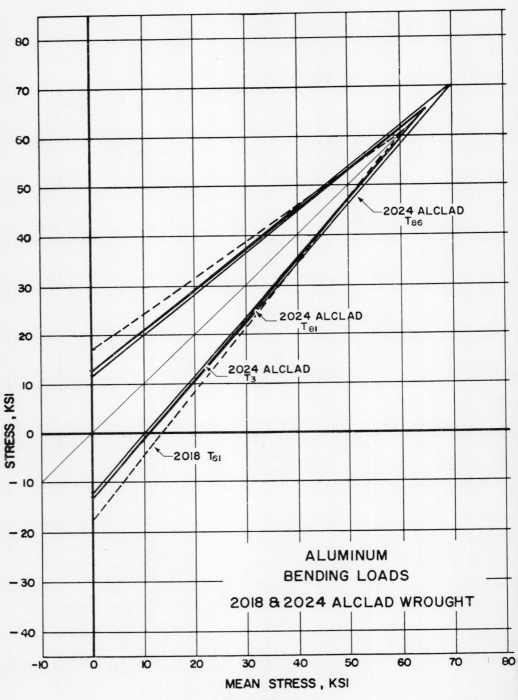

Figure 22–62.

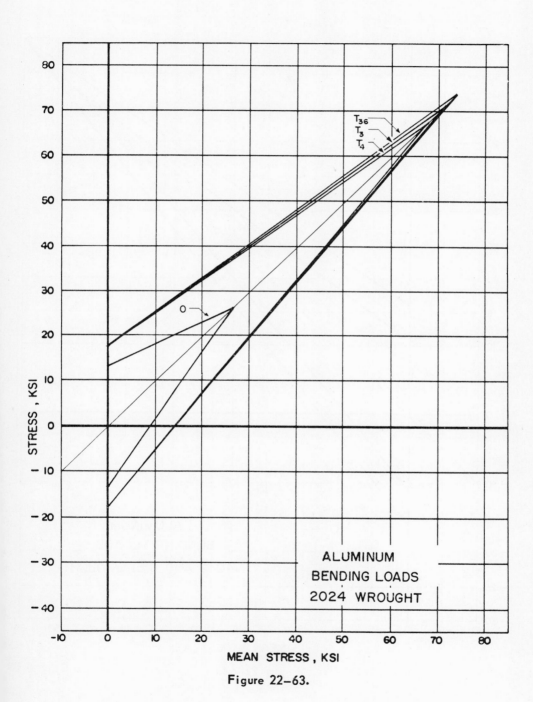

Figure 22-63.

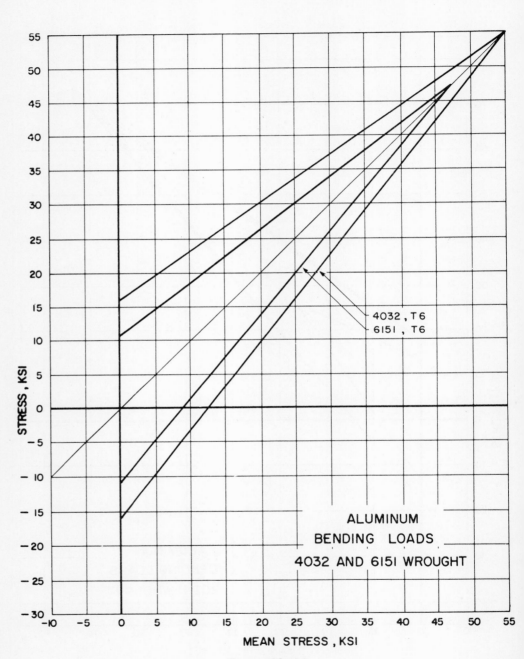

Figure 22-64.

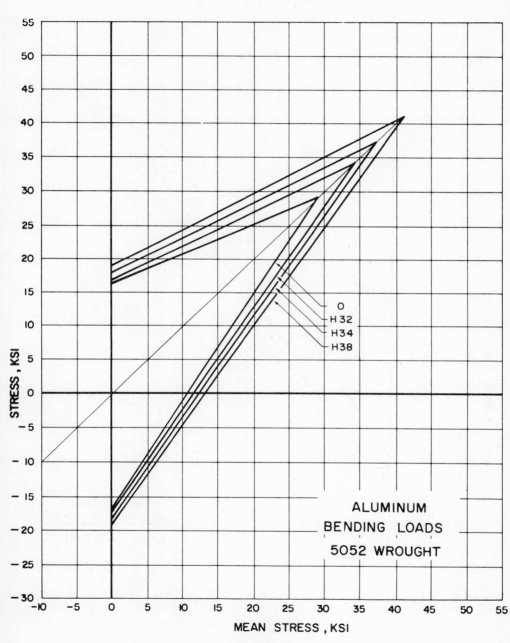

Figure 22–65.

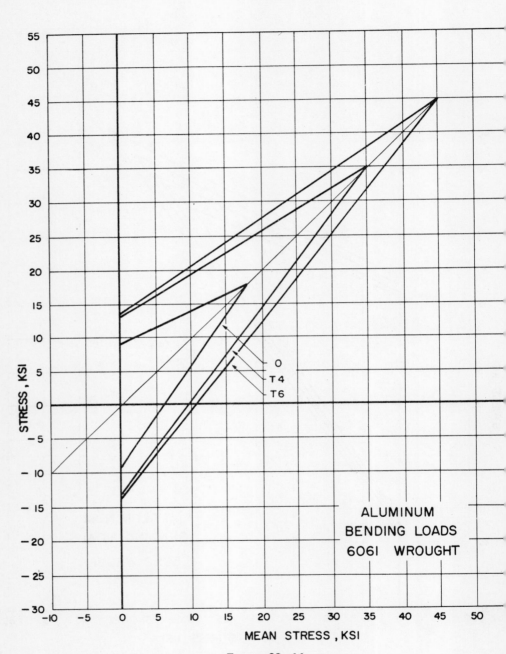

Figure 22–66.

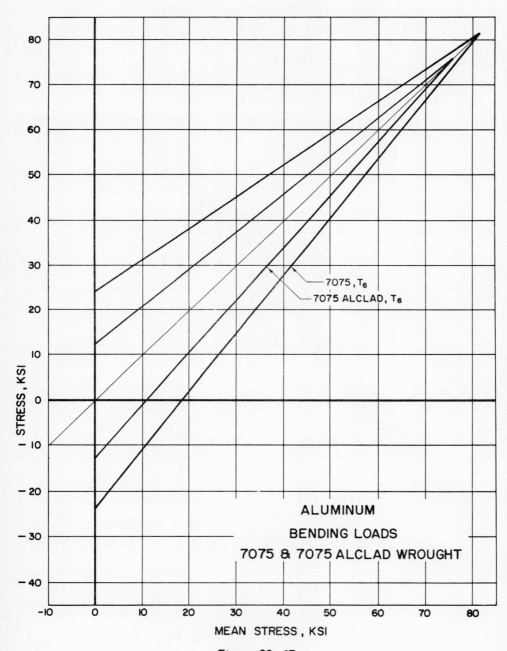

Figure 22–67.

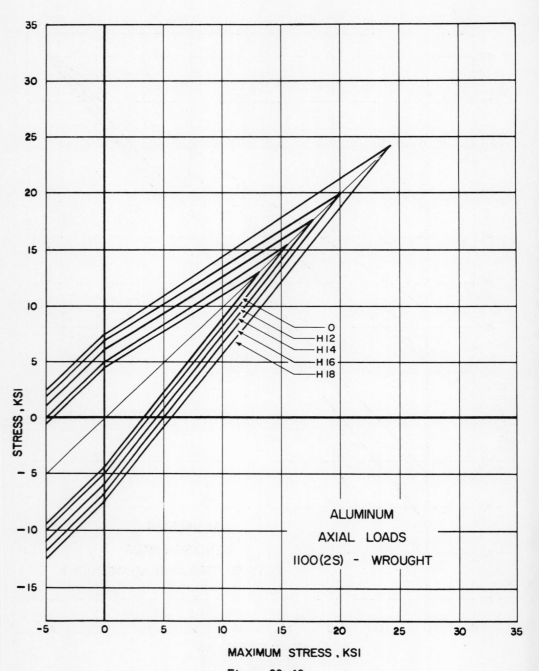

Figure 22–68.

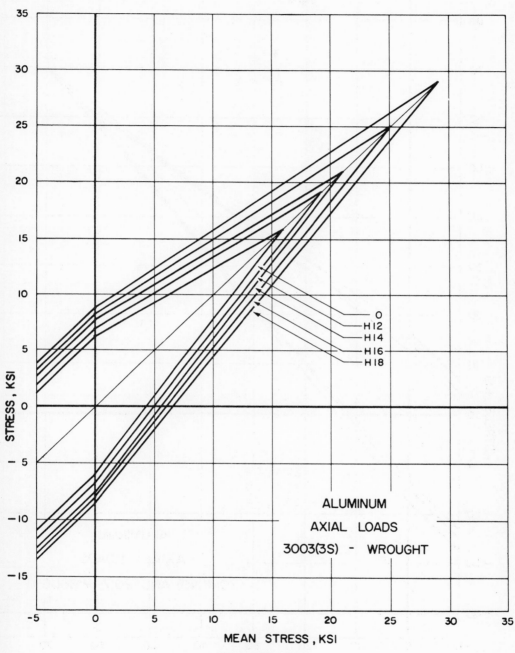

ALUMINUM

AXIAL LOADS

3003(3S) - WROUGHT

Figure 22–69.

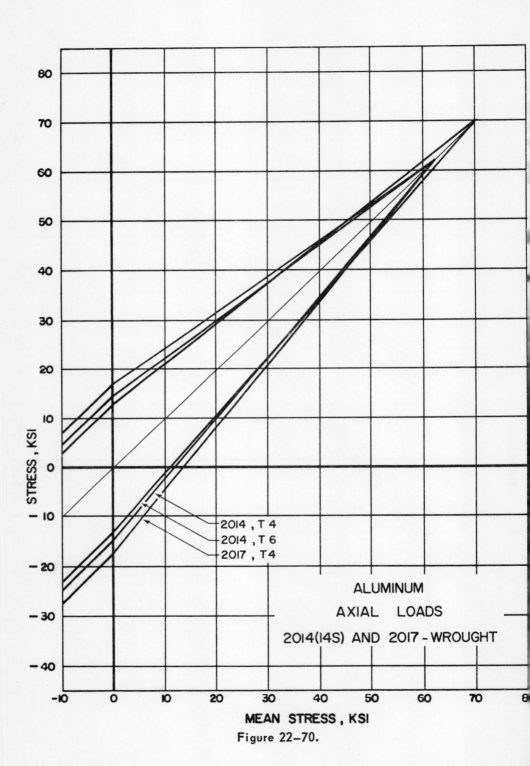

ALUMINUM

AXIAL LOADS

2014(14S) AND 2017 - WROUGHT

Figure 22-70.

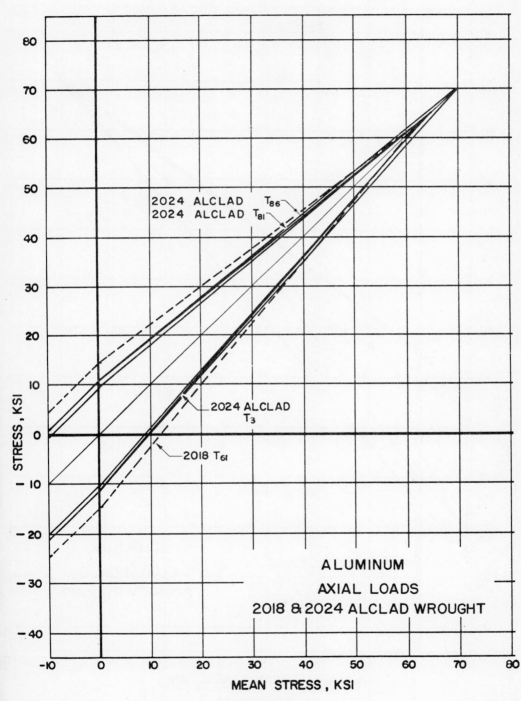

Figure 22–71.

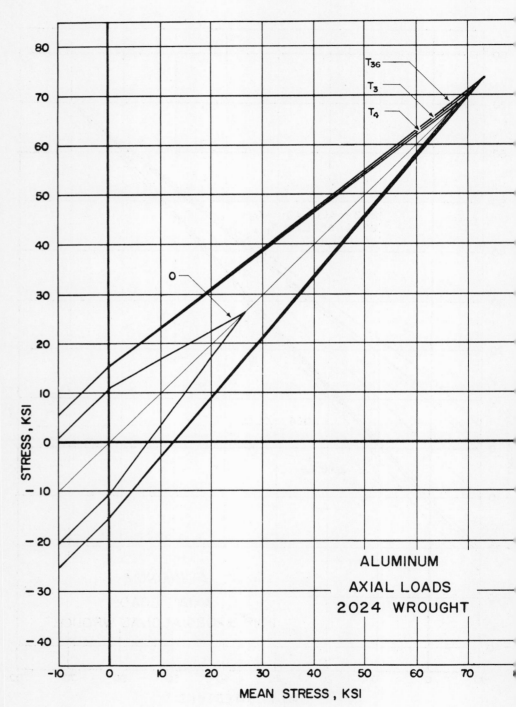

Figure 22-72.

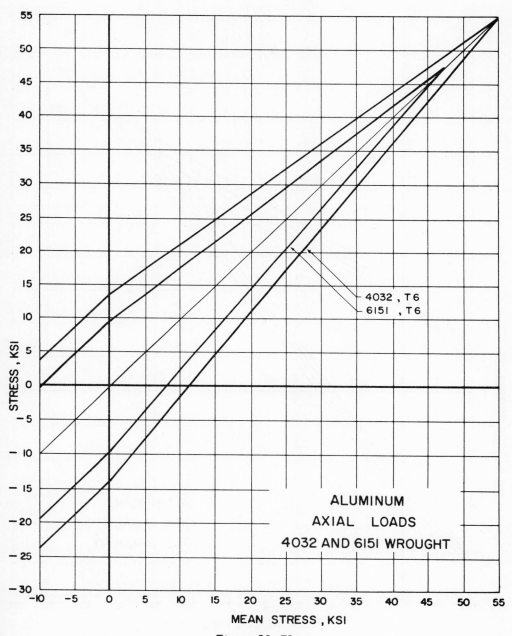

Figure 22-73.

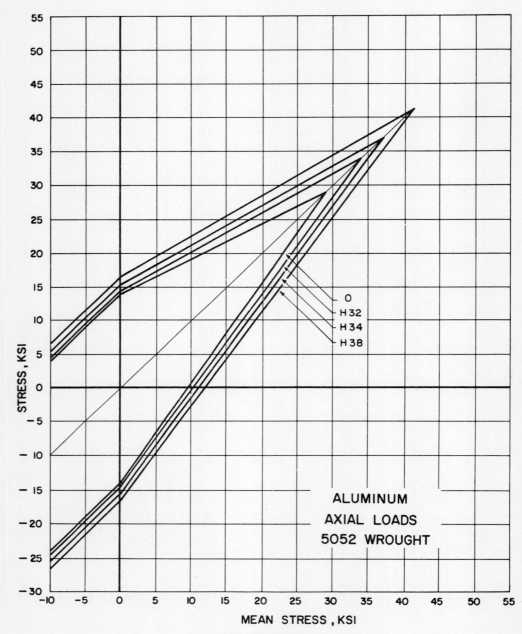

Figure 22-74.

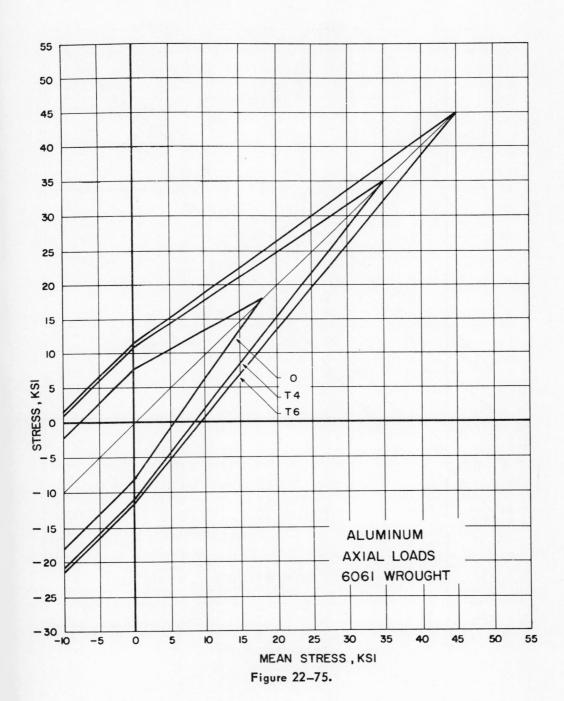

Figure 22–75.

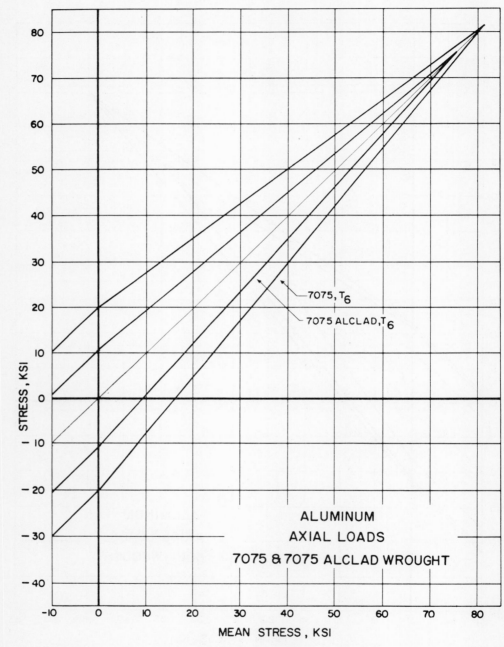

Figure 22–76.

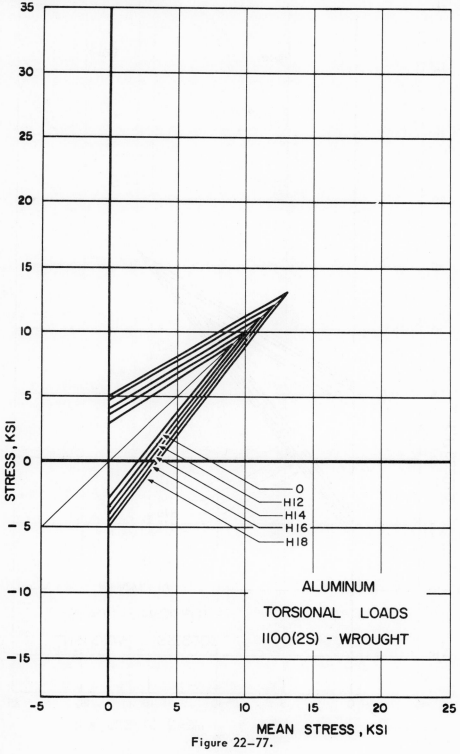

Figure 22-77.

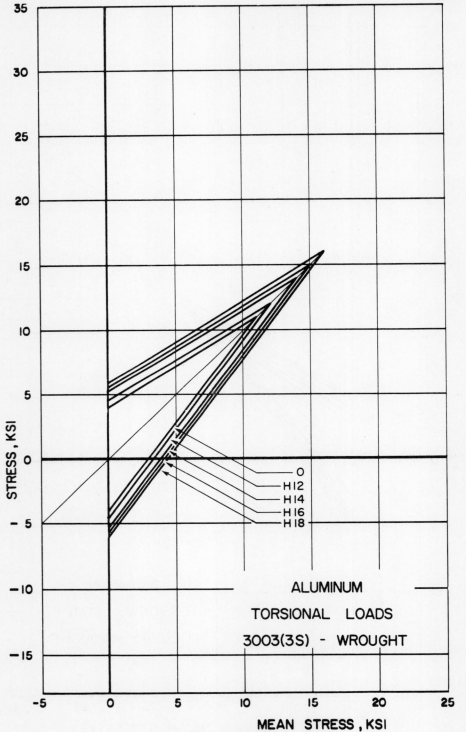

ALUMINUM

TORSIONAL LOADS

3003(3S) - WROUGHT

STRESS, KSI

MEAN STRESS, KSI

Figure 22—78.

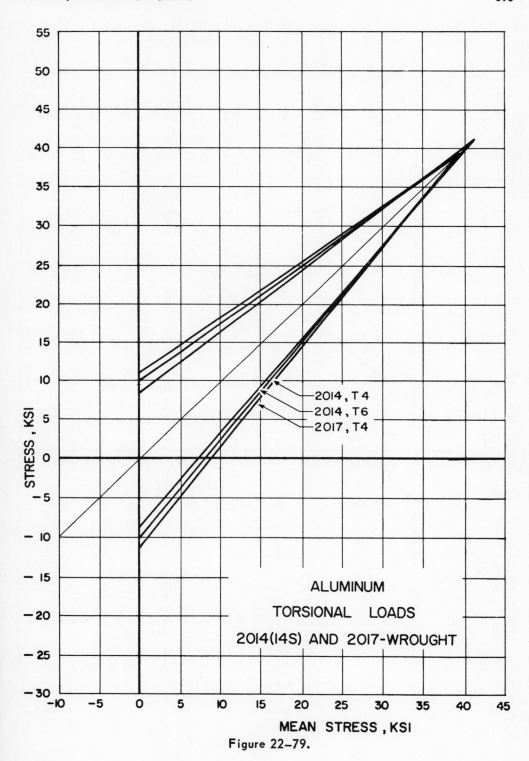

ALUMINUM

TORSIONAL LOADS

2014(14S) AND 2017-WROUGHT

2014, T4
2014, T6
2017, T4

STRESS , KSI

MEAN STRESS , KSI

Figure 22–79.

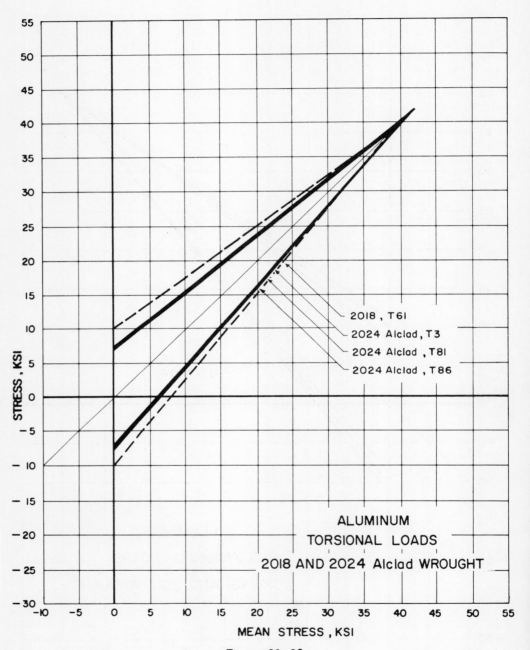

Figure 22–80.

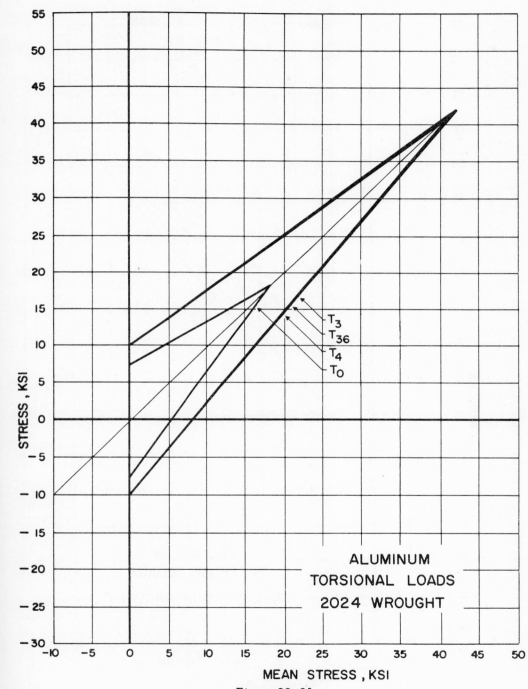

Figure 22–81.

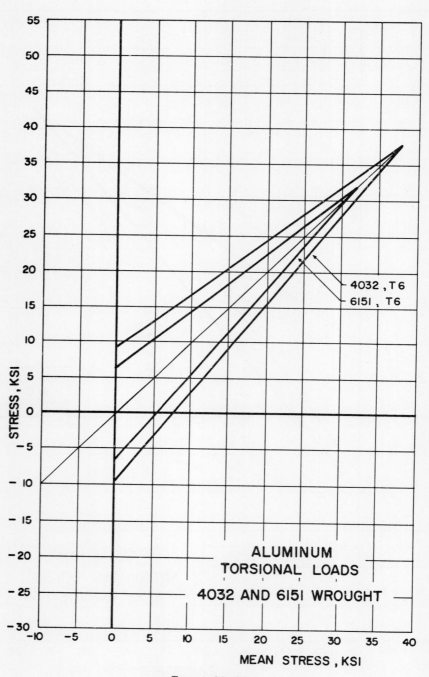

Figure 22–82.

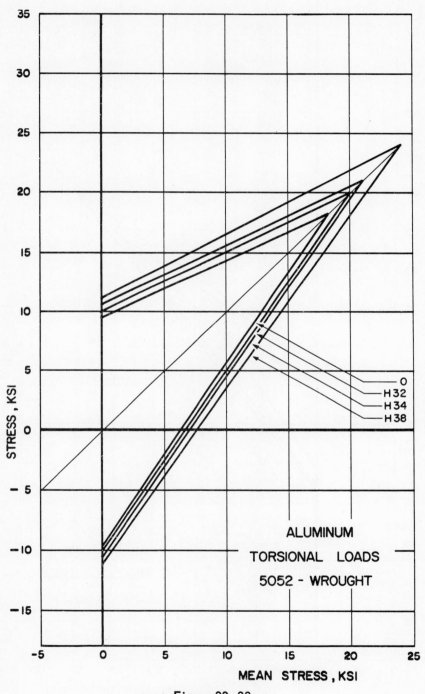

ALUMINUM

TORSIONAL LOADS

5052 - WROUGHT

Figure 22-83.

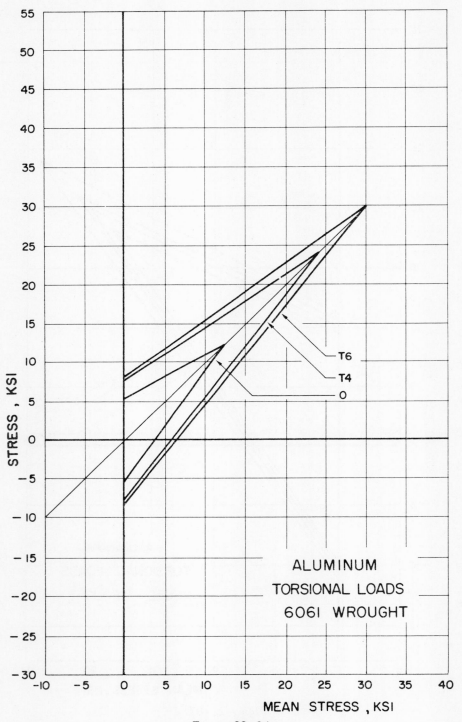

Figure 22—84.

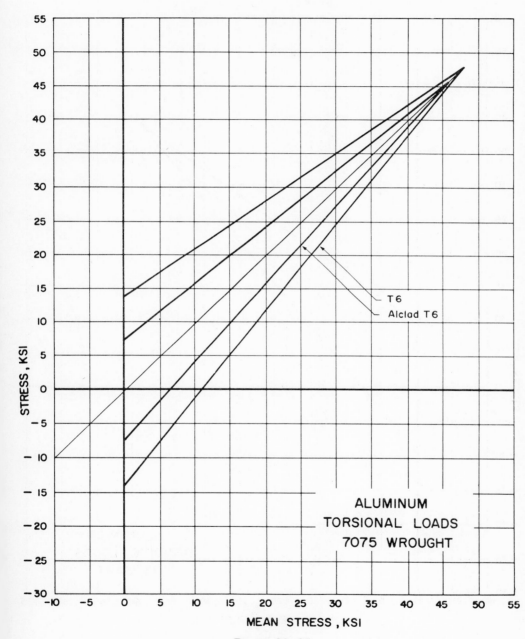

Figure 22–85.

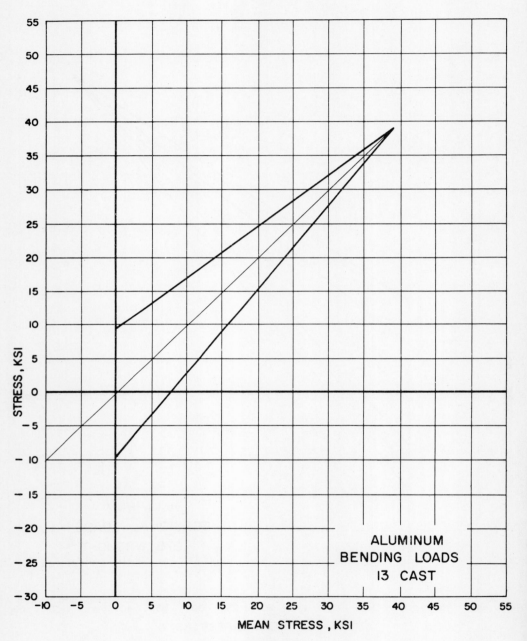

Figure 22–86.

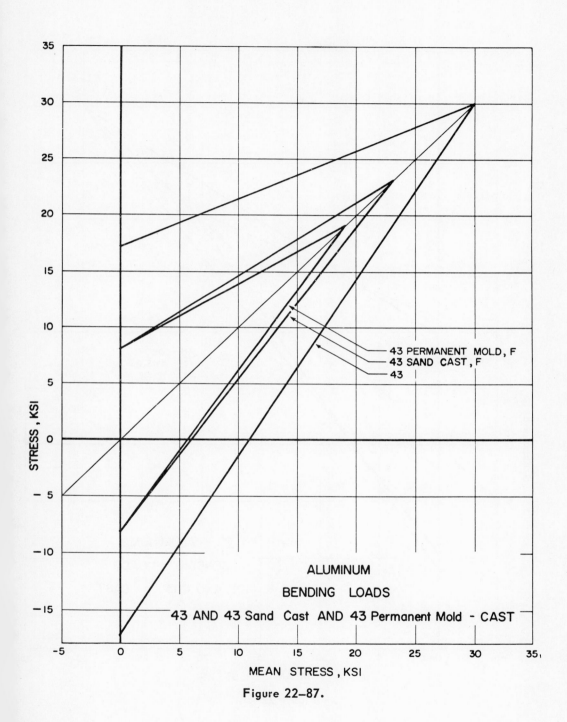

Figure 22-87.

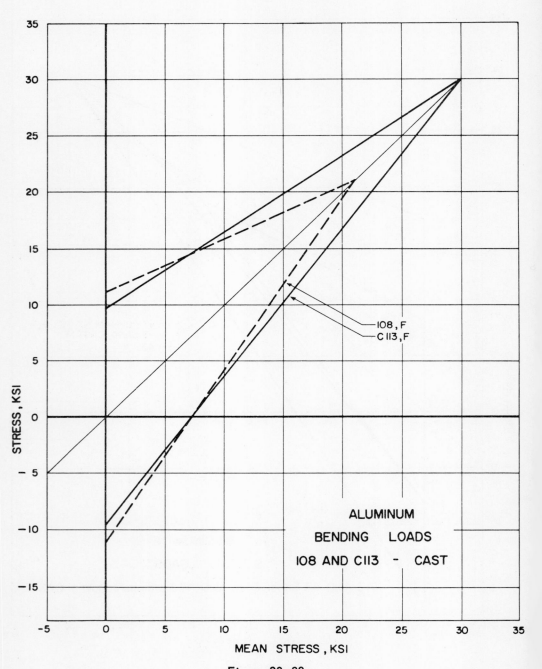

ALUMINUM

BENDING   LOADS

108 AND C113 - CAST

MEAN STRESS, KSI

Figure 22–88.

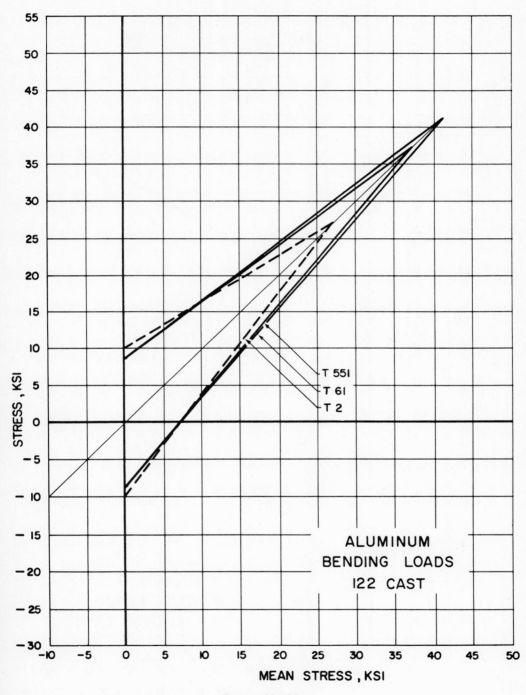

Figure 22–89.

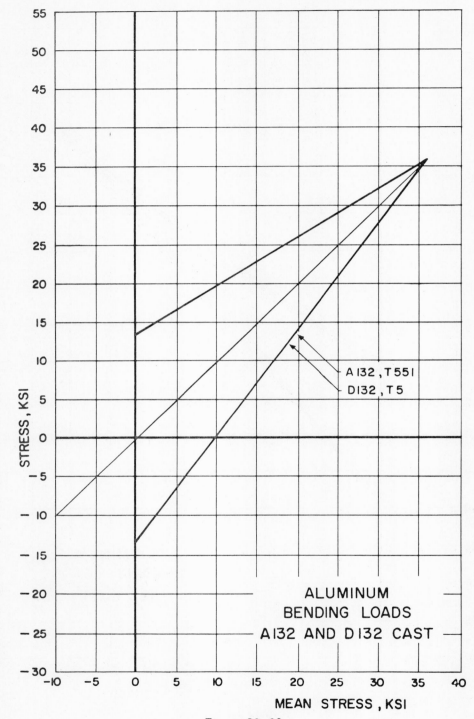

ALUMINUM
BENDING LOADS
A132 AND D132 CAST

A132, T551
D132, T5

STRESS, KSI

MEAN STRESS, KSI

Figure 22-90.

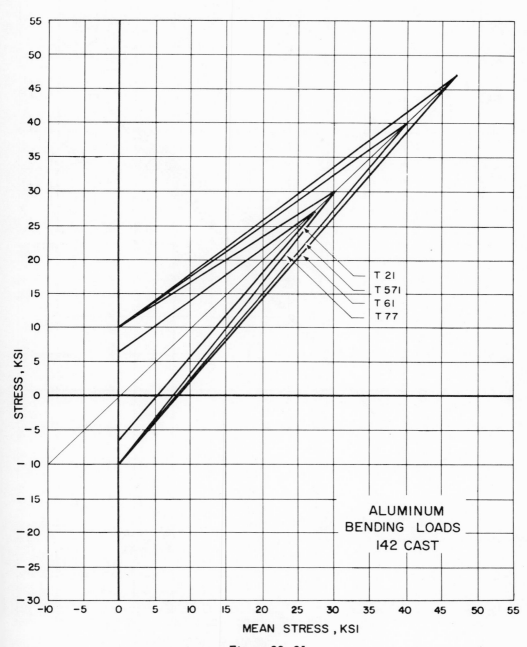

Figure 22-91.

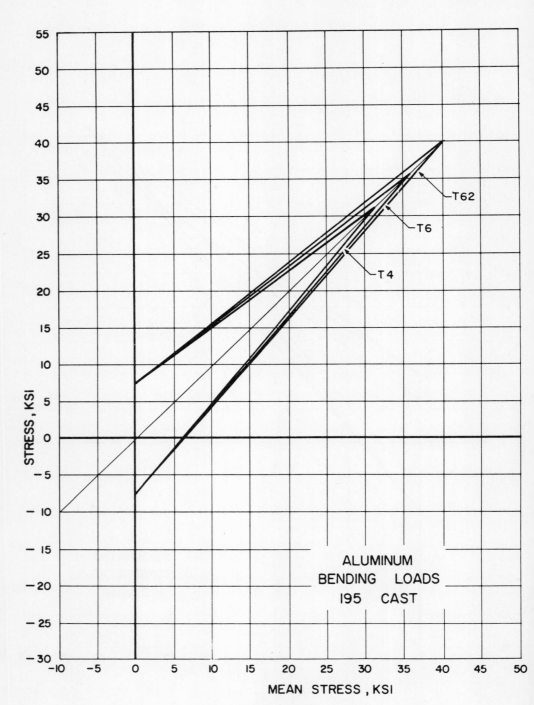

Figure 22–92.

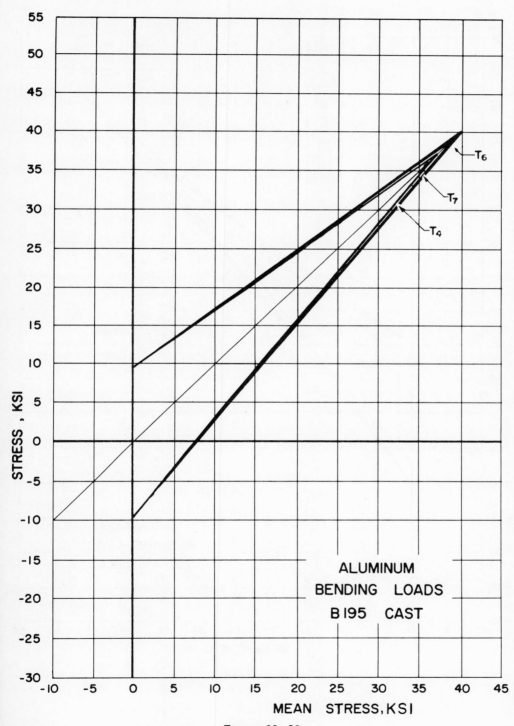

Figure 22-93.

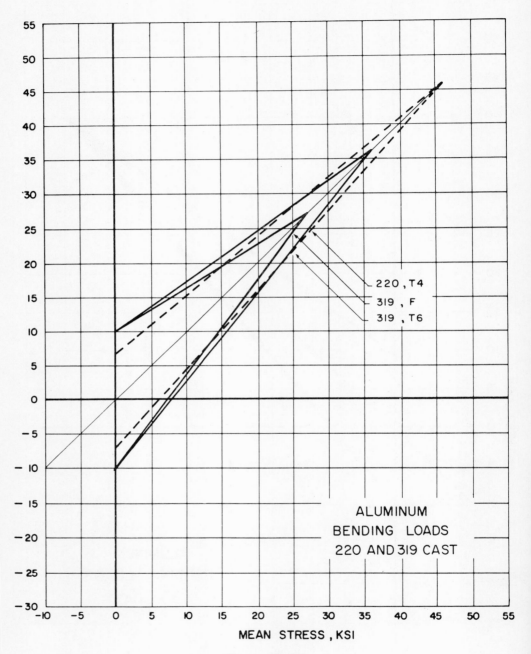

Figure 22-94.

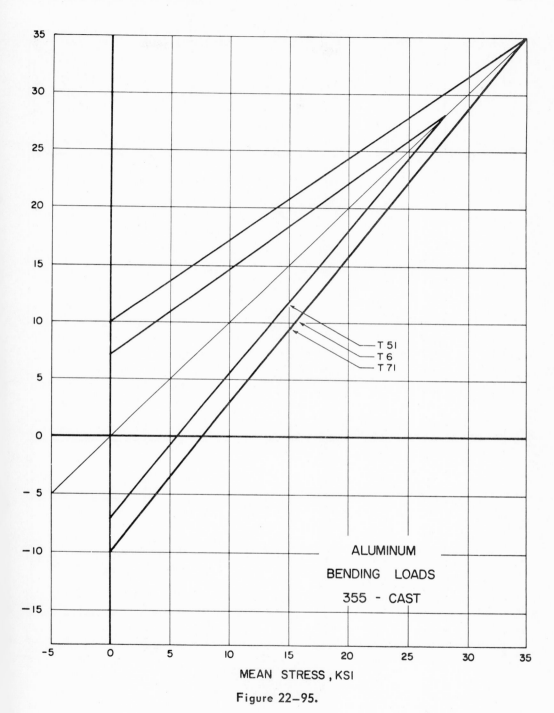

MEAN STRESS, KSI

Figure 22-95.

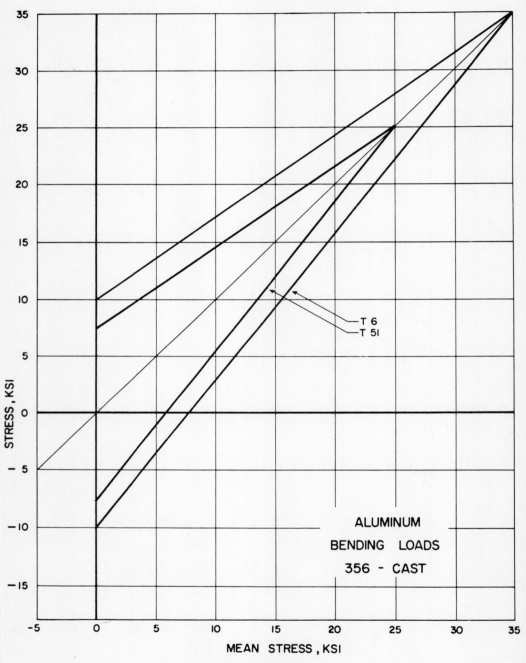

Figure 22–96.

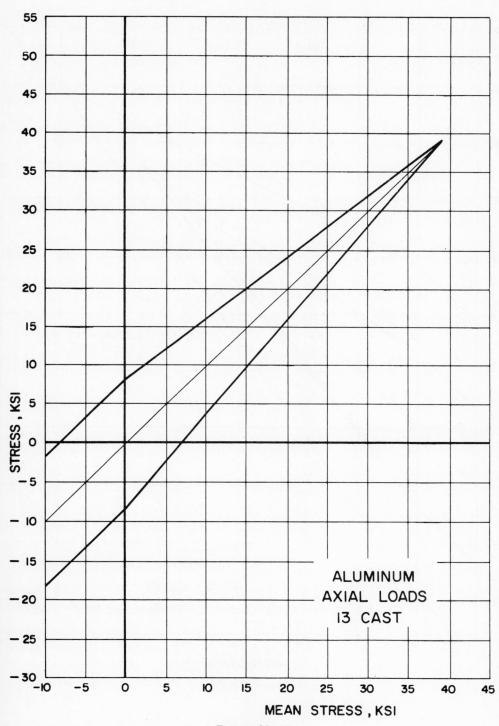

Figure 22-97.

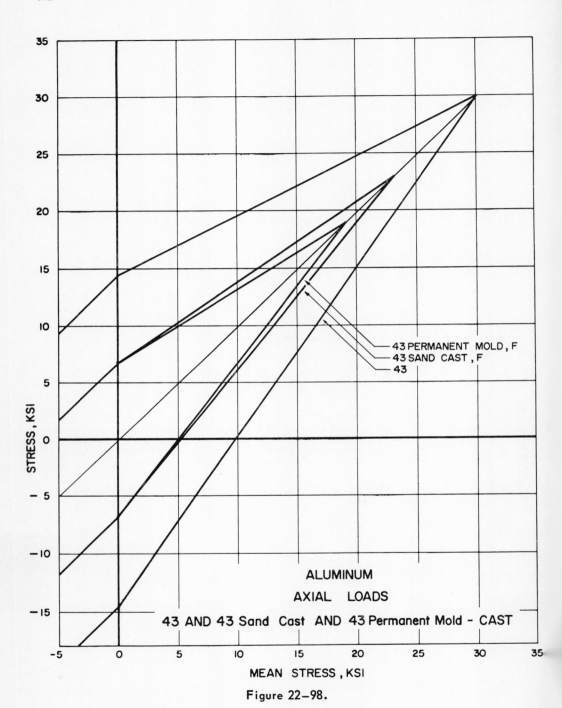

43 PERMANENT MOLD, F
43 SAND CAST , F
43

ALUMINUM

AXIAL   LOADS

43 AND 43 Sand Cast AND 43 Permanent Mold - CAST

MEAN STRESS , KSI

STRESS , KSI

Figure 22–98.

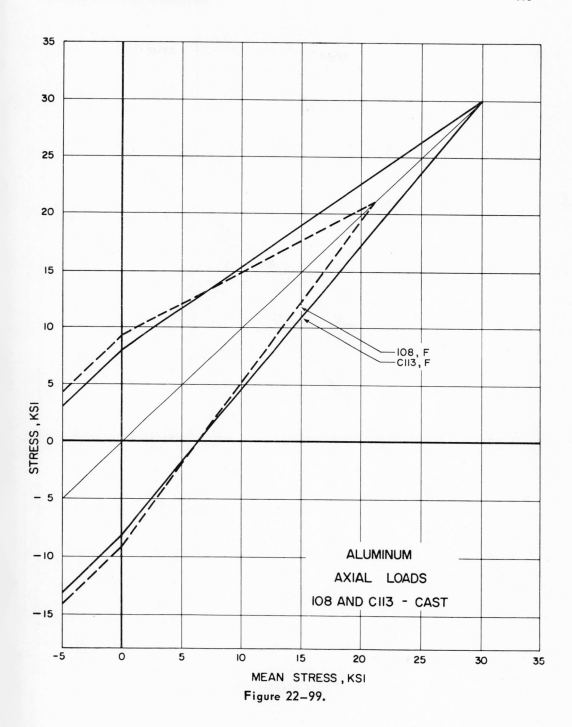

ALUMINUM

AXIAL LOADS

108 AND C113 - CAST

108, F
C113, F

STRESS, KSI

MEAN STRESS, KSI

Figure 22-99.

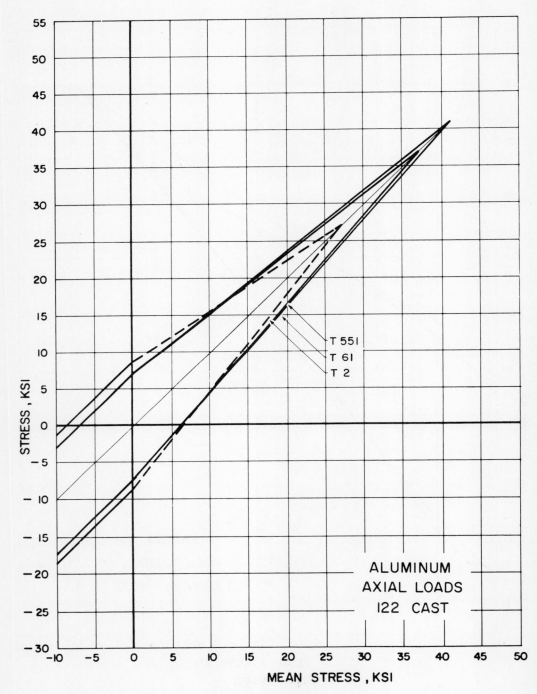

Figure 22-100.

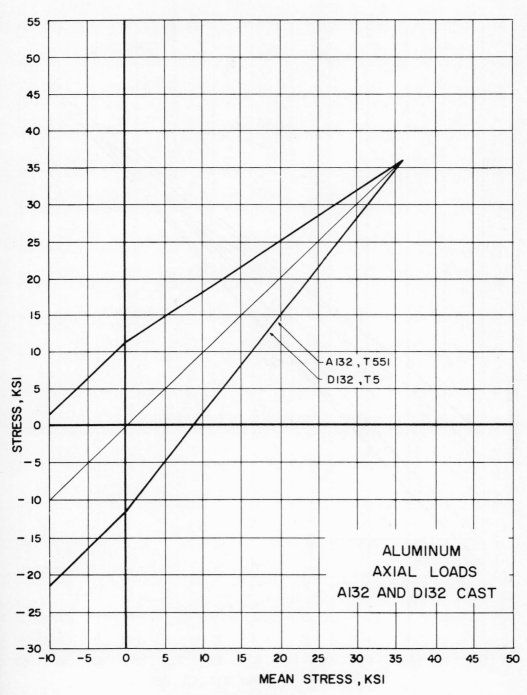

A 132 , T 551
D 132 , T 5

STRESS , KSI

MEAN STRESS , KSI

ALUMINUM
AXIAL LOADS
A132 AND D132 CAST

Figure 22—101.

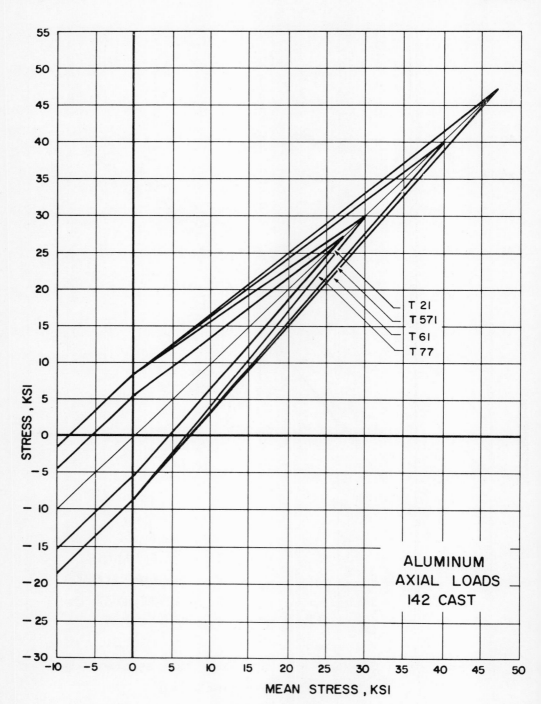

Figure 22-102.

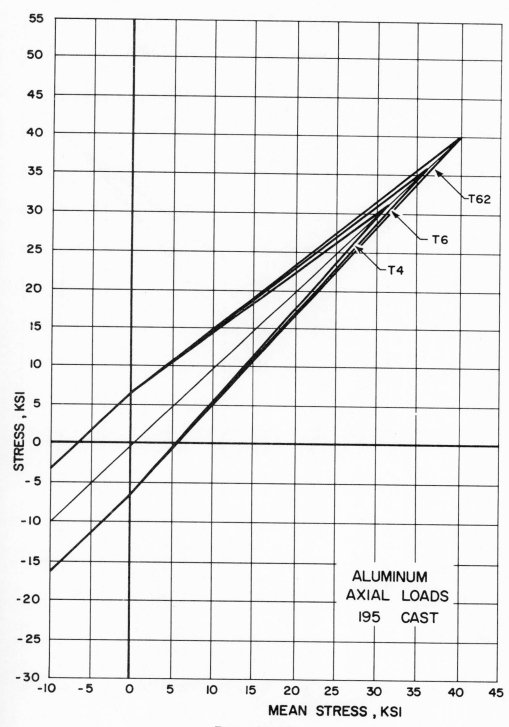

Figure 22-103.

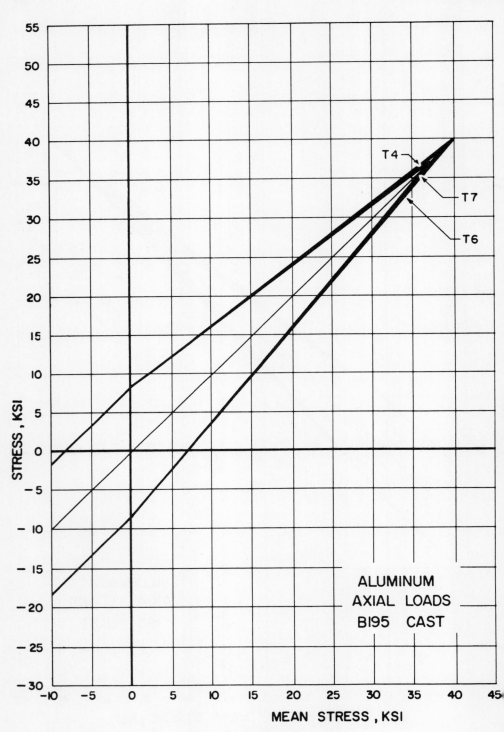

Figure 22-104.

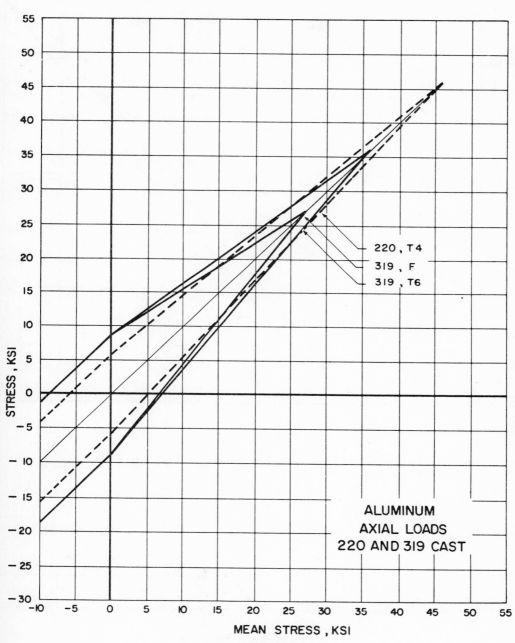

220 , T4
319 , F
319 , T6

ALUMINUM
AXIAL LOADS
220 AND 319 CAST

STRESS , KSI

MEAN STRESS , KSI

Figure 22-105.

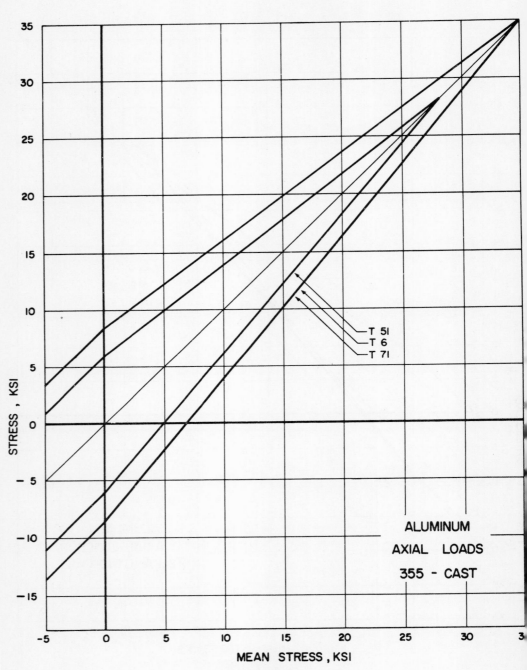

Figure 22–106.

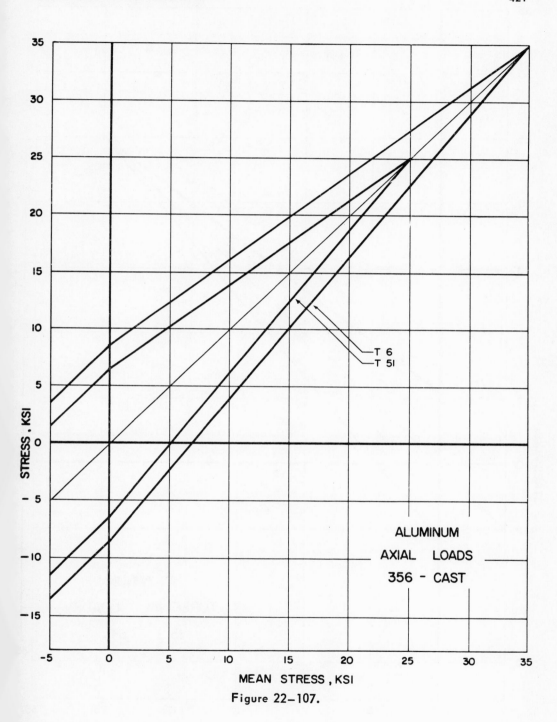

Figure 22–107.

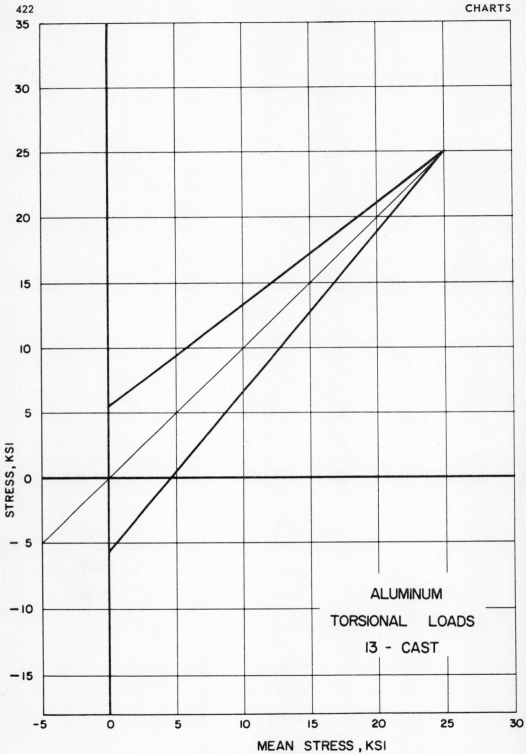

Figure 22-108.

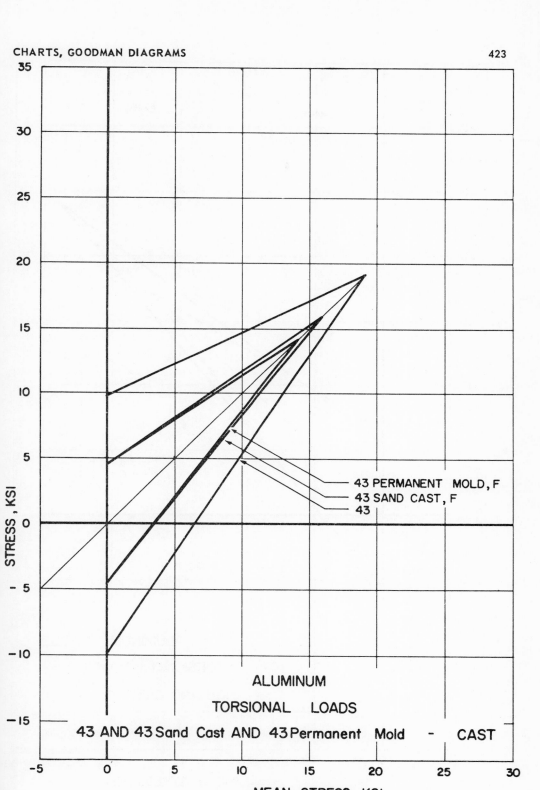

Figure 22-109.

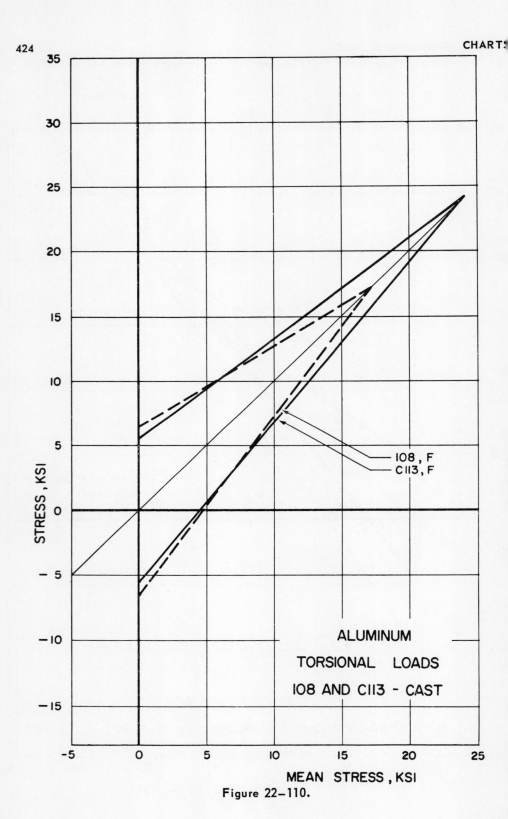

Figure 22–110.

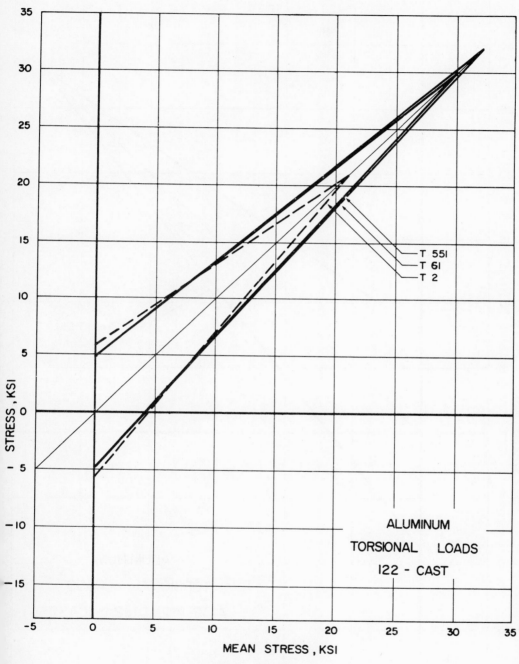

T 551
T 61
T 2

ALUMINUM
TORSIONAL LOADS
122 - CAST

- STRESS, KSI

MEAN STRESS, KSI

Figure 22–111.

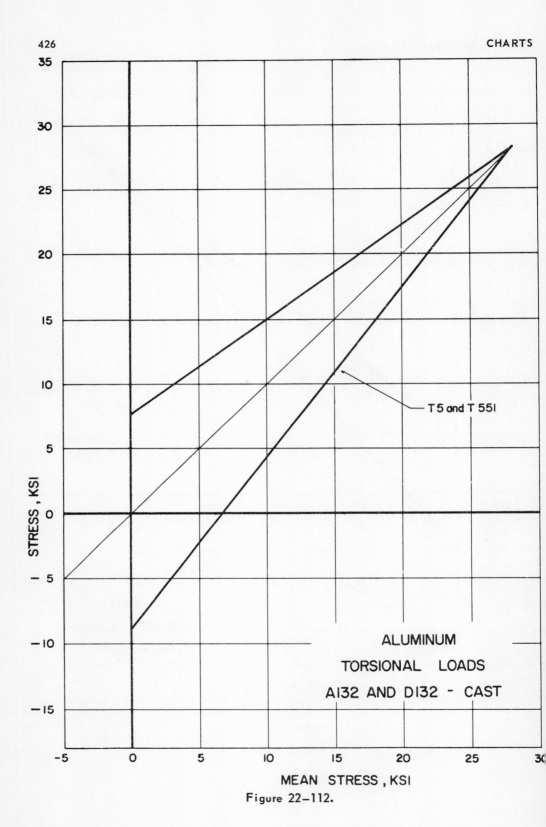

T 5 and T 551

ALUMINUM

TORSIONAL LOADS

A132 AND D132 - CAST

MEAN STRESS , KSI

Figure 22-112.

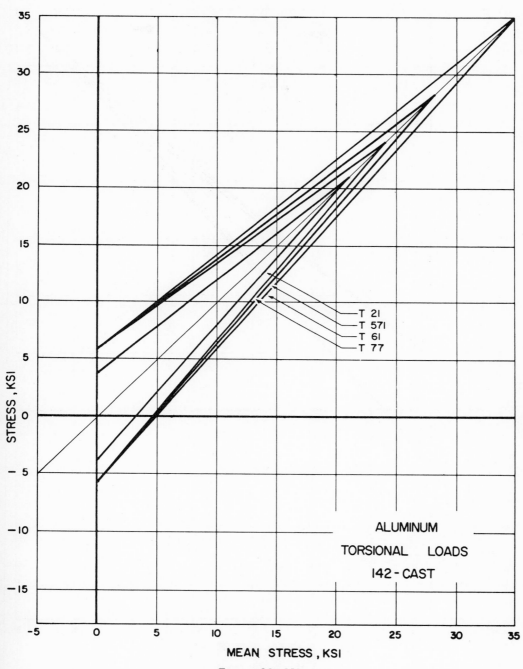

Figure 22–113.

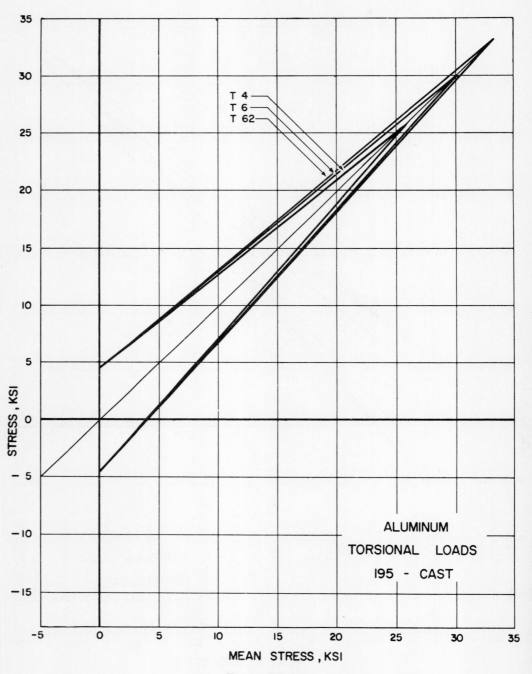

Figure 22–114.

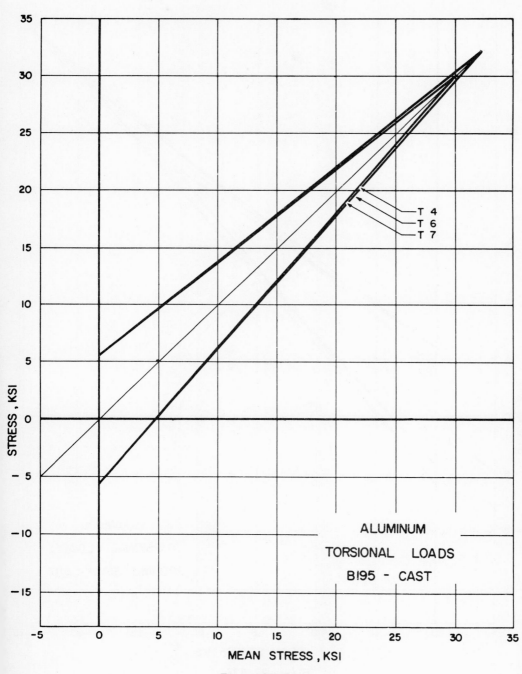

Figure 22—115.

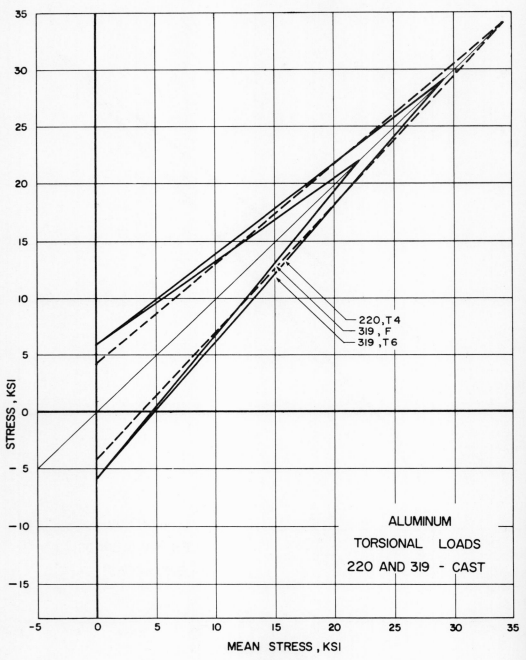

Figure 22-116.

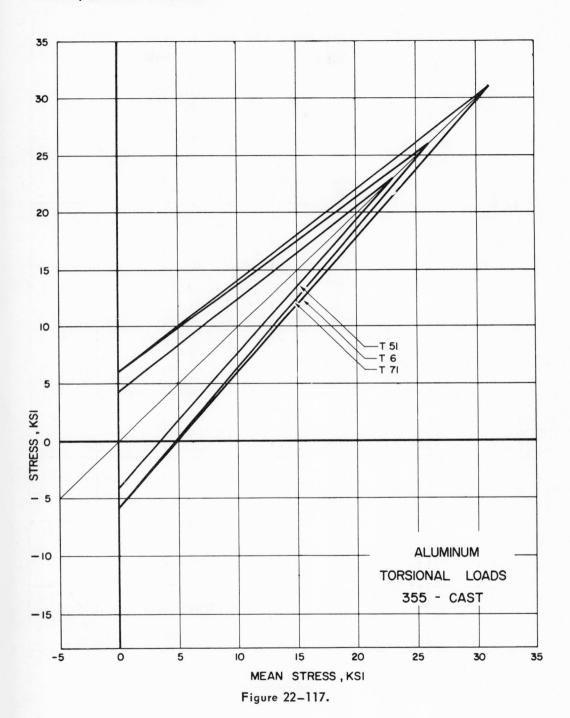

Figure 22–117.

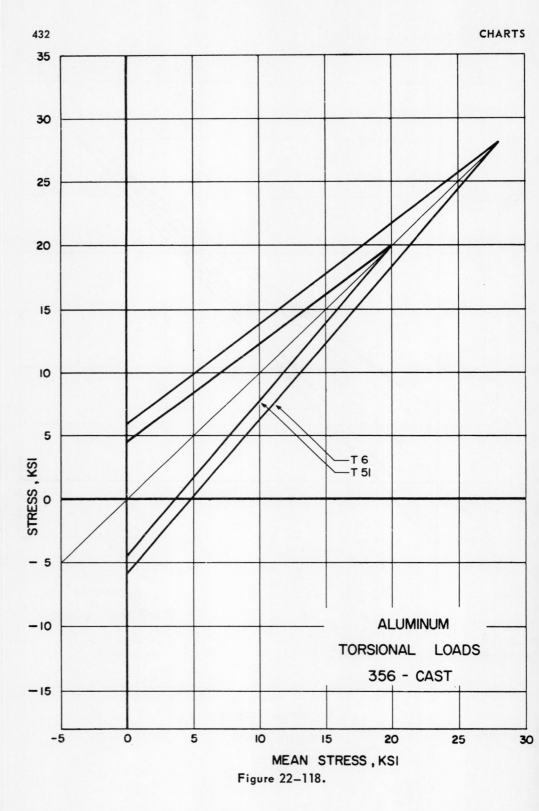

Figure 22-118.

MISCELLANEOUS TABLES, MATERIAL PROPERTIES

TABLE 23-1

For All wrought Steels:
Modulus of elasticity in tension or compression, $E = 30 \times 10^6$ psi (for wrought iron, $E = 28 \times 10^6$ psi).
Modulus of elasticity in shear or torsion, $G = 11.5 \times 10^6$ psi (for wrought iron, $G = 10 \times 10^6$ psi).
Yield strength in torsion (shear) frequently falls between $0.5s_y$ and $0.6s_y$. Use .577

Notes. (a) Minimum values. (b) Annealed. (c) Q & T 1000 stands for "quenched and tempered at 1000°F," etc. (d) *Ultimate stress in shear* has been arbitrarily taken as approximately

Material AISI No.	Condition (c)	Ult. str., ksi		Ten. Yd. S_y, ksi	Elong. 2 in. %	Red. Area %
		S_u	$S_s(d)$			
Wrought Iron Wrought Steel	As rolled	48(a)	36	25(a)	35	
B1113	Cold finished	83	62	72	14	40
B1113	As rolled	70		45	25	40
C1020	As rolled	65	49	48	36	59
C1020	Normalized	64	54*	50	39	69
C1020	Annealed	57	43	42	36.5	66
C1020	Cold drawn	78	58	66	20	59
C1022	As rolled	72	54	52	35	67
C1030	As rolled	80	60	51	32	56
C1035	As rolled	85	64	55	29	58
C1045	As rolled	96	72	59	22	45
C1095	Normalized	141	105	80	8	16
C1118	As rolled	75	56	46	32	70
C1144	Q & T 1000	118	88	83	19	46
1340	Q & T 1200	113	84	92	21	61
2317(c)	Q & T 1000	106	79	71	27	72
2340(e)	Q & T 1000	137	103	120	22	60
3150	Q & T 1000	151	113	130	16	54
3250(e)	Q & T 1000	166	122	146	16	52
4063	Q & T 1000	180	135	160	14	43
4130	Q & T 1100	127	95	114	18	62
4340(e)	Q & T 800	222	185(f)	200	12	48
4620	Case hard.	148	110	116	17	58
4640(e)	Q & T 1000	152	104	130	19	56
5140(e)	Q & T 1000	150	113	128	19	55
8630(e)	Q & T 1000	133	99	115	18	62
8640	Q & T 1000	167	125	145	15	52
8760	Q & T 800	220	165	200	12	43
9255	Q & T 1000	180	135	160	15	32
9440	Q & T 1000	152	104	135	18	61

Tables 23-1 through 23-8 reprinted with permission of the publisher from Design of Machine Elements by Faires.
Third Edition Copyright 1955 by The Macmillan Company.

Wrought Ferrous Metals

Endurance limit of a polished specimen, reversed bending, approximately $S_u/2$.
Endurance limit in reversed torsion, approximately .557.
Poisson's ratio is about 0.25 to 0.3.
Density is about 0.284 lb. per in.^{3} (0.28 lb. per in.^{3} for wrought iron).
Coefficient of linear expansion is 0.000 006 in. per in.-°F (0.000 006 3 for wrought iron).

(.82) tensile ultimate); except starred * values which are test values. (e) 1-in. specimen.
(f) Torsion. (g) Mill annealed. (h) Cold drawn.

BHN B	Rock. Hard.	Izod ft-lb.	Machin-ability (i)	Some typical uses; remarks.
	B60		50(h)	ASTM A85-36, A41-36
170	B87		135	Free cutting; high sulfur
138	B76			Free cutting; high sulfur
143	B79	64	64	Structural steel; plate
131	B74	72		Carburizing grade
111	B66	80		General purpose
156	B83		62	Misc. machine parts are cold forged
149	B81	60	70(h)	General purpose
179	B88	55	60	Machinery parts
190	B91	45	57	Machine parts. May be heat treated
215	B96	30	51	Large shafts.
285	C25	3	39	Tools, springs. Usually heat treated.
149	B81	80	82	Free cutting; not usually welded
235	C22	36	65(b)	Free cutting. High sulfur
293	C31	95	45(g)	Manganese steel
220	B97	85	55(h)	(3½% Ni)—Gears, pump liners, etc.
285	C30	50	31	(3½% Ni)—Gears, etc.
300	C32	46		(1.25% Ni, 0.8% Cr) Gears, bolts, shafts, etc.
340	C36.5	30	55(b)	(1.85% Ni, 1.05% Cr) Gears, etc.
375	C40	59		(0.25% Mo) Shafts, bars, etc.
280	C29	85	65(b)	(0.95% Cr, 0.20% Mo) Shafts, forgings, pins
422	C45	17	16	(1.85% Ni, 0.8% Cr, 0.25% Mo) General purpose
302	C32	42	65(b)	(1.85% Ni, 0.25% Mo) Core properties
310	C33	41	55(b)	(1.85% Ni, 0.25% Mo)
300	C32		60(b)	(0.80% Cr) Gears, shafts, pins, etc.
262	C26	74	65(b)	(0.55% Ni, 0.5% Cr, 0.2% Mo)
330	C35	36	60(b)	(0.55% Ni, 0.50% Cr, 0.20% Mo)
429	C46	19	50(b)	(0.55% Ni, 0.50% Cr, 0.25% Mo) Tools, gears, bolts
352	C36	7	45(b)	(2.00% Si) Springs, chisels, tools
311	C33	73	60(b)	(0.45% Ni, 0.4% Cr, 0.11% Mo)

TABLE 23-2

Notes: (a) ASTM and SAE specifications are not identical. Do not buy according to these numbers without referring to the specifications themselves. (b) Machinability, relative values, AISI B1112 = 100%. (c) 1.2-in. dia., 18-in. supports. (d) Test results suggest that the flexural strength of cast iron in *symmetric* sections computed from $S_f = M/Z$, is about $1.9S_u$ to $2S_u$. (e) Endurance limit of cast iron varies from $0.4S_u$ to $0.6S_u$. (f) Minimum values. Typical values may range 10–40% higher. (g) ASTM 35 and higher are considered to be high-strength, and are definitely more expensive. (h) For cast iron, at 25% of ult. stress; varies with

Material, Spec. No.		Ult. Strength, ksi				Transv. Strength lb. (c)	End. Lim. S_n' ksi	Ten. Yd. S_y ksi
		S_u	S_{uc}	S_{us}	Tors.			
Gray Iron (g)		(d)	(d)				(e)	
ASTM	SAE(a)							
20	110	20(f)	80	32		1800(f)	8(i)	
25		25(f)	100	35		2000(f)	10(i)	
30	111	30(f)	105	41	40	2200(f)	12(i)	
35(g)	120	35(f)	115	49	45	2400(f)	17.5	
40(g)	121	40(f)	125	52	54	2600(f)	19.5	
50(g)		50(f)	150	64	67	3000(f)	25.5	
60(g)		60(f)	175	60	76	3400(f)	27.5	
Malleable Iron								
ASTM No.	Grade							
A47-33	32 510	52	(o)	48	58		25.5	34
A47-33	35 018	55	(o)	43	58		27	36.5
A220-44T	43 010	70	(o)	60(i)			35(i)	50
A220-44T	70 003	90(f)	(o)	80(i)			45(i)	65
Nodular Cast Iron(j)								
90-65-02 (as cast)		100			90(i)		34(i)	72
80-60-05 (as cast)		90			81(i)		30(i)	62
60-45-15 (annealed)		70			63(i)		24(i)	55
Cast Steel					Condition (l)			
ASTM	SAE(a)							
A27-46T		60(f)	60(f)		Annealed		25	30(f)
A27-46T	0030(k)	65(f)	65(f)		Normalized		28	35(f)
A157-44		70(f)	70(f)		N and T		33	45(f)
A27-46T		70(f)	70(f)		Normalized		31	38(f)
	080	80(f)	80(f)		N and T		35	45
	0050	85(f)	85(f)		N and T		38	50
A148-46T	090	90(f)	90(f)		N and T		41	60(f)
A148-46T	0105	105(f)	105(f)		Q and T		49	85(f)
A148-46T	0175	175(f)	175(f)		Q and T		77	145(f)

Cast Ferrous Metals

section size and chemical analysis. (i) Estimated. (j) No Society standards for ductile (nodular)cast iron at this time; International Nickel Co. Nos. The number indicates minimum properties; e.g., 90-65-02 indicates S_u = 90 ksi, S_y = 65 ksi, and 2% elongation, minimum, in approximately 1-in. section. (k) 0.3% C, nominal. (l) N and T, normalized and tempered; Q and T, quenched and tempered. (m) Charpy impact, keyhole notch, 70°F, ft-lb. (n) Charpy impact, V-notched. (o) Take as equal to S_u.

Mod. Elas., psi $E \times 10^{-6}$	Shear Mod., psi $G \times 10^{-6}$	BHN B	Izod ft-lb.	Density lb/in.^{3}	Mch. (b)	Usual Min. Wall Thick.	
(h)							
10		150		0.253		t = 1/8 in.	
14		160		0.253		t = 1/8 in.	
14		180	23	0.254	80	t = 1/4 in.	
15		200	25	0.257	65	t = 3/8 in.	
16	5.5	220	31	0.262	55	t = 1/2 in.	
18	7	240	65	0.269	50	t = 1/2 in.	
19	8	260	75	0.269		t = 3/4 in.	
						Elong. 2 in., %	Red. Area, %
25	10.7	120	12	0.264	120	12.5	
25	10.7	130	16	0.264	120	20	
		170		0.265	90	10	
		220		0.265	80	3(f)	
25	9.2	240	2.7(n)	0.26		4	
25	9.2	210	2.7(n)	0.26		7.5	
25	9.2	160	7.5(n)	0.26		20	
30	11.5	120	30(m)	0.284	55	30	50
30	11.5	130	30(m)	0.284	60	30	53
30	11.5	140	35(m)	0.284	65	28	55
30	11.5	140	30(m)	0.284	65	28	50
30	11.5	160	35(m)	0.284	70	26	43
30	11.5	175	30(m)	0.284	70	24	40
30	11.5	190	26(m)	0.284	70	24	50
30	11.5	235	28(m)	0.284	60	18	42
30	11.5	380	10(m)	0.284		8	15

TABLE 23-3

Average Properties of Steel –
Various Sizes and Conditions

(a) Abbreviations: W-Q & T 1000 means "water quenched and tempered at 1000°F"; O-Q & T 1100 means "oil quenched and tempered at 1100°F;" etc.

AISI No.	Condition (a)	Rod Dia. in.	Ult. Str. S_u ksi	Ten Yd. S_y ksi	Elong. 2 in., %	Red. Area, %	BHN B	Izod ft-lb.
C1015	As rolled	½	61	45.5	39	61	126	81
	Annealed	1	56	42	37	69.7	111	83
	Normalized	½	63	48	38.6	71	126	85
	Normalized	1	61.5	47	37	69.6	121	85
	Normalized	2	60	44.5	37.5	69.2	116	86
	Normalized	4	59	41.8	36.5	67.8	116	83
C1117	As rolled	½	70.6	44.3	33	63	143	60
	Annealed	1	62	40.5	32.8	58	121	69
	Normalized	½	69.7	45	34.3	61	143	70
	Normalized	2	67	41.5	33.5	64.7	137	83
	Normalized	4	63.7	35	34.3	64.7	126	84
C1030	As rolled	½	80	51	32	54	179	55
	Annealed	1	67	49	31	57.9	126	51
	Normalized	½	77.5	50	32	61.1	156	69
	Normalized	4	72.5	47	29.7	56.2	137	61
	W-Q & T 1000	1	88	68	28	68.6	179	92
C1137	As rolled	½	93	55	26	63	192	61
	Annealed	1	85	50	27	54	174	37
	Normalized	½	98	58	25	58	201	69
	Normalized	2	96	49	22	51	197	21
C1040 (See Fig. 19)	Annealed	1	75	51	30	57	149	32
	Normalized	1	85	54	28	55	170	48
	Normalized	2	84	53	28	53	167	51
	Normalized	4	83.5	49	27	51.8	167	39
	W-Q & T 1000	½	109	81.5	23.8	61.5	223	75
	O-Q & T 1000	2	92	59.7	27	59.7	187	75
	W-Q & T 1000	2	101.7	69.5	24.7	63.6	207	85
	O-Q & T 1000	4	90	57.5	27	60.3	179	61
	W-Q & T 1000	4	99	64	24.7	60.2	201	62
C1050	As rolled	½	102	58	18	37	229	23
	Annealed	1	92	53	23.7	40	187	12
	Normalized	½	111	62	21.5	45	223	17
	Normalized	4	100	56	21.7	41.6	201	20
	O-Q & T 1100	½	122	81	22.8	58	248	22
	W-Q & T 1100	½	119	88	21.7	60	241	51
	O-Q & T 1100	2	112	68	23	55.6	223	20
	W-Q & T 1100	2	117	78.5	23	61	235	24
	O-Q & T 1100	4	101	58.5	25	54.5	207	21
	W-Q & T 1100	4	112	68	23.7	55.5	229	15

TABLE 23-4

Typical Properties of Heat Treated Steels

To get the strength or Brinell number for any other tempering (drawing) temperature, make a straight line interpolation between the values given. Extrapolation to lower temperatures might sometimes give a reasonable estimate, but extrapolation should not be relied upon. (a) Do not interpolate using this value.

AISI No. (Quenching medium)	Size	Tempered at, °F	Ult. Str. s_u ksi	Ten. Yd. s_y ksi	BHN B	Elong. 2 in. %	Izod, ft-lb.
C1035	1"	600	118	87	240	11	40
(water)	1"	1000	102	73	200	22	57
	1"	1300	85	57	170	29	93
C1095	½"	800	176	112	363	11	6
(oil)	½"	1100	145	88	293	17	6
	4"	1100	130	65	262	17	5
C1137	½"	700	135	115	277	12	13(a)
(oil)	½"	1000	111	88	229	23	61
	2"	1000	105	63	217	23	31
2330	½"	600	210	195	429	13	39
Nickel	½"	1000	135	126	277	20	77
Steel	½"	1300	107	91	217	26	109
(water)	4"	1000	105	85	207	26	87
4140	½"	500	270	241	534	11	8(a)
Cr-Mo	½"	800	210	195	420	15	21
(oil)	½"	1200	130	115	277	21	83
	4"	1200	112	83	229	23	87
4150	½"	800	228	215	444	10	12(a)
Cr-Mo (oil)	½"	1200	159	141	131	16	53(a)
5150	½"	800	210	195	415	11	17(a)
Chromium	½"	1000	160	149	321	15	39
(oil)	½"	1200	127	117	269	21	59
6152	½"	700	246	224	495	10	9(a)
Cr-V	½"	1000	184	173	375	12	30
(oil)	½"	1200	142	131	293	18	65
	2"	1200	121	94	241	21	45(a)
8630	½"	800	185	174	375	14	58
Ni-Cr-Mo	½"	1100	137	125	285	20	95
(water)	4"	1100	96	72	197	25	104
8742	1"	700	226	203	455	11	14(a)
Ni-Cr-Mo	1"	1200	130	110	262	21	67(a)
(oil)	4"	1200	118	91	235	22	
9261	½"	800	259	228	514	10	12
Si-Nn	½"	900	215	192	429	11	13
(oil)	½"	1200	147	124	311	17	35(a)
9840	1"	700	237	214	470	11	10(a)
Ni-Cr-Mo	1"	1200	140	120	280	19	65(a)
(oil)	6"	1000	151	131	302	16	

TABLE 23-5

Typical Properties of the Core of Carburized Steels

Carburizing is done at about 1700° F. A tempering temperature of 300° F produce maximum case hardness; 450°F results in improved impact strength.

Notes. (a) Nominal size of specimen, 1 in. (b) 1/2-in. specimen. (c) 2-in. specimen. (d) 4-in. specimen. (e) Abbreviations: "SQ & T 450, O," single quench and temper at 450°F, quench in oil; "DQ & T 300, W," double quench and temper at 300°F, quench in water; Q, quench; P, pot. (f) Of the order of other hardnesses shown. (g) Case thickness depends on temperature and time of carburizing; for example, at 1700°F for 4 hr., the case should be of the order of 0.05 in.; at 1700°F for 8 hr., about 0.06 in. As seen from the values given, these are not hard and fast rules.

AISI No.	Condition (e)	Core Properties						Case	
		Ult. Str. S_u ksi	Ten. Yd. S_y ksi	Elon. % 2"	Red. Area %	BHN B	Izod ft-lb.	Rock. Hard. R_c	Thick. in. (8 hr.)
C1015 (b)	SQ & T 350, W	73	46	32	71	149	91	C62	0.048
C1020 (a)	DQ & T 300, W	85	55	33	65	170		(f)	(g)
C1020 (a)	SQ & T 300, W	80	50	30	60	160		(f)	(g)
C1117 (b)	SQ & T 350, W	96	59	23	53	192	33	C65	0.045
2115 (a)	DQ & T 300, O or W	90	60	30	70	185	70	(f)	(g)
2317 (a)	DQ & T 300, O	95	60	35	65	195	85	(f)	(g)
2317 (a)	DQ & T 300, W	100	65	30	60	210	70	(f)	(g)
2515 (a)	DQ & T 300, O	170	130	14	50	352	40	(f)	(g)
3115 (a)	DQ & T 300, O	100	70	25	55	212	55	(f)	(g)
3215 (a)	SQ & T 300, O	141	110	17	50		45	(f)	(g)
E3310 (b)	SQ & T 450, O	180	149	14.5	58	363	57	C57.5	0.047
E3310 (b)	DQ & T 300, O	177	143	15.3	58	352	47	C61	0.047
3415 (a)	SQ & T 300, O	130	95	18	52	285	55	(f)	(g)
3415 (a)	DQ & T 300, O	135	105	19	55	300	60	(f)	(g)
4320 (b)	Direct Q from P 300, O	217	159	13	50	429	32	C60.5	0.060
4320 (b)	DQ & T 450, O	145	94	21.8	56	293	48	C59	0.075
4620 (b)	DQ & T 300, O	122	77	22	56	248	64	C62	0.060
4620 (b)	DQ & T 450, O	115	77	22.5	62	235	78	C59	0.060
4820 (b)	SQ & T 300, O	207	167	13.8	52	415	44	C61	0.047
4820 (b)	SQ & T 450, O	205	184	13	53	415	47	C57.5	0.047
8620 (b)	SQ & T 300, O	188	149	11.5	51	388	26	C64	0.075
8620 (b)	SQ & T 450, O	167	120	14.3	53	341	29	C61	0.076
8620 (b)	DQ & T 300, O	133	83	20	56	269	55	C64	0.070
E9310 (b)	Direct Q from P 300, O	179	144	15.3	59	375	57	C59.5	0.039
E9310 (b)	SQ & T 300, O	173	135	15.5	60	363	61	C62	0.047
E9310 (b)	DQ & T 300, O	174	139	15.3	62	363	54	C60.5	0.055
E9310 (a)	SQ & T 300, O	159	122	15.5	57	321	68	(f)	(g)
E9310 (c)	SQ & T 300, O	145	108	18.5	66	293	93	(f)	(g)
E9310 (d)	SQ & T 300, O	136	94	19	62	277	93	(f)	(g)

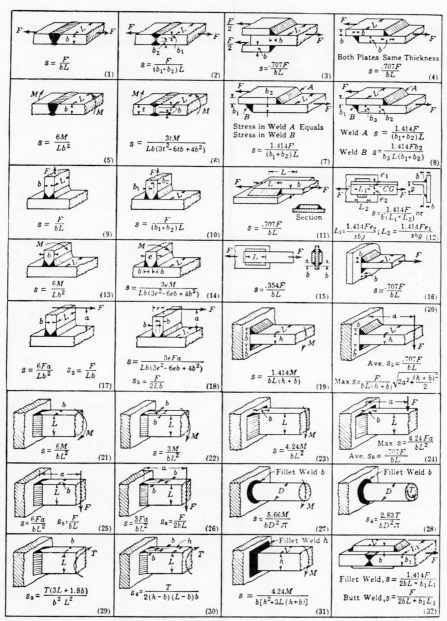

After Jennings, Reference 16, reprinted with permission.

Figure 23–1. Stresses in Welds.

TABLE 23-6

Typical Properties of

Notes. (a) TS, thermosetting; TP, thermoplastic. (b) National Electrical Mfg. Assoc. grades. (c) Flatwise. (d) For 1/3 to 1-in. dia. Reduce 15% for sizes 1 to 2 in. (e) For 1/8 to 1-in. dia. Reduce 10% for sizes 1 to 2 in. (f) Min. values, Much higher values obtainable.

Material	Type (a)	Condition (k)	Ult. Str., S_u ksi	Comp. Ult. Str., S_{uc}	Flex. Str., (g)
Phenol-formaldehyde					
Grade X (b)	TS	L. sheet	14	35	23
Grade XX (b)	TS	L. rod	8.5(d)	20	15(e)
Grade C (b)	TS	L. rod	7.5(d)	20	17(e)
Grade A (b)	TS	L. rod	6(d)	15	10(e)
Wood flour filler	TS	M	6(f)	24(m)	9(f)
Nylon-phenolic	TS	L, RT.	42.6	31.8	46.8
Urea-formaldehyde (f)	TS	M, CF.	5.5	20	10
Polyvinyl Chloride (f)	TP	M, P.	5		
Methyl Methacrylate (f)	TP	M	4	8	9
Polystyrene (f)	TP	M	5	11.5	6
Nylon FM-1 (at 77°F.)	TP	M	10.5	15	12
Cellulose Acetate (f)	TP	M	3.2	13	3.4
Polyethelene (f)	TP	M	1.7		1.7
Tetrafluoroethylene (f)	TP	M	2	1.7	2

Typical Properties of

Notes. (a) Coef. of thermal expansion near room temp., a in. per in.-°F. (b) Approx. average values of ult. strength of 403, 410, and 416 are given by $S_u = 5 + 0.465$ (BHN) in KSI (3). (c) Varies with details of heat treatment and cold working. (d) Cold worked, full hard.

Material AISI No.	Ult. Str. S_u, ski (c)	Ten. Yd. S_y ksi (c)	End. Lim. S_n' (e)	Mod. El. $E \times 10^{-6}$ (f)	Elong. 2 in. % (c)	Red. Area, % (c)
302, annealed	85	40	34	28	57	70
302, cold rolled	140	100	70(d)	28	30	
303, annealed	85	40	35	28	55	60
304, annealed	85	40		28	62	70
316, cold rolled	125	90		28	30	
347, annealed	90	40	39	28	50	65
410, heat treated	150(b)	130		29	20	65
410, cold rolled	191(b)	140		29	6	
416, annealed	78(b)	40		29	31	55
430, annealed	75	45		29	25	45

a Few Plastics

(g) Bending strength, symmetric sections. (h) Specific gravity. (i) Aver. water absorption. 24-hr., 1/4-in. thickness, per cent. (j) 48-hr. immersion. (k) CF, cellulose filled; L, laminated; M, molded; P, plasticized; RT, room temperature. (l) When used for gears, let S_n = 6000 psi.

Elong. %	Rock. Hard.	Mod. El., $E \times 10^{-5}$	Sp. Gr. (h)	Izod, ft–lb. (f)	% H_2O Ab- sorp. (i)	Typical Trade Names
	M100	4–20	1.35	1.3(c)	1.4	Bakelite (l)
	M100	4–20	1.35	1.0(c)	0.65	Formica (l)
	M100	3.5–15	1.35	3.2(c)	1.2	Micarta (l)
	M90	3.5–15	1.65	1.8(c)	0.65	Synthane (l)
0.4–0.8	M100	12	1.4	.32	0.8	
	M118	12	1.45	.24	0.4	Bakelite, Formica, Plaskon
			1.2		0.05	Geon, Saran, Vinylite, Marvinol
5–15	M60	6	1.16	0.2	0.3(j)	Lucite, Pexiglass
1–5	M85	1.7–7	1.06	0.2	none	Lustrex, Styron, Textolite
54	M90	2.9	1.14	0.5	1.5	Nylon
12–50	M40	1–4.4	1.27	0.8	2	Lumarith, Plastacile, Textolite
30–500		0.15	0.92		0.01	Polythene, Bakelite
300–400			2.1	2	none	Teflon

Some Stainless Steels

(e) Endurance limits for stainless steels may be estimated at $0.4S_u$, up to tensile strength of about 160 ksi *(18)*. (f) Varies some with condition: annealed, cold worked, stress relieved. In shear, for cold drawn spring wires, $G \approx 10.6 \times 10^6$ psi.

BHN (aver.) (c)	Density	Izod ft–lb. (c)	$a \times 10^6$, (a)	Remarks
150	0.286	90	9.4	Austenitic. Hardenable by cold work only
250	0.286		9.4	302, 303, 304 are 18-8 stainless steels.
140	0.286	90	9.6	Austenitic, Hardenable by cold work only
150	0.286	100	9.5	Austenitic. Hardenable by cold work only
240	0.286		8.9	Austenitic. Hardenable by cold work only
160	0.286	100	9.3	Austenitic. Hardenable by cold work only
310	0.279	60	5.7	Hardenable by HT. Martensitic. Q&T1000F
400	0.279	20	5.7	Max. hardness. Martensitic
160	0.278	80	5.7	Hardenable by HT. Martensitic
165	0.277	30	5.4	Ferritic. Not hardened by HT

TABLE 23-7

Typical Properties of

For *Aluminum alloys*, let the torsional ult. = $0.65S_u$; torsional yield str. = $0.55S_y$. For *Magnesium alloys*, let the flexural strength (symmetric sections) be the average of the tensile and compressive strengths. See note (k).

Abbreviations: H, hard; 1/4H, 1/4 hard; H14, temper designation meaning 1/2 hard; HT, heat treated; T4, temper designation meaning solution heat treated.

Notes: (a) At 0.5% total elongation under load. (b) At 0.01% offset. Proportional limit =

Material (ASTM No.)	Condition	Ult. Str., ksi		Ten. Yd. S_y ksi	End. Str., S_n ksi at No. cycles
		S_u	S_{us}		
COPPER ALLOYS					
Admiralty metal (B111)	Annealed	53	24(o)	22(a)	18 at 10^7
Aluminum bronze (B150-1)	Annealed rod	80		40(a)	28 at 8×10^7
Aluminum bronze (B148)	Cast, HT	90		40(a)	
Beryllium copper (B194)	HT	200	96(o)	171(b)	50 at 10^8(h)
Cartridge brass (B134, No. 6)	1/2H, rod	70	42	52(a)	22 at 5×10^7
Manganese bronze (B138-A)	1/2H, rod	84	48	60(a)	(q)
Naval brass (B124, No. 3)	1/4H, rod	69	43	46(a)	15 at 3×10^8
Phosphor bronze (B139C)	1/2H, rod	80		65(a)	22 at 10^8(r)
Silicon bronze (B98-B)	H, rod	70	45	55(a)	30 at 3×10^8
Yellow brass (B36-8)	Spring H	91	47	61(a)	20 at 10^8
Yellow brass (B36-8)	1/2H	61	40	50 (a)	
ALUMINUM ALLOYS					
3S (B209)	H14, hard	21	14	18(c)	9 at 5×10^8
11S (B211)	Cold worked	53		47(c)	12.5 at 5×10^8
17S (B211) (p)	T4, HT	62(p)	38	40(c) (p)	18 at 5×10^8
24S (B211)	T4, HT	68	41	46(c)	18 at 5×10^8
72S (B209)	T6, HT	82	49	72	23 at 5×10^8
85 alloy (B85)	Die casting	40		22(c)	17 at 5×10^8
MAGNESIUM ALLOYS					
(Alloy A10, B80-47T)	Cast	22	18	12(c,k)	10 at 5×10^8
(AZ61X, B107-45T)	Extruded bar	45	21	32(c,k)	17 at 5×10^8
AZ80X, B91-45T)	Forged, aged	50	23	34(c,k)	16 at 5×10^8
LEAD AND TIN ALLOYS					
Babbitt (B23-46T-8)	At 77°F (1)	10	Comp. yd. = 3.4(m)		3.9 at 2×10^7
Babbitt (B23-46T-8)	At 212°F (1)	5.4	Comp. yd. = 1.7(m)		
Tin babbitt (B23-46T-1)	At 68°F (1)	9.3	Comp. yd. = 4.4(m)		3.8 at 2×10^7
MISCELLANEOUS					
Hastalloy B	Rolled, annealed	130		60(c)	66 at 10^8(n)
Monel	Hot rolled	80	56	40(c)	31 at 10^8
Platinum alloy	Annealed	45			
Titanium (MST Grade III)	Annealed	80		72(f)	50
Titanium (MST Grade III)	Full hard	125		110(g)	60
Zinc, Zamak-5 (XXV)	Die cast	47.6	38		8 at 10^8

Some Non-Ferrous Metals

100 ksi. (c) At 0.2% offset. (d) BHN. (e) BHN with 500 kg load. (f) Proportional limit = 40 ksi. (g) Proportional limit = 50 ksi. (h) End. strength in reversed torsion, 25 ksi. (i) a in. per in.-°F, coef. of thermal expansion. (j) Varies with size of test specimen. (k) Yield point in compression; alloy A10, 12 ksi; AZ61X, 21 ksi; AZ80X, 28 ksi. (l) Chill cast. (m) At 0.125% set. (n) At 1200°F, after water quench and aging. (o) Estimated. (p) For rolled structural shapes, S_u = 55 and S_y = 32 ksi. (q) For manganese gear bronze, use S_n = 17 ksi. (r) For phosphor gear bronze, SAE 65, use S_n = 24 ksi.

Mod. El. $E \times 10^{-6}$	Mod. El. Sh. $G \times 10^{-6}$	Elong. % 2 in. (j)	Rock. Hard.	Density lb./in.^{3}	$a \times 10^6$ (j)	Percentage Composition
15	5.8	65	F75	0.308	11.2	71 Cu, 28 Zn, 1 Sn
17	6.5	22		0.274	9.6	10 Al, other ≈ 1%
17	6.5	15	B90	0.267	9.5	10 Al, other ≈ 1%
18.4	6.4	2.8	400(d)	0.297	9.8	2 Be, 0.35 Ni
16	6.4	30	B80	0.308	11.1	70 Cu, 30 Zn
15	5.8	19	B90	0.308	11.8	58 Cu, 39 Zn, plus
15	5.8	27	B78	0.304	11.8	60 Cu, 39.25 Zn, 0.75 Sn
16	6.4	33	B85	0.318	10.1	92 Cu, 8 Sn
15	5.8	15	B80	0.316	9.9	96 Cu, 1.5 Si, plus
15	5.8	3	B90	0.306	11.3	65 Cu, 35 Zn
15	5.8	23	B70	0.306	11.3	65 Cu, 35 Zn
10	3.80	16	40(e)	0.099	12.9	1.2 Mn
10.3	3.85	15	95(e)	0.102	12.7	5.5 Cu, 0.5 Pb, 0.5 Bi
10.4	3.85	22	105(c)	0.101	12.7	4 Cu, 0.5 Mg, 0.5 Mn
10.6	4.00	22	120(e)	0.100	12.9	4.5 Cu, 1.5 Mg, 0.6 Mn
10.4	3.85	10	150(e)	0.101	13.1	5.5 Zn, 2.5 Mg, 1.5 Cu, plus
10.3	3.85	3.5		0.101	11.7	4 Cu, 5 Si
6.5	2.4	2	E64	0.066	14.4	10 Al, 0.1 Mn
6.5	2.4	15	E67	0.065	14.4	6 Al, 1 Zn, 0.2 Mn
6.5	2.4	6	E82	0.066	14.4	8.5 Al, 0.5 Zn, 0.15 Mn
4.2		5	20(e)	0.36	13.3	80 Pb, 15 Sb, 5 Sn
		27	10(e)	0.36	13.3	80 Pb, 15 Sb, 5 Sn
7.3			17(e)	0.265		91 Sn, 4.5 Sb, 4.5 Cu
30.7		40	B96	0.334	5.55	62 Ni, 30 Mo, 5 Fe
26	9.5	40	B85	0.319	7.8	67 Ni, 30 Cu, plus
		35	90(e)			10 Rhodium
16		25	A59	0.162	4.7	
15.5		12	A62	0.162	4.7	
		7	91(e)	0.24	17.2	4 Al, 1 Cu, 0.04 Mg

TABLE 23-8

Miscellaneous Endurance Limits

Notes: (a) Manganese steel. (b) Number of cycles is indefinitely large unless specified. Cy. = cycles. (c) Estimated (not a test value). (d) Depends on the number of cycles.

Material	Condition	S_n ksi at No. of Cy. (b)	$\dfrac{S_n}{S_u}$	S_y ksi	$\dfrac{S_y}{S_n}$
Wrought iron	Longitudinal	30	0.65	30	1.00
Wrought iron	Transverse	28.5	0.60	28	0.98
Cast iron	ASTM 30	12	0.38		
Cast iron	ASTM 30	16 at 10^5			
Cast iron	ASTM 30	21 at 10^4			
Cast steel, 0.18% C	As cast	31.5	0.45	36	1.14
Cast steel, 0.18% C	Cast and annealed	34.5	0.45	37	1.07
Cast steel, 0.25% C	As cast	27	0.40	40	1.48
Cast steel, 0.25% C	Cast and normalized	35	0.46	45	1.29
Cast steel, 1335(a)	As cast	32	0.40	44	1.37
Cast steel, 1335(a)	Cast and normalized	45	0.41	57	1.27
Cast steel, 1335(a)	Cast, quenched, tempered	45	0.41	70	1.55
Cast steel, 4340	Cast, quenched, tempered	64	0.40	148	2.32
Cast steel, 8630	Cast, quenched, tempered	52	0.45	85	1.63
Wrought 1014	Cold drawn	35(c)	0.50(c)	60	1.71
Steel 1020	As rolled	45 at 10^4		48	1.08
1020	As rolled	40 at 10^5		48	1.20
1020	As rolled	33 at 10^6		48	1.45
Wrought 1020	As rolled	32	0.50	48	1.5
Steel 1035	Cold drawn	46(c)	0.50(c)	78	1.69
1035	In air	40.6	0.46	58	1.43
1035	In brine	24.6		58	2.36
Wrought 1035	In sulfur	10.6		58	5.48
Steel 1117	Cold drawn	40(c)	0.50(c)	68	1.70
1137	Cold drawn	50(c)	0.50(c)	89	1.78
1141	Cold drawn	55(c)	0.50(c)	95	1.73
Wrought 2317	In air	52	0.61	50	0.96
Steel 2317	In brine	31.6		50	1.58
2317	In sulfur	23.9		50	2.09
2320	Hot rolled rod	48	0.50	51	1.06
Wrought 2320	Carburized, case hardened	90	0.53	140	1.56
Steel 3120	Carburized, case hardened	90	0.64	100	1.11
6150	Heat treated	96	0.46	190	1.98
Nitralloy N	Nitrided	124	0.65	180	1.45
Nitralloy 135, modified	Un-nitrided	45			
Nitralloy 135, modified	Nitrided	90	0.66	140	1.56
Nitralloy 135, modified	Notched and un-nitrided	24			
Nitralloy 135, modified	Notched and nitrided	80	0.59	140	1.75

and Endurance Strengths

(e) For creep rate of 0.0001%. (f) Stress for rupture in 100 hr.

Material	Condition	S_n ksi at No. Cy. (b)	$\dfrac{S_n}{S_u}$ (d)	S_y ksi	$\dfrac{S_y}{S_n}$
Stainless steel 303	Cold drawn bar	50	0.50	60	1.20
Stainless steel 316	Annealed bar	38	0.37	35	0.92
Stainless steel 403	Annealed bar	40	0.53	45	1.12
Stainless steel 410	Quenched and tempered, 1200°F	49	0.53	60	1.22
Aluminum 17S	Forged, heat treated, aged	15 at 5×10^8	0.24	40	2.67
Aluminum 24S	Tempered, age hardened	40 at 10^5	0.59	46	1.15
Aluminum 24S	Tempered, age hardened	31 at 10^6	0.46	46	1.48
Aluminum 24S	Tempered, age hardened	25 at 10^7	0.37	46	1.84
Aluminum 24S	Tempered, age hardened	20 at 10^8	0.29	46	2.30
Aluminum 52S	Wrought, half hard	19 at 5×10^8	0.51	29	1.53
Aluminum 122	Sand cast, heat treated	8.5 at 5×10^8	0.21	30	3.54
Aluminum 122	Permanent mold, heat treated	9 at 5×10^8	0.19	36	4.00
Aluminum bronze	Extruded, heat treated	34 at 7×10^7	0.44	50(c)	1.47
Aluminum bronze	Sand cast, heat treated	30(c)		40	1.33
Cartridge brass	0.08" spring wire	22 at 10^8	0.17	65(c)	2.96
Cartridge brass	Half hard, 0.04" strip	18 at 10^8	0.29	52	2.89
Commercial bronze	0.08" hard wire	23 at 10^8	0.31	60(c)	2.61
Leaded tin bronze	Sand cast, heat treated	12(c)		18(c)	1.50
Low brass	Spring hard, 0.04" strip	24 at 2×10^7	0.26	65	2.70
Low brass	0.08" spring wire	26 at 10^8	0.21	68(c)	2.61
Manganese bronze	Sand cast, heat treated	21(c)		30(c)	1.43
Phosphor gear bronze	Sand-cast SAE 65; heat treated	24(c)		17(c)	0.85
Silicon bronze A	Half-hard rod	30 at 3×10^8	0.39	45	1.50
Silicon bronze B	Hot rolled	16 at 5×10^7		15(c)	0.94
Silicon bronze B	Extruded	19 at 5×10^7		45(c)	2.37
Silicon bronze B	Cold drawn, 72% reduction	30 at 3×10^7	0.32	69(c)	2.30
Silicon bronze B	0.08" hard wire	25 at 10^8	0.28	67	2.68
Hastalloy B	1200°F	66 at 10^8			
Hastalloy B	1500°F	34 at 10^8		18(e)	0.53
Magnesium (ASTM B80-41T)	Cast, heat treated, aged	9 at 5×10^8	0.25	19	2.11
Magnesium (ASTM B91-41T)	Forged bar, 3.5x4 in.	15 at 3×10^8	0.32	26	1.73
Monel	Annealed, 60°F	36 at 10^8	0.51	35	0.97
Monel	Annealed, −100°F	38 at 10^8	0.54	35	0.92
Monel	Cold drawn	52 at 10^8	0.61	75	1.44
Monel	Annealed. In brackish water	29 at 10^8	0.41	35	1.20
Stellite 21	Room temperature	37 at 10^8	0.36	82	2.21
Stellite 21	1200°F	44 at 10^8	0.49	51(f)	1.16
Stellite 21	1500°F	33 at 10^8		22(f)	0.67